COMMUNITY PROBLEMS

Community Problems

By

JENNETTE R. GRUENER, Ph.D.

School of Social Work,
University of Missouri

and

DEBORAH MacLURG JENSEN, R.N., M.A.

Instructor in Nursing Education and Sociology,
Department of Adult Education,
University of Missouri

ILLUSTRATED

ST. LOUIS
THE C. V. MOSBY COMPANY
1954

Press of
The C. V. Mosby Company
St. Louis

PREFACE

This book is intended primarily for the use of nurses to help them integrate social and emotional aspects in their clinical fields. It may, however, be valuable to other workers in the health field whose function it is to study the total patient situation and to help him make a better adjustment. The core of nursing content today is total patient needs. Since every patient has been conditioned by and is a part of the community in which he lives, every worker must consider not only the patient but also the community. She must also understand the resources as well as the problems found. Every personal problem presented by a patient goes back to and is influenced by family and community conditions. Because of this conditioning of every patient by the community in which he lives, every nurse must consider the community in relation to the patient. She needs to understand the social problems in the community and the many social welfare resources in the community. Problem areas exist in every city and town, such as poor housing, lack of recreational facilities, high incidence of disease. Lack of adequate health resources as well as ignorance of existing facilities result in many health problems.

All nurses now have an introductory course in sociology usually during the first or second term in the school of nursing. This book presupposes certain basic sociological information; in fact, most workers in the health field have had an introductory course in sociology or the social sciences in high school before coming to college. This book has been called *Community Problems* because every social problem is a community problem. No problem can operate or exist in a vacuum; it exists only in a community setting, and as the student will soon realize when she begins to study these problems, very few, if any, exist absolutely alone and isolated but are related to other problems and community conditions. In many schools of nursing a course called Social Problems (sometimes now called Community Problems) is given following the introductory course in sociology. For such a course this book may be valuable. It is hoped, however, that the book will be used beyond the limits of any course and that the student will find valuable information herein as she gets experience in the different clinical areas and is confronted with community problems.

It is not intended that this book take the place of more comprehensive textbooks in the field of Social and Community Problems. Reference has been made to standard text and reference books in these various fields, and it is hoped that the reader will investigate the sources given when more detailed information is required. The authors have attempted to select material from the tremendous amount of information now available that would be of greatest value to the nurse particularly and to other health workers who need a ready reference to the most commonly found community problems in their field. It is hoped that, when possible, the student will supplement information here by going to sources indicated in the references.

In the Appendix for Teachers a suggested bibliography is given, listing those books and magazines which should be available either in the institutional library or the educational library. No glossary has been included in this book because very few new terms are used. As stated above, this course is built on a broad sociological base which the student has had either in high school or in college.

This book started out as a revision of Part 2 of *Sociology and Social Problems* by Jensen. As stated above, the title *Community Problems* seems to describe better the area which the authors wished to emphasize in this book. Very little material from the previous edition has been included, because as the authors developed the concept of the nurse caring for the patient in his total environment, they realized more and more that "social problems in nursing service" had developed into "community problems."

The authors are indebted to many people for help in analyzing and presenting the material included in this book. To their associates in the field of Sociology and Social Problems the debt is very great; particularly are they indebted to Mrs. Honora Camden, School of Nursing, Washington University, for reading the total manuscript in its final stages and giving valuable suggestions.

Columbia, Mo.   JENNETTE GRUENER
St. Louis, Mo.   DEBORAH M. JENSEN

FOREWORD

This book reflects a rich background of experience in working with the community problems centered around the emotional and social aspects of individuals and families. Interspersed throughout is a great appreciation of the impact or influence of the racial, religious, and cultural patterns of the various groups.

Mrs. Jensen's familiarity with the educational needs of all nurses would qualify her to have a special kind of insight into the needs of schools of nursing and hospitals. Dr. Gruener from a closely related field has been able to illuminate and clarify areas that we may not think of as strictly nursing. A broader view is generally recognized today as very essential in the concept of complete nursing care. By lending understanding and additional knowledge, the book should become a valuable contribution to nursing education.

The approach to illness as one of the community problems is a point of view which we are trying to stress more in schools of nursing. The student nurse will be exposed to a good introduction to community health as she studies this book.

The authors' discussion of the various diseases with constant emphasis on the effect on the community should serve to acquaint the student with the necessity to study disease as a part of the whole patient rather than as an end in itself.

HONORA WILLS CAMDEN, R.N., B.S., A.M.

St. Louis
Assistant Professor and Assistant Director, Community Health and Guidance Programs, School of Nursing, Washington University

CONTENTS

**B. Community Problems
in the United States**

I. PROBLEMS AFFECTING TOTAL HEALTH

COMMUNITY PROBLEMS

A. BACKGROUND AND SOCIOLOGICAL SETTING

CHAPTER 1

GENERAL INTRODUCTION

FRAME OF REFERENCE

As a background to the understanding of contemporary community problems, the nurse should, if possible, have a good background in general sociology. The understanding of social groups, social institutions, and of the community, both from the structural and functional point of view, will be very valuable, as will also the basic understanding of the factors involved in social change, disorganization, and reorganization. Social problems develop when there are marked inequalities in the social organization. It may be said that problems become evident when individuals and groups deviate from the accepted normal (or what the group thinks is right) in any particular culture and when the rest of the group becomes aware of that deviation. The nurse must have an understanding of community problems, especially those which have some relation to or are accentuated by illness. The problem of maintaining the people's health today cannot be adequately solved without an understanding of other community problems. Modern society has become so complex that the physical and mental problems are inextricably woven with the economic and cultural. To limit oneself to the treatment and prevention of disease without considering also the cost of illness, housing, poverty, old age, problems of childhood, to mention a few, would be to limit one in the results that he gets.

Thus a basic knowledge of sociology enables the nurse to understand community problems more intelligently. Disease and ill health are now regarded as one of the many problems found in modern communities. No problem appears independently; it is interrelated in cause, effect, and treatment with other problems.   The nurse cannot limit her knowledge to the field of health and disease, but must understand her community in the broadest sense of the word.   The aims and objectives for the nurse in approaching any study of community problems might be outlined as follows:

1. To appreciate the part played by social factors in the illness problems of individual patients (especially with reference to their bearing on medical and nursing care, recovery from illness, or adjustment to disability), in order to understand better the behavior of patients and thus improve their nursing care.

2. To develop ability to discover clues to social problems connected with illness as they are revealed in the behavior of the patient and his family or associates, and in available recorded material.

3. To gain understanding of the processes of medical-social diagnosis and treatment as they are practiced by medical-social workers in collaboration with professional associates both in the hospital and in the community, and to learn how to cooperate with such groups in meeting the problems of patients and their families.

4. To consider some of the more persistent and characteristic social problems which have been studied in individual cases in their wider social setting, and to gain further knowledge of the agencies and methods used by the community in meeting them.

5. To review and carry further through reflective experience and application the study of facts and concepts learned in other courses, especially psychology and sociology, so that better understanding of individual behavior and community problems and the nurse's responsibility for them may result.[1]

In her contact with patients in the home, clinic, or hospital, the nurse is often aware of the major social problems, either incidental to or accentuated by the illness.   An understanding of these problems is essential to complete nursing care.   An understanding of community agencies and resources will help the nurse in working with the patient and his family in attempting to solve their problem.

---

[1] A Curriculum Guide for Schools of Nursing, ed. 3, New York, 1937, Committee on Curriculum of the National League of Nursing Education, pages 225-226.

THE NATURE OF COMMUNITY PROBLEMS

Community problems have their definition in the values of people and groups. Apart from the values of individuals and groups, problems cannot be defined. Problems always suggest conflict of values. This conflict may exist at different levels. For example, it may exist at what might be called the definition of the problem, what is the problem. There may also be conflict about the factors that lead to the situation or the cause or causes of the problem. There may also be conflict about what steps should be taken, what program of action is necessary to reduce or to treat the situation adequately.

No problem stands out as an isolated phenomenon in group life. Social and community problems are interdependent and one may often be the cause of the other. Thus illness in the wage earner or homemaker may contribute to neglect, dependency, or delinquency in children. The economically handicapped may develop physical or mental illness or show antisocial behavior in other ways. The problems of the aged may be complicated by physical or mental illness.

THE NATURAL HISTORY OF PROBLEMS

One may be aware in studying community problems that there seems to be a natural history common to all problems. Roughly this natural history may be described as follows: *First stage,* when individuals and groups develop an awareness that a problem exists; *second stage,* the policy determination or official views to be taken. At this stage there is often debate over what needs to be done. This may focus in the program of interest groups. First of all, there may be discussion by neighborhoods or unorganized groups, consciously or unconsciously forming public opinion. Then there may be discussion by organized groups such as educational groups, taxpaying groups, real estate groups, men's and women's clubs. There may be also, as the situation develops, discussion by specialists and administrators in the fields of health, education, recreation, crime, and many others. In the policy determination stage, individuals and groups do not always agree on a solution and are not always willing to accept or even consider a solution that may have been proposed by experts. The *third stage* might be called the reform stage and would describe that period when organized groups or administrative units formulate plans and put these plans into action. This may, in certain instances, include legislation.

Fig. 1.—The patient should always be considered in his family and community setting.

For example, in the realm of medical and health care all communities agree that there is a problem in this area. They agree that all individuals are not getting adequate health care. The reasons for this are many and complex and would be presented differently by different individuals and groups, but the fact is that there is a problem. In our country, what action should be taken is still highly controversial. In the recent past and at present one might describe what different groups feel should be done about this problem as follows:

1. Do nothing other than what has already and is being done by private philanthropy, with the idea that anything you do is likely to make the situation worse. These groups would allow some tax-supported medical care of a limited nature to those in the very lowest income brackets and would probably insist on a "means test."

2. Support limited public health measures including quarantine, pure food and drug laws, public sanitation, control of water supply, handling of food, etc. That this, with a combination of private, voluntary systems and philanthropy should meet the problem satisfactorily is held by some groups.

3. Some groups feel that more extended public health facilities should be set up, including tax-supported clinics and hospitals for many individuals, and particularly for those with chronic, long-term, and mental conditions.

4. Compulsory health insurance, such as is found in some other countries, has been advocated by some groups in this country.

5. State medicine, that is, all medical practice under the direct supervision and administration of the state, as is found in a few other countries today, is recommended by some.

All of these approaches to the problem of providing adequate health care in this country have been discussed. Probably most individuals and organized groups feel that a combination, perhaps of Numbers 2 and 3, if carried out in all communities might meet the situation most satisfactorily. See Section C for fuller discussion of some of these plans.

In the treatment of social problems and in any plans proposed, there is quite likely to be conflict between the laissez faire attitude and directed social change. Directed social change, as a result of social planning and under effective control, may be resisted by many organized groups because these plans will inevitably mean change. Change is always disorganizing even for a temporary period as it disturbs established patterns. Many of our contemporary problems cannot be presented or completed until radical changes take place in the social structure. The whole program of social planning described in Section C gives evidence of some of these changes. Many of these changes, in fact most of the changes in the field of community welfare, will in some way be related to the nurse's work.

So complex has our social structure become and so interdependent is each part with others that no one issue or problem can be adequately studied or treated by itself. The nurse is most interested in helping to do her part in the treatment and prevention of disease. However, she soon realizes that the success of her activities may rest on situations outside the immediate nursing and medical picture but closely related to them. The relation between poverty and disease has been recognized for a long time. The patient may not get medical or nursing care when he needs it, not because it is not available but because he cannot pay for it. Perhaps he does not even have carfare to go to a free clinic in his community.

THE NURSE AND COMMUNITY PROBLEMS

Recognition of the total social situation is, of course, basic to its understanding. In nursing situations the student learns the importance of observation. She learns what to observe and the significance of her observation. Much of the plan of treatment outlined by the doctor may depend on the record of the nurse's observation. She also learns the art of listening and of interpreting and recording her observations.

These clinical records are also of service to other nurses and professional workers rendering service to the patient. Training in the observation of social symptoms is one of the newer developments in nursing and is essential in all fields of nursing. Many nurses are not yet as aware of the need to observe and record social symptoms as keenly as they feel their responsibility in the clinical field. The technique of learning is the same as for medical and nursing symptoms, and in many schools students are given help by clinical instructors. When students make nursing care studies or patient care studies the instructor has an excellent opportunity to point out the social symptoms and to show their relation to the medical and nursing situations.

The nurse is sometimes made more aware of the existence of a problem if a social worker is also interested in the patient. Conferences between nurses and social workers help to bring these workers closer together in working out plans for any patient. The nurse in other instances may become aware of the existence of social problems from listening to the patient's conversation. With very little encouragement, patients talk to the nurses who are giving bedside nursing, and often their conversations center about their troubles and their family's difficulties. The young nurse should be guided by the clinical instructor for the interpretation of these problems and their relation to the medical and illness situation.

Often, having recognized that a problem exists, the next thing to decide is what should be done about it. It may be that the social worker should be consulted, and in this the young student will be guided by her instructor. It may be that the nurse can give the necessary help in situations where budgeting or food planning for the family seem to be at the base of the trouble. It may be that the patient is unduly worried about the outcome of his illness and sometimes he will talk to the nurse about his fears. It may be wise, in many instances, to consult his doctor since these fears may be the result of incomplete or erroneous information about his condition. A thorough explanation from his doctor may do much to relieve him of these worries.

The nurse soon learns to accept all social information concerning her patients in an interested yet professional way. She must learn to consider the patient's personality and his reserves. To be successful in her contacts with patients, she learns to be sensitive to his moods and will avoid any discussion of his personal affairs where others may hear. When the social service department, the clinic, or the hospital clears cases with the Social Service Exchange, the nurse will get some knowledge of the patient from the study of the record. She will at least learn what social agencies have had contact with the patient, and, from a knowledge of the type of services rendered by these agencies, she will get some idea of the problems that he has had.

The fears and insecurity, which may be evident during the nurse's contact with the patient, are very real and must be understood by her if she is to give complete nursing care. The importance of the nurse's studying the whole patient as well as expertly carrying out technical procedures is stressed today. This implies that she must study each of her patients and try to appreciate the background and experiences out of which his present attitudes become fixed. She needs to be aware not only of the medical and nursing problems associated with the patient and his disease, but also of the social problems which have developed or become accentuated because of the disease situation.

The nurse in the community who is faced with such problems, either financial or emotional, or the more involved adjustment situations in personal relationship will turn to the resources of her community, which from experience she knows are best suited to help with any individual problems. She may start by studying the information obtained from the Social Service Exchange about the patient and his family. Social agencies that know the patient now, or knew him in the past, may be better equipped to help him in his present difficulty. From her detailed analysis of the patient and his present situation and from her knowledge of the functions of existing social agencies in her community, the nurse will decide where she may advise the patient to get help in his present situation.

Thus it is important for every nurse, in the hospital as well as in the public health field, to know the resources in her community. The cooperation which she is able to give to workers of other agencies will depend not only upon her understanding of the patient's problem, but also upon her knowledge of how the various agencies function and what help they can give in any particular problem.

THE INTERVIEW

The successful detection and treatment of social and health problems is often dependent on successful interviewing by the professional workers attempting to help the patient and his family. It is most important for the nurse to train herself in the techniques of interviewing. Some references will be found at the end of this section in this area. A few of the most important techniques are presented here.

The interview is a technique of obtaining evidence. The nurse needs to understand the patient as an individual and in order to do this she must be familiar with his background and his family group. She needs to know his personal likes and dislikes, his antagonisms, as well as his attitudes to himself in illness and health, to other individuals in his family, in his work and social groups in the community. Most of this information she can get only from the patient's conversation. This information, to be of greatest help, must be given spontaneously by the patient in the way and at the time when he wants to give it and can seldom, if ever, be adequately obtained in a formal question and answer period. It is strange that while the nurse is frequently interviewing many individuals, as well as patients, very little formal instruction in the technique of interviewing has been given. Some of the fundamental principles in interviewing are described here. It is not intended that this description or the techniques mentioned here in any way cover the field of interviewing, and the nurse should utilize opportunities to improve her interviewing technique by any facilities or opportunities available in her agency or community.

In the beginning, students may feel confusion, difficulty, and even embarrassment when talking to patients or other professional workers or when listening to these individuals discuss what she feels are "personal" situations and problems. It is not unusual for students beginning in this field to feel that they are prying into the patient's personal and family affairs. Sometimes students unwittingly may find themselves in difficult situations with patients, families, doctors, or other community and health workers because of tactlessness in getting or using such information. It is very important from the very beginning that the nurse consider all such information in a matter-of-fact way, that it be considered confidential and the patient and his family must have the greatest confidence that the nurse will hold all of these matters in the strictest confidence so that mutual respect can be established between the patient and his family and the nurse. No valuation should be placed on this information as far as passing judgment on it is concerned. The fact that a patient and his family may have different standards or place different valuation on certain of their activities and behavior must not be accepted as right or wrong by the nurse. The fact that a patient's standards may be different or even unacceptable for the nurse should not in any way create either rejection of the patient and his activities or create the situation where the patient feels that the nurse is passing judgment, and usually unfavorably, on him and his behavior. The nurse does not necessarily have to show approval or disapproval of the patient's behavior, but he must be assured that he will be accepted for what he is and not because he has or has not met certain standards. The student will soon learn by the patient's behavior and conversation that often feelings of inferiority and insecurity are covered up by complaints demanding service, rejection of hospital and health routines and authority, and sometimes by boasting and misrepresentation of facts.

Techniques in Interviewing.—Little of any interview is the direct question and answer technique. It is used only in obtaining necessary identifying information, and this is usually done in the first interview where such information as the address, marital status, age, number of children, place of work, etc., is obtained. Once this information has been obtained and perhaps verified, the direct question and answer part of any interview is usually at an end. The interview has sometimes been described as a specialized conversation. It has also been descrived as a series of interacting relationships between two or more people where every response becomes a stimulus for another response, and after each stimulus and response period, a new level of relationship is attained by the interviewer and interviewee respectively. Every interview should be considered as a reciprocal process with much give and take. For example, the nurse may initiate and perhaps guide the interview in the beginning, but she may soon find that she is answering many of the patient's questions in regard to himself, his condition, his social problems, resources in the community, and all this lays the ground for a more satisfactory acceptance on his part of his responsibility to himself and his problems. In first interviews the nurse must be concerned not only with getting information but on establishing rapport on which later contact can be developed. The willingness of the patient to participate in his program for rehabilitation, medical and social, may depend on the success of these early interviews. The aims of any first interview might be summarized as follows:

1. To give the patient an opportunity for a fair and unhurried hearing.
2. To establish as early as possible a good basis for further interviews.
3. To get a deeper insight into the difficulties of his situation by securing clues and other sources of information.
4. To begin as soon as possible the process of developing self-help and self-reliance.

The nurse is often so eager to help the patient and to influence him to do what she thinks is the "right" thing that she may forget that real and lasting therapy, medical or social, is dependent on the patient's activity, interest, and willingness to work out his own problems.

As stated above, very little of any interview is conducted by the direct question and answer method. The nurse must be alert and must approach each interview with as much preparation as possible. It is very annoying to most individuals to be asked the same questions over and over again. In fact, in hospitals and clinics it is not uncommon to find patients who, having been asked questions about the same things by many, many individuals, doctors, nurses, social workers, occupational therapists, etc., have memorized certain routine answers to these questions. In fact, sometimes patients have been found who have set answers written down to these rather set questions. All professional workers must refrain from institutionalization in their interviews. It is so easy to get into the habit of asking set questions when we wish to get certain types of information. Very often, of course, the kind of question that is asked will initiate in the patient's mind the kind of answer that we want or that he thinks we want, and it will not give us the complete picture which is necessary if we are to understand the total situation.

The nurse should study all data that has been accumulated about any patient. For this she is likely to read the patient's clinical chart either in hospital, clinic, or health agency in the community. All facts in this chart should be understood and, if indicated, she will want to talk with other nurses or doctors who have an interest in the patient. She will also want to study information from social service records or from the records of any other professional workers interested in the patient that may be available to her.

In all interviewing, observation is a very important technique. The nurse has a great advantage in the area of observation since she has been taught it is important. Ever since entering the school of nursing she has been shown the importance of observing the patient when she is performing certain nursing duties. She has been taught the importance of observing and accurately reporting the patient's symptoms and progress as an aid to diagnosis and therapy. While some of the instruction may stress clinical signs and symptoms, the nurse today is also taught to observe the total patient. His attitudes and moods should be noted. His reaction to the hospital, to doctors, to nurses, to members of his family, to other patients should be observed. In the home, the student should observe family relationships, noting particularly their strength as well as antagonisms. Watching the facial expressions is very important in any interview. This has been pointed out by certain experts in this field.[2] It is pointed out that embarrassment, such as might be portrayed by flush, an unconscious wince, or argumentative tone of voice, or a desire to evade certain topics, may disclose certain difficult problems which the patient wishes to avoid at that particular time. It is very important that some fixed and rather stereotyped attitudes be considered in interviewing. For example, in many instances the nurse and the doctor may be associated with authority. Young students may feel that it is easier to use the authoritarian advantage in getting the patient to carry out certain treatments rather than taking the necessary time and effort to explain all steps to the patient and to help the patient to understand, accept, and put forth effort necessary for him to participate fully in the complete health picture.

In addition to observation, the student soon learns the importance of listening. The nurse must avoid too evident direction of any conversation. She will soon recognize the importance of letting the patient choose not only the subject but also the time at which he wishes to talk and the topics that he wishes to discuss. Very often particular topics on which the patient wishes to concentrate in conversation will, in themselves, be an indication of the importance of certain aspects of the problem to him, and equally the avoidance of certain aspects of the situation may indicate reluctance on his part to discuss these topics. Perhaps, when better understanding has been established, these reserves may be broken down. In asking questions, in guiding the conversation, the student must understand that it is important to talk in terms that will be understood by the patient. Unconsciously the nurse quickly picks up hospital slang and institutionalized ways not only of asking questions but also of discussing certain situations. It is interesting to note the patients who have been in hospitals or clinics frequently pick up much hospital slang and can talk in a very familiar way about many of the hospital routines. However, not all patients can do this. Again, the student remembers that the average person in the community today is much better educated in matters of health and disease than his parents. Therefore, it is not surprising to find individuals very well informed. Mass communication, health programs in school and industry, in addition to the health teaching that has been carried on for many years by doctors, nurses, medical-social workers, and

---

[2]Young, Pauline: Interviewing in Social Work, New York, McGraw-Hill Book Company, Inc., 1935, page 58. (See also references at the end of chapter.)

other members of the health team, are definitely having results so that the nurse must avoid either talking over the patient's head or talking down to him. Either approach may handicap her in getting or in establishing the desirable relationship.

An accurate record should be kept of every interview. It is not considered the best technique to appear with notebook and pencil at the patient's bedside in hospital, clinic, or home. However, it is very important that the interviewer make full and detailed notes about each interview just as soon as possible. Most student nurses are encouraged to have a small notebook which may be carried in the uniform pocket. Into this notebook would go observations, the results of conversations, information obtained from records, from various conferences, from talking to the patient's family or to anyone interested in him. Observations and conversations noted down as soon as possible can be elaborated later on when the complete record is being made.

CONCLUSION

The nurse has a great advantage over many other workers in establishing satisfactory relationship with the patient and his family, since she is looked upon as a person who has helped the patient, who can do something to relieve his immediate health problem, and in whom the patient and his family have confidence. Therefore, she should do everything to make him comfortable physically and mentally by carrying out her professional nursing duties as efficiently as possible and at the same time incorporating all of the techniques necessary to establish good personal relationships with him and his family.

STUDY QUESTIONS AND PROJECTS

1. Describe what may make a situation a community problem.
2. Select one problem in your community and trace its history. At what stage is it now and what is being done about it?
3. For what reasons should the interviewee always play the dominant part during an interview?
4. What are the characteristics of a successful interview?
5. Write down in detail an interview in which you have been
   (a) an interviewee
   (b) an interviewer
6. Show from Number 5 how your position will influence your part in any interview.

REFERENCES

Cuber, John F., and Harper, Robert A.: Problems of American Society: Values in Conflict, New York, 1949, Henry Holt and Co., Inc.

Fairs, Robert E. L.: Social Disorganization, New York, 1948, The Ronald Press Co.

Fenlason, Anna F.: Essentials in Interviewing, New York, 1952, Harper & Brothers.

Gillan, J. L.: Social Pathology, New York, 1946, D. Appleton-Century Company, Inc.

Halliday, James L.: Psychosocial Medicine: A Study of the Sick Society, New York, 1948, W. W. Norton & Company, Inc.

Herman, Abbott, P.: An Approach to Social Problems, Boston, 1949, Ginn and Company.

Lee, A. M., and Lee, E. B.: Social Problems in America, New York, 1949, Henry Holt & Company, Inc.

Mowrer, Ernest R.: Disorganization: Personal and Social, Philadelphia, 1942, J. B. Lippincott Company.

Phelps, H. A., and Henderson, David: Contemporary Social Problems, ed. 4, New York, 1952, Prentice-Hall, Inc.

CHAPTER 2

TEAMWORK

INTRODUCTION

In no area of activity is teamwork more necessary than that of the finding, diagnosis, treatment, and prevention of community problems. It has been stated that no problem is the result of one single cause. A multiplicity of causes have led to the existence of the problem. It has also been pointed out that seldom, if ever, is a problem an individual one but it involves the family or groups and the community. The nurse today very soon learns that in the strictly medical therapeutic sense, the doctor and the nurse can no longer work alone. Great developments in the whole broad field of medicine and health have resulted in many specialized fields and many professional and sub-professional workers in these fields. Take, for example, the many workers in the hospital. In addition to the doctor and the nurse today, there will be found dietitians, medical technicians, librarians, occupational therapists, physiotherapists, medical-social workers, recreation workers, religious workers, just to name those most frequently found. In the broader community, other workers soon become familiar to the nurse. One might mention ministers, teachers and other individuals in the broad field of education, specialized social workers such as those in the field of child welfare, those who have special interests in the field of crime and delinquency, those who have specialized interest in the unemployed, the physically handicapped, the aged, just to mention a few. With many of these workers the nurse is in close association and a free interchange of information and activities is essential if the patient is to profit by these specialized services. The integration of all of these services presents a problem to every health agency, including the hospital. In addition to the personnel looked upon strictly as hospital personnel, that is perhaps the dietitian, the laboratory technician, the occupational physiotherapist, it is quite likely that the medical-social worker will be the person whose work must be understood by the nurse and with whom she will work most closely both in the hospital and in the community. Therefore it is essential that she understand the field of social work, particularly that specialized area known as medical-social work.

THE SOCIAL WORKER

Medical-social work is a specialized field within the broad area of social case work. Too often in the past the impression has been that the medical-social worker is interested primarily in the economically handicapped. The nurse recognizes by now that many problems are not strictly economic in nature and as a result of the very complex society today many forces tend to disrupt the individual and the family's way of life. Because of the complexity of our society, many of these problems cannot be dealt with satisfactorily by the individual or even by his family. The object of all social work is to help the individual to use his own and the community's resources in solving his problems. Social case work is a skilled technique of working with individuals to help them remove the obstacles to their effective functioning. Skilled understanding and consideration are necessary to deal satisfactorily with the problems of personal relationship and with illness or any other problem.

Increasing emphasis by doctors for the social as well as the medical study of patients has greatly increased the demand for trained medical-social work. Medical-social work is a specialized form of general social work and gives services to individuals where medical-social problems cease to predominate. The medical-social worker is trained to help the physician and the nurse achieve the goal not only of curing the disease but also of preventing its occurrence or recurrence and of helping the patient and his family find the most satisfactory adjustment to the situation. The medical-social worker, then, is a member of the health team together with the physician and the nurse.

Functions of the Medical-Social Worker.—This specialized type of social work developed because of the recognition of the importance of social factors in the diagnosis, prevention, and treatment of disease. The relationship between disease and such factors as poverty, ignorance, inadequate diet, poor housing, occupational conditions, and many others is being studied by doctors, social workers, and public health nurses. The activities of the social workers are many but might be summarized as follows:

1. Inquiry into the social situation of patients and the reporting of these findings to the responsible physician.

2. Determining the factors in the social situation pertinent to the patient's health, analysis of inter-relationships and formulating these as medical-social diagnosis.

3. Defining objectives and the role which the social worker is to play in helping the patient to achieve the possible goal. Both Steps 2 and 3 are performed in collaboration with the physician and often with the nurse.

4. Interpretation of the meaning of the medical-social situation to: (a) the patient group; (b) cooperating professional persons or agency. In some cases social treatment ends at this point since both groups can be counted on to carry on effectively by themselves.

5. Integration of services: (a) within the hospital, emphasis largely on the social aspects; (b) without the hospital, emphasis largely on medical aspects as having social significance. This varies from the fourth classification in that the social worker more definitely plans with and endeavors to influence the action of both groups, remaining in and playing a part in the situation longer.

6. Performance by the worker herself of more specific services relating closely to the adjustment of the patient and requiring an understanding of the whole person and his total situation. Through the process of specialization and division of labor among the various professions these fall to her.

Social case work, particularly for the chronic and physically disabled, and the arrangement and management of convalescence is in many instances worked out with the public health nurse. Thus, interprofessional relationships and understanding are necessary if the patient is going to benefit from these services.

The actual medical treatment suggested is often the key for the social treatment. Radical changes in the patient's habitual ways of behaving may not only necessitate interpretation from the medical-social worker but also help during the adjustment period. These may involve changes in diet, in work, in prolonged periods of rest, and others. Thus the social worker is concerned mainly with the social problems which develop directly because of the medical condition and treatment. She facilitates and extends medical treatment, especially after the patient leaves the hospital. She may provide special apparatus, arrange for diet, convalescent care, transportation to and from the clinic, and so forth.

Much of the medical social treatment, however, is concerned with the adjustment of the patient's social role and relationships. She is concerned with studying and treating the physical and economic strains due to the illness and the emotional aspects. Often this means the provision of occupation or recreation during convalescent periods and during chronic illness. The importance of occupational therapy in keeping up morale is being recognized in general hospitals and in psychiatric institutions.

Medical social treatment has a strong environmental basis. This may mean adjustments, temporary or permanent, in the physical environment. An obvious example is the case of the cardiac patient who should not climb steps, and whose removal from second or third floor to ground floor is indicated. Change in occupation or in place or mode of living may be needed and may call for the specialized services of the medical-social worker.

Interpretation is Another Important Phase of Medical-Social Treatment.—This may be summarized as follows:

1. Interpretation of the social factors may contribute a great deal to the diagnostic process.

2. Interpretation may be given to other professional workers either without or within the hospital. The interpretation of the medical-social problem may be given to nurses as well as doctors, to occupational therapists, nutritionists, and other individuals interested in the patient.

3. Interpretation must always be given to the patient and his group, particularly when there are conflicts and problems in adjusting to the illness or in carrying out the treatment.

Thus it can be seen that the medical-social worker is concerned mainly with relating medical and social factors and in the study of the treatment of problems growing out of such relationships. This service may be needed particularly in recurrent and chronic diseases, in cases of physical handicaps and invalidism. She, together with the doctor and the nurse, individualizes the patient. Because of her detailed study of the patient in all his social relationships, she is able to contribute to other members of the medical team facts which may influence the progress of the medical treatment.

THE NURSE AND MEDICAL-SOCIAL WORK

It is obvious by now why the nurse needs to understand and cooperate with the medical-social worker. The nurse is an active member of the medical team of which the doctor is the leader. Because of the highly specialized medical treatment that has developed, many specialists may function in this medical team. The dietitian, the occupational therapist, and others in addition to the medical-social worker, the nurse, and the doctor may be involved in sharing responsibility for satisfactory medical treatment. It is essential then, in order to obtain good results, that each member of the team appreciate the work of the others and cooperate to the fullest extent, so that the patient may get the greatest benefit from their combined efforts. The nurse, because of her close and prolonged contact with the patient, can, if she has been so trained, make pertinent observations on the physical and emotional state. These observations, if accurately reported and recorded, may contribute to the total picture presented, and may influence the trend of medical and social treatment being followed.

THE OCCUPATIONAL THERAPIST AS A MEMBER OF THE TEAM

An occupational therapist is a professional person trained in the field of occupational therapy. This is rather a new field as an organized profession; however, the theory behind it is very old. During World Wars I and II, the need for the services of the occupational therapist was evident and gave great stimulus to this field. Between World Wars I and II, it developed in civilian hospitals and clinics. Occupational therapy has been described as any activity, mental or physical, prescribed by a physician for its remedial value. The aims are to arouse an interest and confidence in the patient and to exercise his mind and body to help overcome his disability and to reestablish security for vocational and social activity. The theory underlying occupational therapy is that through activity, physical and mental exercise and satisfaction, better communication with individuals and with one's environment, takes place. When one's normal activity is interrupted by disease or injury, an individual may lose his initiative temporarily or may have to change their accustomed activities. When a patient remains inactive, he often develops a sense of helplessness and isolation which in themselves will slow up his convalescence. Through manual, creative, recreational, educational, or cultural activity, under the direction of a physician, the occupational therapist works out special remedial programs for the individual patient. The therapist varies her media and technique to suit the age and sex of the patient, as well as his physical or mental condition. Occupational therapy, which was started and carried out first within hospitals, is now extended to outpatient departments and to patients in their own homes. While the individual help given to the patient is at first often a means of physical rehabilitation, it serves, however, in restoring the patient's confidence in himself and in preparing the patient for returning to group activity and for holding a job in the community.

THE PHYSICAL THERAPIST

With development in the whole field of rehabilitation, the work of the physical therapist has become increasingly important. Many nurses are accustomed to a physical therapy department and have an understanding of the activities of the physical therapist. However, with increasing emphasis placed on rehabilitation for many different types of patients, as well as those traditionally handicapped or the chronically ill, the activities of the physical therapist become more important. The physical therapist often makes contact with patients much earlier in their convalescence than in the past and often with the nursing staff works out activities for muscular development and for the carrying out of body mechanics.

OTHER SPECIAL SERVICES

The role of the most frequently found professional workers comprising the team has been described. Other workers would include the nutritionist, the vocational counseling expert, the special workers in the field of education, music, and other fields where certain services may seem to contribute to the treatment or the rehabilitation of the patient.

CONCLUSION

In this complex diagnostic, therapeutic, and preventive situation, it is recognized, of course, that good teamwork is essential. If the patient and his family are to benefit from skills represented by these different professional workers, integration and cooperation must exist between them. An understanding of the activities of the other workers is essential for each member of the team. Accompanying this understanding, of course, will be genuine interest in each patient and concern for providing as complete care as possible. It is important in order that patients and their families get the greatest benefit, as well as from the point of view of economy, that every effort be made by each worker to use the contribution of other members of the team as extensively as possible.

Working together also involves a knowledge of community agencies and of the resources which are available through these agencies and which certain professional workers can arrange. The division of responsibility is often outlined by the agency. Collaboration and the sharing of information is necessary and this is often accomplished through group conferences where all of the workers interested in the patient come together regularly to evaluate the situation and to pool their information and ideas and to make plans for his future treatment.

STUDY QUESTIONS AND PROJECTS

1. What is implied by teamwork in social diagnosis and therapy?
2. Name and describe the functions of other workers on the health team.
3. Describe medical-social work and show what it may contribute to medical diagnosis and treatment.
4. Analyse the history of any patient as found in the records to show (a) how teamwork between different professional workers contributed to his total recovery or (b) how the absence of teamwork slowed up and prevented good recovery.

REFERENCES

Bachmeyer, Arthur C. (ed. by): The Hospital in Modern Society, New York, 1943, The Commonwealth Fund.

Cooley, Carol H.: Social Aspects of Illness, Philadelphia, 1951, W. B. Saunders Company.

Robinson, Canby: The Patient as a Person, New York, 1937, The Commonwealth Fund.

Sensenich, H.: Teamwork in Rehabilitation, Am. J. Pub. Health **40**:969, 1950.

Stattel, Florence M.: The Student Occupational Therapist, American Journal of Occupational Therapy **2**:162-164, June, 1948.

Thornton, Janet, and Knauth, Majorie Straus: The Social Component in Medical Care, New York, 1937, Columbia University Press.

Upham, Frances: A Dynamic Approach to Illness, New York, 1949, Family Service Association of America.

CHAPTER 3

THE NATURE OF COMMUNITY PROBLEMS

A PROBLEM OF SETTING

The nurse in her contact with an ill patient is concerned first with ameliorating the physical condition of the patient, but she is soon aware that the illness is but one of the many problems surrounding him, and that she is but one of the many persons concerned with helping him recover. As has been admirably stated by Dr. Koos,[1] the patient is first an individual in his own right, then a member of a family, of the community, of the labor force; and all of these affect his adjustment to his illness. Thus, the nurse must be aware of the patient as a person and in respect to the milieu which surrounds him. To help her understand this, the bulk of this book is dedicated.

The nurse, furthermore, whether working in a hospital, with a public health agency, or in a doctor's office, is also aware of the community in which she is working and the resources there for helping persons. Troubles seem to beget troubles, and many have observed the interrelatedness of health and welfare problems; ill health means loss of job or lessening of earning, which means less financial security, perhaps producing more illness. Undoubtedly any nurse will encounter many persons who desire nothing further from the nurse than her professional skill. Personal and financial problems can be solved insofar as these patients are concerned. On the contrary, many patients have multiple needs. Even if these needs are not within the sphere of competence of the nurse, she can only understand her patient and be most helpful to him when she is aware of the larger forces which impinge on the patient and on which he depends. The importance of the family is considered in a following chapter. This chapter emphasizes social problems of the community resulting from social and personal disorganization.

---

[1]Koos, Earl L.: The Sociology of the Patient, New York, 1950, McGraw-Hill Book Company, Inc.

Social problems may be academic in the by and large, but when they actually touch the individual it is because they have become localized in the immediate environment. As has been said in a recent study:

> It is always well to remind ourselves of the simple truth that it is in the community that people have troubles and seek solutions for them. The community is the place where people benefit much or little from services provided in their behalf. Here must converge all the particular ideas about what these services should be, what degree of protection they should afford against the hazards of modern living, and what enhancement they should bring to family and personal well-being. This is true even when the services are paid for out of a federal or state pocket and carried out by a hierarchy of ascending administrative levels.[2]

The community, then, is the place where one notices social conditions and forms one's judgment of whether or not the conditions seem to be favorable for fostering social progress or hindering it. If they seem to be negative, such as disease producing, they tend to be regarded as problems, conditions which should be corrected. Particularly if these conditions may be deemed harmful to large numbers of people, a strong compulsion to remedy them or mitigate their effects is widely felt. Obviously value judgments are being made when conditions are termed good or bad. No universally accepted standards exist to identify social problems, although many are looked upon with disfavor or taboo in varying cultures. Social problems are related to the social groups in which they are found because they represent threats to the integrity of existing social organization.

SOCIAL ORGANIZATION AND SOCIAL CHANGE

Social organization may be considered as comprising all those processes which build up group life and enable it to meet crises and conflict situations so that the group survives and carries on its accepted tasks. Social organization also includes all those relationships which persons and groups find satisfactory, enabling them to function effectively. Any society at any time is a product of its past culture and its manner of adapting to changes brought about by mechanical inventions and new ideas. While there may be some primitive cultures today,

---

²Buell, Bradley, and Associates: Community Planning for Human Services, New York, 1952, Columbia University Press, page 7.

and there have been in the past, where social organization is static, the concept of social organization must be a dynamic one. Social changes are occurring rapidly, compelling societies to make some adjustments to them. Some changes can be incorporated into the culture patterns very readily; others require for acceptance many corollary changes in other inventions or modification of prevailing ideas. The length of time between the social changes and their acceptance into the existing social organization is called by the sociologists "cultural lag."

Early scientific ideas advanced by Galileo were met with great resistance on the part of the society of his time, because of their contradiction of firmly held beliefs. Great conflict followed their pronouncements, and, of course, Galileo was forced to say he was wrong. The invention of the automobile, while viewed with initial skepticism, proved so useful and enjoyable it was rapidly assimilated into the culture. Nevertheless, many changes were necessitated by the introduction of this new machine. Garages and filling stations had to be erected to service it; better roads were demanded to facilitate traveling; different accommodations for those touring were needed. A new system of marking roads and drafting road maps was established. Traffic rules and lights were required, accidents led to growth of insurance provisions and safety education courses. No doubt exists, however, that the automobile has become a firmly fixed part of our culture and that the existing social organizations have adapted to this minor social upheaval.

Social changes do not necessarily create social problems, for a social problem can only exist when society regards conditions as troublesome. The offending situation must be so out of harmony with prevailing values that it calls attention to itself. If a society is unconcerned about the deaths of children or the health of people because a low value is placed on human life, high infant mortality and morbidity rates will not be causes of alarm. If girl children are economic liabilities to a family, and it is an accepted custom that they be virtually sold for prostitutes, then prostitution will be no problem to that society. One might say that few social problems were created by the automobile until the number of fatal accidents increased so greatly. In a society such as ours, which places a high value on human life, needless fatalities have been a cause of concern and efforts have been directed toward correcting conditions causing them. So social change is always occurring and will inevitably affect the existing social organization and institutions. To the extent that the culture resists or has difficulty accommodating itself to the changes, social problems may develop. The present age in which we live is experiencing some rapid social change, particularly from highly technical results of the discovery of atomic energy.

CONCEPTS OF SOCIAL DISORGANIZATION

In the process of adapting to social change, disorganization may result in one or more of the basic social institutions. Several concepts of social disorganization exist,[3] but, as used here, disorganization of social institutions or personal disorganization affecting existing social institutions constitute our limited discussion of the subject. Social disorganization may result from conflicts between man and his environment, as widespread famine or floods; or it may result from conflict between social groups, as wars or strikes. So long as personal disorganization concerns only a few persons who are cared for by their family, society is not affected. But when personal disorganization becomes so widespread that individual capacity to care for them is taxed, the community is threatened because of their presence and measures must be taken to provide some means of care, personal disorganization has affected social institutions. Such conditions are commonly seen in the mentally ill, the juvenile and adult offenders, the alcoholics.

Whatever the cause for the breakdown in the orderly arrangement of community affairs, both social and personal disorganization affect individuals and society. Breakdowns in social institutions may cause unemployment, breed family distintegration, cause despair and personal deterioration. Society is undermined if too many individuals are existing and working against the established goals or are incapable of contributing to society.

Degrees of social organization and disorganization exist. At any one time, some disorganizing factors may have interrupted or slowed the orderly assimilation of social changes, not severe enough to disrupt all social forces. Widespread and sweeping social disorganization usually results only from war or catastrophes. Social disorganization, too, tends to be cumulative, that is, disrupting aspects influence more and more social processes until eventual breakdown. This can be seen in disturbances to economic institutions as in a steel strike. First, the steel production stops; factories using the products are next affected;

---

[3]The student is referred to Elliot, Mabel A., and Merrill, Francis E.: Social Disorganization, Rev. edition, New York, 1950, Harper & Brothers; Faris, Robert E. L.: Social Disorganization, New York, 1948, The Ronald Press; Bloch, Herbert A.: Disorganization: Personal and Social, New York, 1952, Alfred A. Knopf, Inc.

carriers of steel may have to slow down their activities; buying power of the workers is curtailed and, if steps are not taken to avert it, large scale social disorganization can result. Some crisis situations develop, however, due mainly to epidemics, floods, typhoons, tornadoes, sometimes called "acts of God," because of man's inability to avoid them. In the wake of such events, a community is left with business and trade interrupted, channels of communication destroyed, persons homeless, normal safety and sanitary measures out of balance, imminence of further disruption through accidents or disease, anxiety and fear upsetting the people. Sometimes martial law must be invoked to prevent looting and wholly undisciplined behavior. The orderly process of community life is curtailed for an indefinite time. To a certain extent communities have been able to forestall such outbreaks due to progress in scientific knowledge. No longer do epidemics of the "black plague" or cholera sweep a country. Warnings of typhoons can avert some disaster. Floods can be partially controlled.

Communities may also plan against disruption on a wide or small scale. Most towns and cities have some plans for a disaster whereby emergency shelters are erected, communications are reestablished, food supplies are made available. The American Red Cross has been active in this area as nurses may well be aware since they are members of such teams. Civilian Defense plans in World War II, which were not used, fortunately, had prepared against an emergency from enemy attack. At the present, plans for civilian defense are reactivated.

Inevitably a relationship between personal disorganization and social disorganization exists because of the effect of social breakdown on the individual and the effect on the community of personal breakdown on a large scale. Indices of social breakdown which can be found in any community are measured usually in human terms, the numbers of persons on relief, on strike, sick, alcoholic, offenders, the relation of divorces to marriages, all involve community problems from personal breakdown. Societal factors may be found from poor housing, unsanitary conditions, poor roads, inability to control disease or fire.

Later in this book many problems both of social and personal disorganization are discussed. As examples of the effects of social disorganization, minority and transient problems are discussed here. Personal breakdown is exemplified by the problem of the prostitute.

MINORITY PROBLEMS IN A COMMUNITY

The basis of conflict between groups of people in every society stems from competition, jealousy, and prejudice. In this country our Constitution mentions life, liberty, pursuit of happiness, and equal opportunities for all. Actually many barriers are placed in the attainment of these goals and groups will fight ruthlessly, emotionally, and doggedly to keep others from having certain opportunities of housing, schooling, and employment.

These differences which lead to tensions and open hostility are more than conflicts between the "haves" and the "have nots" in our society. The problems in this country result from the growth in the United States itself and the principles for which this country has stood. The very democratic nature of our government lured large numbers of immigrants to our shores. The need for labor in industrialization, the growth of the west, and the expansion of cities presented economic opportunity to many. Need for labor in the fields of the south led in large part to the importation of many of the Negro race; perhaps they were the only ones who came involuntarily. Most of the other groups responded to the financial and philosophical advantages, or left undesirable and unattractive situations in their own country. The racial minority groups, Negroid and Mongoloid, in this country have not always been welcomed. Familiar to all readers of newspapers are instances of unfair discrimination against members of these races in employment opportunities. In many places, particularly for the Negro race, school facilities are segregated and are far from being equal to those provided for the majority group. Health facilities are not equal and this is evidenced in the higher infant death rate of nonwhite children and the lower life expectancy than the white. Applied to any specific community, minority prejudices will mean less desirable housing facilities available and fewer employment opportunities. The community will not be deriving the maximum usefulness from its manpower resources, since potentialities of many are being wasted. Maintaining a dual set of services as schools, colleges, hospitals, etc., increases the cost to the taxpayers for these services and may reduce the quality of service offered.

Probably prejudice, often not fully understood, against the members of these racial minorities accounts for the community's action against the members. Prejudice and hostility arise in many instances from a struggle for survival on the part of the lower-economic class where competition for jobs is more intense. Ignorance and indifference are also accountable for attitudes which are assumed toward others. Many of these attitudes and feelings are acquired at a very early age. In a study of race awareness in young children, the author commented, "It is shocking to find that four-year-olds, particularly white ones, show unmistakable signs of the onset of racial bigotry."[4] It is perhaps shocking also to find so much resistance on the part of adults to finding solutions for these problems.

Many dissatisfactions have been voiced with these relations, and efforts have been made to reduce and eventually to eliminate some causes for group tension. Progress has been slow, but there has been progress. Insistence by the federal government and other public agencies that public programs show no discrimination has had some effects. Supreme Court decisions compelling state universities to admit Negro students or to furnish equal facilities have reflected the judicial point of view.

TRANSIENTS AND MIGRATORY WORKERS

Our economic institutions have not entirely achieved satisfactory relations between demand and supply of labor, and have shown evidences of some social disorganization. During the thirties the economic system weakened so that factories were forced to close and millions of persons were thrown out of work. Family life became disorganized; ill-health and malnourishment developed. Unemployment has also resulted from improvement in our inventions so that machines will do the work of men. Unemployment due to technological improvements has been less widely disruptive than a depression, but a sizable number of workers have had to transplant themselves and their families to other jobs in other places.

Nor has there been financial security for the wage earner in industry, and the insecurity has been the greater, the less skilled the worker. At the bottom of the list is the migratory agricultural worker who has had no security in job or home. The need for the unskilled picker of fruits and vegetables varies seasonally and geographically; furthermore, the over-all trend has been down in recent decades due to improved machinery which aids techniques of production. So the opportunity for the migrant is reduced. The migrant worker and his family face countless social and economic problems, some of which are

---

[4]Goodman, Mary Ellen: Race Awareness in Young Children, Cambridge, Mass., 1952, Addison-Wesley Press, Inc., page 218.

enumerated here. The low place of the migrant worker may be seen in these quotations from a recent report of the government's "Commission on Migratory Labor."

> Beyond wanting migrants to be available when needed and to be gone when not needed, they are expected to work under conditions no longer typical or characteristic of the American standard of life. In a period of rapidly advancing job and employment standards, we expect them to work at employment which, for all practical purposes, has no job standards. In saying this, we refer not alone to such matters as bad housing, poor sanitation, lack of medical facilities, and the problems of feeding, rearing, and schooling children. These are conditions which, over the years, have received condemnation; yet despite some improvement, for the most part they remain unsolved problems and there is little organized effort to deal with them. . . . . . Although migratory farm laborers have more need for medical and hospital care than most other segments of the population, the evidence shows, with some exceptions, that they get the least. Child labor is still a serious problem due to poverty and need. Migrant children are among those with the lowest educational attainments found in the United States. Nor are they likely to get educational opportunities so long as they work during school hours and move from place to place with their parents in search of employment. In addition children of migrants suffer from discrimination and social stigma which exclude them from full participation in the community.[5]

Not only are the social conditions in a community affected by the presence of the domestic migratory labor, but a problem of importation of labor for seasonal work and the illegal entrance of laborers from Mexico, the "Wetbacks," place the family man in an unfavorable bargaining condition. Because, further, none of these workers usually stays long enough to become a real part of the community, their problems are of the federal government rather than the state. Suggestions for improving the conditions have included coordination of public programs, elimination of alien contract labor, or, if used with citizens from Puerto Rico and Hawaii, better labor conditions in open contract labor, better housing, facilities for health and welfare programs, educational provisions and elimination of child labor.

---

[5]Migratory Labor in American Agriculture, Report of the President's Commission on Migratory Labor, 1951, pp. 16-17, 155, 167.

This particular problem is somewhat limited. A million migratory farm laborers are leading this migratory life. They work on only about 2 per cent of all the farms. Many of these people have children. Their annual earnings averaged $514 in 1949.[6] Altogether a disadvantage lot, their existence is characterized by absence of some of the basic social institutions.

TYPES OF PERSONAL DISORGANIZATION

Atypical and disruptive factors creating social problems from individual breakdown are found in persons who cannot adapt their lives to the group, as the delinquent, the mentally ill, the alcoholic. Multiplicity of individual breakdowns, far beyond the capacity of the individual family, has compelled society to assume responsibility, lest other members of the community become threatened to the point that normal activities are not pursued. The community faces a danger, its members physically harmed, they may become prey to a criminal. So the offender must be removed from society. Society recognizes some responsibility toward the deviant, too, and may provide a hospital for treatment, or custodial care, or a program for rehabilitation.

Individuals whose personality has been disorganized in some way have been increasing in numbers. One can see this in the statistics of local and state governments reporting on the number of patients in mental hospitals, and schools for the feeble-minded, and the number of patients in other types of hospitals, and in the crime reports of those arrested and committed to state correctional institutions. The mass approach obscures all of the individuality. For each figure reported on court statistics, hospital patient load, or on a casualty list there is a person who is or has been at some time a part of a family group, who may have held a job, who belonged to community life, but now, because of breakdowns, has ceased to be able to function up to the standards of the community and has had to have special attention.

Each of these persons has a unique set of factors which has contributed to his breakdown. Succeeding chapters will elaborate in more detail some of the characteristics and causes which have produced specific patterns in the over-all picture. It is probably obvious that the personality of any individual is molded by the social environment in which he lives and his groups, of which the family is most important. Few babies come into this world with personal breakdown at birth.

---

[6]Ibid., p. 125.

The exceptions are those born mentally deficient, or with severe physical abnormalities to prevent learning, and the psychopaths; all others acquire their patterns of divergence from the normally accepted pattern as they grow. The largest groups of these personally maladjusted who need care or restraint from the community are the mentally ill, the alcoholics, the mentally deficient, the offenders, both juvenile and adult. Physically ill persons likewise need provisions in the community for treatment, but their need stems from some physical defect which is not necessarily of itself a menace to society unless there be some emotional difficulty in adjusting to the illness.

What are the causes of this personality breakdown which is so detrimental to the individual and society? In many instances it is difficult to fix responsibility; even in the case of some organic mental illnesses and feeble-mindedness where a direct cause and effect relationship can be established, many factors seem to operate before the individual develops into one of these maladjusted misfits. Causes may lie in the environment of home, neighborhood, and school; conflicts may develop within the person, as a result of deprivation of affection, strained relations between person and parent or between siblings. A great fright, or severe shock, or loss of a loved one—many factors work on the individual to weaken his defenses, to increase his feelings of hostility, or guilt, so that finally the unacceptable behavior results. Society does not condone the atypical and makes provision, first, for removing him from society and, second, for reforming or rehabilitating him.

If the individual becomes a prey to the impact of his own little world with its impressions on his mind which cannot be destroyed, he must obviously have been an accepted member of society at some time. Knowledge, then, of personality development can act to prevent breakdown, if knowledge is complete and widely enough disseminated. The cost of caring for all of these people is tremendous. The costs to the state includes providing measures for caring for these persons, police, jails, courts, institutions with all the staff and equipment required to maintain them. This cost could probably be calculated if there were complete figures from all over the United States. But the cost to the individual in lack of satisfaction, in unhappiness, in unproductivity is incalculable; the cost to the family in anxiety, perhaps loss of support, is likewise difficult to measure. Society has its loss, too, in that its potential resources of human beings is being wasted—a drain on society instead of a vital, constructive force. Efforts to treat and rehabilitate the individual, therefore, represent help to the person disorganized and an attack on the social problems. Elsewhere in this book some problems of personality disorganization have been discussed, the mentally ill, the mentally defective, the juvenile and adult delinquent. To illustrate points emphasized, the problem of prostitution will be discussed.

PROSTITUTION

Prostitution has persisted as a social problem over many years, and adaptations have been made in the social organization in some countries to allow for this. Prostitution presents a moral as well as a health problem; its moral aspects are determined by the culture and are less amenable to control than the health aspects. Any kind of extramarital relations have been regarded as wrong in present-day society even though a more tolerant attitude toward the reasons behind the asocial behavior is adopted. Yet apparently urgent sexual needs and the lack of adequate and approved methods of satisfying these have been the basis for the development of prostitution. Moral taboos and legal machinery have failed to eliminate prostitution. On the health side, prostitutes are the most frequent carriers of venereal diseases. The spread of venereal disease in this manner has been controlled by physical examination of prostitutes, licensing of houses of prostitution in some countries, and by information on prophylaxis to the males frequenting such places. The problem of prostitution is still with us and transcends national boundaries.

Both prostitutes and those who visit them represent, on the whole, disorganized individuals, unable to get normal satisfactions from their lives. Most prostitutes drift into that occupation because of unsuccessful and unsatisfactory contacts elsewhere. Some are mentally deficient and should receive protection from society. Some are undoubtedly so disturbed that psychiatric help at some point might have helped them. Many of the frequenters of houses of prostitution are likewise drifters and misfits representing a fair degree of personal disorganization. Others who patronize prostitutes infrequently could perhaps be aided in getting some other type of satisfaction in a more acceptable way. One of the disorganizing factors in our modern society is that satisfactory life is denied tens of thousands of individuals living alone in large cities. Many homeless men and women are dependent on commercialized recreation lacking any satisfactory social relationship.

The American community is faced with the problem of what to do about this social problem. Should it attempt to prohibit prostitution? Can the laws be enforced? Should it be regulated by taxation or licensing? Problems of prostitution are serious for a community because there is frequently a link between prostitution and other underworld activities, such as dope peddling, gambling. Nonenforcement of laws against prostitution is evidence of disorganization in a community and instances have been found where police were paid to keep from reporting law violations. The attack on this problem means seeing that suitable laws regarding prostitution are enacted and that they are then enforced. Local citizen crime commissions have done very constructive work in this area.

Another source of control of this problem is to work to prevent its occurrence or those conditions which foster its growth. Strengthening of family relationships, better sex education in families and in school, group recreation facilities, more outlets for the persons without families, will lead to a reduction of these community problems. All along the life of a person, school, church, work situation, adequate counseling and guidance, opportunities for recreation and forming of relationships, should help to offset the many impersonal relationships of modern city life which have proved inadequate for many.

This brief discussion shows that there is no easy answer to any such problem. Remedies must be directed toward (1) helping the individual and (2) preventing the problem from resulting in many social effects. Both areas can use preventive and rehabilitative measures. Any problem must also be studied as to extent and causes. It seems that only recently have we been able to face this problem because its practice breaks some of our most fundamental group values. So far the health aspects have received most attention. Elimination of the need for the satisfactions of prostitution and the profit in it would reduce this problem.

STUDY QUESTIONS AND PROJECTS

1. How do social conditions become a problem to a community? Describe some social problems in your community. What is being done about them?

2. Why is social change resisted? Give examples of social changes and resistances which have been evident. How were the objections handled?

3. How does social disorganization differ from personal disorganization? How are they interrelated?

4. What are the symptoms of personal disorganization? Illustrate with persons known or in fiction who exemplify the process of personal disorganization. What can be done to rehabilitate them?
5. Has your community ever faced an acute disaster? If so, how were community forces organized to enable the people to cope with it?
6. Talk with the chairman of the Disaster Committee of the American Red Cross or the Civilian Defense chairman in your community regarding plans made to prevent community disorganization. Discuss the scope and nature.
7. Describe instances of racial or minority discrimination which you may know. How did it affect the persons involved? Could it have been prevented?
8. Discuss the effects of transiency on the individuals involved, the members of the community in which they reside, and social institutions of the community as economic, school, church.
9. What measures, both remedial and preventive, have been taken to lessen social problems resulting from migratory families?
10. What measures, remedial and preventive, have been taken to lessen social problems of prostitution?

REFERENCES

Benedict, Ruth, and Weltfish, Gene: The Races of Mankind, Public Affairs Pamphlet, Number 85, 1949.

Bloch, Herbert A.: Disorganization Personal and Social, New York, 1952, Alfred A. Knopf, Part I.

Chatto, Clarence, and Halligan, Alice: The Story of the Springfield Plan-One Community's Total War Against Prejudice, New York, 1945, Barnes and Noble.

Clarke, Tom and Perlman, P. B.: Prejudice and Property, Washington, D. C., 1948, Public Affairs Press.

Elliott, Mabel A., and Merrill, Francis E.: Social Disorganization, New York, Revised edition, 1950, Harper & Brothers.

Havighurst, Robert J., and Morgan, H. Gerthon: The Social History of a War Boom Community, New York, 1951, Longmans, Green and Company.

Ogburn, William F., and Nimkoff, Meyer F.: Sociology, Boston, 1946, Houghton Mifflin Company, Parts 5, 6, 7.

Phelps, Harold A., and Henderson, David: Contemporary Social Problems, ed. 4, New York, 1952, Prentice-Hall, Inc., Chapter 1.

Queen, Stuart A., Bodenhafer, W. B., and Harper, Ernest B.: Social Organization and Disorganization, New York, 1935, Thomas Y. Crowell Co.

Sellew, Gladys, and Furley, Paul H.: Sociology and Social Problems in Nursing Service, ed. 2, Philadelphia, 1946, W. B. Saunders Co., Chapters 1, 2.

U. S. Federal Interagency Committee on Migrant Labor: Migrant Labor, A Human Problem; Report and Recommendations, Washington, D. C., 1947, Government Printing Office.

Williams, Robin M., Jr.: The Reduction of Intergroup Tensions, New York, 1947, Social Science Research Council, Number 57, Chapters 1 and 2.

CHAPTER 4

PERSONALITY DEVELOPMENT

INTRODUCTION

In order to understand personality disorganization, and, in fact, to understand the physically ill person, some appreciation of personality development is required. No two individuals are alike. Every human being, however, develops as a result of the interplay of heredity and environment. Each individual starts with what he has inherited by way of body structure, physical constitution, learning capacity, predispositions, all of which are unique to each. The human infant, as has been pointed out frequently, does not enter the world equipped with automatic behavior responses needed for independent existence, as an animal does. He needs considerable help from his environment, both physical and personal. Successive persons in the growing child's life affect him, his parents, his playmates, his school teachers, his community, as well as the customs and habits which prevail in his groups. To develop independence, the child needs to understand, to learn, to reason, to be equipped for a trade or a profession, to get along with others, to acquire moral and spiritual values.

Personality has been defined variously by psychologists and psychiatrists, but in general it can be considered as the individual as a whole, his feelings, attitudes, security, ways of acting and relating to people. Each individual has certain basic needs which change with physical and emotional growth, and each must bring about some satisfactory balancing of inner needs and acceptable behavior according to environmental standards. Thus, behavior is always motivated by inner drives and modified by desire to conform or receive favor from parents and contemporary groups, that is, if we are functioning normally. Frustrations and anxiety develop when needs are not met in a satisfying manner. Every person develops ways of handling these frustrations, some of which are socially acceptable and others indicative of some maladjustment of the individual.

FUNDAMENTAL NEEDS OF THE CHILD

Physically the human infant is completely dependent on others for the satisfaction of his fundamental processes of eating and elimination. He is the most helpless of units. Interaction between the organism and its environment begins in utero. Some individuals still seem to believe that environment is significant only from the time of birth, without recognizing the tremendous importance of, and reaction between, the fetus and its environment. Recent developments of prenatal medical supervision give evidence of the growing importance placed on this period of the infant's growth. Man has changed very little physically in the past several thousand years. Biological evolution of man proceeds at a very slow rate. In fact, the change is almost infinitesimal. Cultural evolution, on the other hand, proceeds much more quickly.

But the infant has more than physical needs. He is desperately in need of love and affection; he has to be handled and cuddled and have the satisfaction of a secure place near a warm human body. Love is as vital to a child as vitamins, and lack of this fundamental affection is worse than the lack of nutritive foods according to some psychiatrists. Through love, the infant acquires a fundamental sense of trust in his parents. Studies show that infants raised in institutions, or deprived of love and affection during the first year of life, bear permanent scars in the personality, for which it is next to impossible to compensate at a later date. A child outgrows this period of complete dependency as he grows out of infancy. He learns when he becomes toilet trained that he cannot always have everything his own way and that certain prohibitions and demands are made upon him. Some distribution of rewards and punishments are required to keep the child from submitting to too rigid a schedule or too great leniency. A child always wants to explore first himself and then the world about him. He needs recognition as a person in his own right. His world expands beyond his family household, and by about three years he has developed some considerable security, has acquired some self-disciplinary habits, has emerged as a person in his own right.

No one is charged with a greater responsibility in helping the child in satisfying these needs than are the parents. Dr. Benjamin Spock, the well-known expert on child care, has said in this respect:

> Solemnly, we agreed that the one thing that is vital is that a child have a pair of good parents who truly love him. With such a start, he can probably put up with some degree of poverty or other social disadvantage because his parents stand

between him and the world, interpreting it to him in the light of their own wholesomeness and helping him to deal with it. He can probably get along without social services, and come through with a personality that is capable of achieving individual happiness and responsible citizenship. Such a stable person will have a good chance of picking up an excellent wife and of getting along splendidly with her, without benefit of marriage counseling. When their children come along, these parents will probably be able to do a good job without the help of child study courses or psychiatrists.[1]

FURTHER STAGES OF DEVELOPMENT

From three until he goes to school, the child becomes more a part of a group outside his family. He becomes identified with his parent of the same sex; if a boy, he wants to be like his father, if a girl, like her mother. Their games reflect their interest in cars, in dolls, as the case may be. It is around this time that the boy frequently expresses his desire to marry his mother when he grows up, or the little girl talks of her children and tells her daddy he is to be the father. Sometimes, of course, this may create a feeling of rivalry between father and son for the attention of the mother. Parents are hard pressed sometimes to give the love and guidance wisely, for the child is so vulnerable to his parents' actions. Years later a psychiatrist may trace the youth's attitude toward authority to his attitude toward his father during an early period of life.

By six the child is off to school with his books and joins with his fellows in learning and growing up. Children tend to like their teachers, particularly if they have been happy at home. The teacher has an important place in the child's world and has great responsibility, in facilitating the blossoming of his personality, or of blocking it, or fencing him in with autocratic rules. A whole new world is opened to him in books. He learns to compete with his contemporaries in class and on the field playground. His socialization is being extended and his ways of relating himself to people are being developed. The child is gaining some independence in his choice of companions, outlets, clothing; perhaps he is beginning to earn money. If a child has had his basic needs for love and affection well satisfied in his preschool years, he can develop a feeling of adequacy as he grows in his early school years.

---

[1]Spock, Benjamin: What We Know About the Development of Healthy Personalities in Children. Children and Youth at the Midcentury—Official Conference Proceedings, prepared by the Midcentury White House Conference on Children and Youth and published and copyrighted by Health Publications Institute, Inc., Raleigh, N. C.

Besides his growth in independence, the child from six to ten becomes much more interested in other children. He wants to play outside the home and be a member of a group. He is interested in a wide variety of games, those stimulating the imagination are most popular at this stage. Usually children from eight to ten or eleven become increasingly loud and boisterous in their play. They want active sports, particularly the boys, and games calling for physical activity and a certain amount of daring. By the time a child is entering his teens, he has gained some independence and is well started on his social maturation.

Adolescence, roughly the period of the teens, is a troublesome one for children and parents. It cannot be dealt with in as little time as can be given here and the nurse in dealing with an adolescent should look for further guidance from the many books written about this period. Physically many changes are taking place in both girls and boys which may be disturbing to them. Social and emotional changes are perhaps the greatest which the child ever faces in his growth to maturity. Relationships with the opposite sex must be worked out and are of great importance during this stage. Perhaps the most difficult problem for the adolescent is the emancipation of himself from his parents, for during this stage the individual develops maturity, ability to become independent emotionally as well as legally. In this move to maturity, also, the adolescent must begin to think of his vocation, how he will earn a living in the future. In this latter area, boys particularly have been experiencing difficulty because of world conditions and an inability to decide just when service in the Armed Forces will fit in.

During this period many frustrations are encountered by the individual and his ways of meeting these are accentuated. If he has been aggressive in the past, he becomes increasingly aggressive and hostile. If he has had difficulty facing his problems, he tends to shrink more and more from difficult situations into daydreaming or other withdrawn behavior. Parents and persons in the child's environment often find it difficult to understand how to help him.

Some insight into problems which bother teen-agers was gained by a questionnaire recently sent to some 6,000 young people by the National Commission on Children and Youth. The number one problem was listed as the draft, second came quarreling of parents which disturbed young people, and the third was sex.[2]

---

[2]Time, December 8, 1952, page 50.

CULTURAL EFFECTS ON CHILD DEVELOPMENT

Each child is born into a culture which sets the pattern for his future development, and completely controls his actions. By culture is meant behavior transmitted from one generation to another, the sum total of ways of doing and thinking of a social group. Thus, material things—ideas, concepts, customs, moral values are transmitted to the growing child. While it is generally accepted that our cultural patterns in the United States are similar, differences exist in certain sections of the country, and among certain enthic group minorities, such as the American Indians. "In fact, so great is the relative importance which sociologists attach to the conditioning power of cultural heritage, that personality is continually spoken of as the subjective side of culture."[3]

From the sociologist's point of view the family also assumes the leading role in its responsibility for passing on cultural content. The groups and community into which the child is born also shape the cultural pattern. Each family passes on to a child values and attitudes which have been conditioning factors and which it accepts as necessary to inculcate in the child. A child also is affected by the larger ideals and customs of his social class status. For sociologists believe that our American society is a class one. Thus, while families today would uphold democracy as the ideal for all, their class horizons may be such that practice is confined to their own group. Parents may feel that all children have a right to education but not to be invited to their homes or to serve as companions for their children. So a child acquires from his parents "prejudice and appreciation, antagonism and cooperation, pride and a rankling sense of injustice."[4] Some studies have been undertaken to determine persons influencing a young child's ethical concepts and moral values. A notable one by Hartshorne and May showed a higher correlation between a child's values and those of his parents than between the child's and other persons with whom he had been in contact, as teachers, Sunday School teachers, friends. The mother and child were more likely to have identical views than the father and child.[5]

The entire attention of the recent Midcentury White House Conference on Children and Youth was centered on healthy personality

[3]Bossard, James S.: The Sociology of Child Development, New York, 1948, Harper & Brothers, page 120.
[4]Hartshorne, H., and May, M. A.: Testing the Knowledge of Right and Wrong, Religious Education 21:539-554, October, 1926.
[5]Ibid., page 131.

development. Many social institutions share responsibilities with the family. Those discussed at the Conference included the church and synagogue, the school, health services, social services, vocational guidance and placement services, working conditions and employment, use of leisure time, the law courts, and protective services. It was further emphasized at the conference that many disciplines converge on the child in these agencies so that a child has many adjustments to make unless indeed there is more integration between these services for the benefit of the child. Professional personnel involved are lawyers, judges, doctors, nurses, teachers, psychologists, social workers, psychiatrists, ministers, a formidable battery of experts to aid and help the child and his family in the shaping of personality. What, then, is the contribution of each of these?

THE CHURCH

Many children are born into a religious setting and early realize that there is some Divine Being who shapes the course of events and to whom his family does homage. Even though church attendance may be casual, the parents usually were married in church, the child is baptized, his godparents visit him. His playmates attend Sunday School. He hears the church bells ring on Sunday. He realizes the difference in pace of activities on that day. Whether or not each child may recognize its effects, it has been generally agreed, with the exceptions of agnostics, that "religion uniquely provides a sense of security and independence from materialistic goals and gives self-respect and respect for others based on a knowledge of God as Father and of all men as brothers."[6] This security is necessary for the child and he has a right to be brought into contact with it through religious teachings. The church also provides the child with standards of conduct and motives for behavior. Standards of right and wrong, of kindness to others, of human rights, of the value of the individual, have a religious base which the child needs to shape his own life.

According to the conference reports, one-half of the children in the United State today are not now reached by religious teaching through a church or synagogue. It may be that some of these are reached in school or at home. Thus these children are being denied some fundamental values, a faith and an inner security to which they

---

[6]Church and Synagogue, Summary, Proceedings of Midcentury White House Conference on Children and Youth, 1951, page 174.

are entitled. The other half of the children attend Sunday School and church and are in contact with religious teachings. The church shares with the family in establishing basic values and standards of conduct. The church exercises its functions through education and religious teachings of children and parents in the church, in the effect and example of its ministers, priests, and rabbis, in its opportunities for children and young and old to have the experience of working and playing together in church service clubs and recreational activities. Many churches go even further and allow their facilities to be used by other agencies in the community.

THE SCHOOLS

The school, an important social institution permanently influencing development, keeps the child many hours a day and the child spends from eight to twelve years in school, sometimes more. The tasks of the school are well understood, although this might be argued since perennial discussion arises of curriculum content, type, and scope of extracurricular activities. Schools are charged with providing the child with basic learning so that he can live in society, read, write, and communicate with others, master some fundamental skills as arithmetic, learn something of the land in which he lives, acquire some vocational skills. But to the young child school means his teachers; on the classroom teacher rests vital responsibility for the personality development of a child.

Teachers must have training in understanding the individual child as well as skill in teaching a certain subject. But the country is facing now a shortage of teachers. Increasing numbers of children are entering schools so that facilities are taxed to the utmost. Many teachers are called upon to assume burdens under which it is difficult to give each child his due attention. Teachers are inadequately trained in many states. In rural areas, college work is not always required. Salaries of teachers are low. All this means good personnel is lacking for such a vital part of a child's life. The school has the opportunity to educate a child in the true sense of the word, culturally and vocationally, and inculcate him with democratic ideals. The established goal is for each child all the education suited to his capacities, although this ideal is far from achieved. In many small school systems, the curriculum is limited to what the teacher can teach. In some systems the curriculum is inflexible and not geared to the child's needs. Vocational training opportunities are frequently inadequately equipped or lacking. Provisions for testing a child and studying his individual needs so that his program can be suitably adapted are insufficient. The needs of the retarded child and the child needing special services because of physical or mental handicaps are sparsely provided. Many a gifted child, too, is slowed down to keep pace with the average.

No contradiction exists in what the basic responsibility of the school is, namely to prepare each child individually for personal fulfillment and effective participation in democratic life. Despite the many negative aspects mentioned above, progress is seen in the adaptation of some curricula to meet individual needs, in emphasizing the real problems of the community, in stimulating the child to participate in activities around him. But improvements are needed in emotionally stable and adequately prepared teachers, adaptable curriculum, better facilities and equipment, special services to children.

HEALTH AND SOCIAL SERVICES

Other community institutions may be found which have a part in shaping the personality development because of contact with child and his parents. Probably these services particularly in the health field concentrate on the remedial aspects of the situation, nursing care for the ill, operations for the crippled, economic aid for the poor. A second aspect is a preventive one, using knowledge to prevent the occurrence of a disease, of an accident, of family breakdown. Still another aspect is the emotional effect of the physical or social condition on the child and his family.

Since the nurse is especially interested in health problems because of her training, she must be aware of the place of health services on personality development. Necessary goals are similar to those in education, giving the individual the best physical development within our knowledge and the ability to make the most of this. One of the first prerequisites is the individualization of health service. "Good health workers recognize differences among people and respect the dignity of individuals."[7] Nurses and doctors, too, need to appreciate not only the medical findings but the emotional aspects of the condition. In the awareness of the close relationship between parent and child can be seen the fear of the child at being separated even for so routine an

---

[7]Witmer, Helen, and Kotinsky, Ruth: Personality in the Making, New York, 1952, Harper & Brothers, page 321.

occasion in the nurse's life as a tonsillectomy. A child needs to know something about what will occur, when he will see his parents again. A child (or even an adult) undergoing a serious operation needs some understanding of its nature to allay his anxiety. Other factors also enter in. If a husband is away or in service, a mother may hesitate to carry through even emergency treatment of a child. Her anxiety is conveyed to the child. Despite more widespread educational programs regarding physical ailments than has ever been known in this country, many families are abysmally ignorant of the meaning of illness, of precautions for contagious disease, of the importance of diet, as in diabetes, of suitable remedies. The rural health nurse, particularly, encounters the use of many home remedies which have enjoyed curative reputations for several generations. Sometimes when the right way to handle things seems so clear to the nurse, it is most frustrating to realize that the patient does not respond, whether from anxiety or ignorance. Each patient represents a separate situation.

In the section of this book where some specific physical conditions are discussed at more length, this approach will be reinforced, that the patient is a person, a member of a family, and of other social groups, a composite of fears and understanding. The health field, like the educational arena, needs more and better trained personnel. Many rural areas are without public health nurses and inadequately supplied with doctors. Hospital facilities are lacking in many parts of the country. A positive health program or regular check-up does not always exist. The physical examinations for draftees have revealed appallingly large rejections for physical reasons. All told, the health services can contribute even more vitally to personality development.

The term "social services" covers a wide area, but here it is restricted to services designed to help families and individuals function more effectively both on their own, in groups, and in the community. It is carried on by persons called "social workers," whose aims are to help the individual cope with his social situation so effectively that he will not need the aid of the social worker. Obviously the difficulties with which families need help most are economic dependency threatening the existence of family life; substitute provisions when there is no home, or for a portion of the day as day care services when the mother is absent; support or counselling with problems beyond the power of the family to solve itself, as friction between family members, budgeting help, understanding of children; and fourth, services in connection with social institutions as schools and hospitals. All of these except the second are based on help to the family unit. Where there is no family unit, the individual, whether a child or an older person, needs some substitute care. Implicit in the practice of social work is the goal to help the family or individual get on his own feet, and in so doing the right of the individual to make his own decisions is recognized.

Social workers operate under funds from public taxes and private donations alike. They also are attached to organizations in the community well-recognized by the individual. As Dr. Spock stated in the quotation cited at the beginning of this chapter, if all children had adequate parents, and here the term adequate is used broadly, there would be no need for social services. True, financial assistance might be needed, but this could be provided through social insurances and the more personalized help through the social case worker would be superfluous. The social worker's chief contribution to personality development is in the support given to basic family groups, and to children in his activities outside the family group to the end that the child will develop healthily into a responsible citizen. This professionalized service embraces modifying the environment, giving information regarding available resources, giving insight into problems, and helping the individual through interest and support to face and work through his difficulties. Since children need activities within groups, the social group worker plays a major role in making these meaningful for the individual. So whether the assistance is material or personal, the members of the family are helped and the growing child aided in his development.

The agencies through which social workers endeavor to bring help to troubled people are public welfare agencies, family and children's agencies, children's institutions, child guidance and mental hygiene clinics, hospitals, health clinics. Even in industry the services of a social worker have been found valuable, for workers do not leave their troubles behind when they punch the time clock. The social worker, psychologist, and psychiatrist know, too, that behavior can be modified during growth and personality traits can be changed. Dr. Franz Alexander says in this respect :

> It is only recently that students of personality have become impressed by the fact that personality development does not stop at a certain age, that significant changes take place in all phases of the life curve and particularly that the formative experiences of early years do not leave irreversible effects.

Many of the adverse influences of early childhood can be corrected by later experiences in life. Indeed, psychoanalytic therapy is based on this view.[8]

Perhaps a little more should be said regarding the services for leisure time or recreational activities for the growing person. At certain stages in one's life, group membership is very important. It is almost impossible for one to live an isolated existence and the opportunity for group participation and for group leadership should be provided all, if it is directed to desirable ends and not a destructive experience as in some juvenile gangs. Because there is such individual difference between persons, a variety of activities should be available. Interests of children from low-income homes, lower class children, are likely to be in more lively and aggressive activities than for children of the middle classes. Heterosexual outlets of a wholesome nature are required to develop ideals and actions which will make for the most well-adjusted personality.

Another phase of the development of personality occurs in preparing the individual for work and a satisfactory employment experience. "The relation between satisfactory accomplishment and sound personality development has long been recognized . . . Obviously, a good work life grows out of the whole series of events underlying all healthy development."[9]

This means that other efforts in personality development must concern the preparation for employment. Schools have responsibilities here as indicated previously and many are performing them through vocational courses, for both regular students and adult educational courses. Because some special training is necessary for the handicapped, specified services with funds from the federal government are available to help in obtaining this training. Local agencies may be found to give some of this help. The tragedy of the square peg in the round hole results in much dissatisfaction on the job which may spread to family discontent and eventual breakup. To assist the person in his choice of employment various testing devices have been standardized and vocational counselors may be found who will discuss opportunities with the youth and adult. Efforts are made where the facilities are found to help the person get located where he can give the most service and obtain the most satisfaction.

[8]Alexander, Franz: The Dynamics of Personality Development, Children and Youth at the Midcentury, op. cit., page 101.

[9]Witmer and Kotinsky: op. cit., page 291.

It is essential that everyone work and it is traditional that everyone do so in our society, so the youth must take stock and plan for the future. The community meantime has some responsibilities in providing employment services. The government has assisted in this by establishing state employment offices not only for giving job information and placement but also for handling unemployment insurance.

Before leaving the social services, the reader should consider the law enforcement agencies. Those most concerned with the development of personality are the courts handling cases of juveniles, either delinquents or neglected children. The juvenile delinquent is an example in most instances of an already maladjusted personality. Admittedly there are minor offenses which might be indulged in by almost anyone, and in which the perpetrator might get caught. But the asocial, malicious, hostile, aggressive delinquent is a product of his family and environment and already a subject for treatment. He must be helped, rehabilitated, if possible. The persons who are slated to help him in addition to those already mentioned as family, school, church personnel, and the social workers in the existing social agencies, are the court workers, the police, probation offcers, judges, and, if the offender is committed to an institution, the institutional personnel. The greatest challenge to personality development is flung to these persons working with juvenile or youthful offenders. Some are almost beyond help at this point. Emphasis on recognition of early symptoms of maladjustment, therefore, and the procurement of treatment or help at an early age is necessary. The judge of the juvenile court or the court which handles juvenile problems is in a strategic situation. He has the final authority in all cases, although frequently moved by the reports of the social worker or probation officers. It is this judge, too, who in cases of alleged neglect of children by parents has the authority to break up the home, to remove children from their parents if circumstances warrant. Does this judge have training which prepared him for this important position? All too frequently he has training in law but not in the psychology of family relations and the understanding of personality development. Judges are often elected; many do not want to handle juvenile cases; they do not understand them. Some outstanding judges there are, but not enough. Similarly, many probation officers are ill-trained and disinterested. Studies of correctional institutions have repeatedly shown that the personnel is poorly paid, illtrained, and frequently sadistic in attitude. In so vital a field for training operations, such poor equipment in personnel is found.

CONCLUSION

This chapter has served to outline briefly the development of the personality, and to indicate the many persons and institutions affecting its development. With all the chances for damage, it is heartening that so many of us do grow to maturity able to function effectively, but it is discouraging, as shown in the preceding chapter, that there are so many instances of personality breakdown. With more study, symptoms of maladjustment can be more precisely recognized and the final breakdown prevented. This book treats of many phases of maladjustment, mentioning the extent of the problem and various preventive and treatment devices in more detail. This chapter has endeavored to point out that many personality disorders are acquired characteristics and can be helped and perhaps prevented; that the personality grows following certain big patterns and the growing child needs certain things at specified stages of his development; that a number of factors in the personality and the environment converge on a child or an adult to produce the final breakdown. It should perhaps be stressed that all persons develop similarly and that the so-called normal person must make the adjustments to environment of things and persons. The normal person does it more easily, although there are all sorts of fears tied up with certain aspects of his life. All face anxiety at times. But most people weather the adversities without becoming mentally ill, or behaving in some antisocial way.

STUDY QUESTIONS AND PROJECTS

1. Discuss the significance of heredity and environment for the nurse.
2. In what ways does modern health teaching consider both heredity and environment?
3. Observe some young children in a nursery or nursery school. Note and discuss individual differences in the child, behavior patterns, initiative, relationship to other children, and symptoms of aggresive or withdrawn behavior.
4. Discuss some customs or traditions in your own family which have influenced your behavior.
5. Describe instances you know of or from fiction where parents' attitudes and reactions have affected a child. Trace the influence on the child's behavior.
6. Write down for class discussion differences in speech and customs of persons from different parts of the country, different nationality backgrounds.
7. From your own experiences in school indicate specific instances in which the school, teachers, schoolmates, principal helped or hindered you. Describe instances where you were made to feel inferior, embarrassed. How could they be avoided? Describe instances where you were given confidence, made to feel comfortable, stimulated to learning.

8. Similarly discuss ways in which churches can aid the personality development of the child.
9. Try to think how persons in your life outside the family have influenced your development. Discuss the ways in which this was done.
10. Read and discuss the articles in the *Proceedings of the Midcentury White House Conference on Children and Youth,* 1950, as to personality development of children (Articles suggested, pages 53-70; 77-90).

REFERENCES

Averill, Lawrence A., and Kempf, Florence C.: Psychology Applied to Nursing, ed. 3, Philadelphia, 1946, W. B. Saunders Company, Units III, V, and VI.

Bossard, James H. S.: The Sociology of Child Development, New York, 1948, Harper and Brothers, Part VI.

Bowlby, J.: Maternal Care and Mental Health, New York, 1951, Columbia University Press, World Health Organization, Monograph Series, No. 2.

Cunningham, Bess V.: Psychology for Nurses, New York, 1946. D. Appleton-Century Company, Inc., Chapters 10-14.

Gesell, Arnold, and Ilg, Frances L.: Infant and Child in the Culture of Today, New York, 1943, Harper and Brothers.

Gessell, Arnold, Ilg, Frances L., Ames, Louise Bates, and Bullis, Glenna E.: The Child from Five to Ten, New York, 1946, Harper and Brothers.

Jenkins, Gladys G., Shacter, Helen, and Bauer, William W.: These Are Your Children, Chicago, 1949, Scott, Foresman and Company.

Midcentury White House Conference on Children and Youth: Proceedings, Raleigh, N. C., 1951, Health Publications Institute.

Plant, James S.: Personality and the Cultural Pattern, New York, 1937, Commonwealth Fund.

Reynolds, Martha M.: Children from Seeds to Saplings, New York, 1951, McGraw-Hill Book Company, Inc.

Spock, Benjamin: The Common Sense Book of Baby and Child Care, New York, 1946, Duell, Sloan and Pierce.

Staff of the Division on Child Development and Teacher Personnel: Helping Teachers Understand Children, Washington, 1945, American Council on Education.

Witmer, Helen L., and Kotinsky, Ruth: Personality Development in Children, New York, 1952, Harper and Brothers.

CHAPTER 5

CHANGING FAMILY PATTERNS*

INTRODUCTION

For the nurse, the family is one of the most important social institutions. Most of her work is with individuals in families. When she is not concerned with individuals in the family group, she is aware of the influence of the family in the development of each family member. Much of her health teaching will be ineffective unless it concerns the family. The hospital nurse realizes the force of family influence on the patient; his anxiety at separation and longing for visits are seen time after time. Thus, a good understanding of this basic social institution in contemporary society is essential for the nurse.

FUNCTIONS OF THE FAMILY

The structure and the functions of the family as we are familiar with them today are flexible, but through the ages, and in every culture, some type of family organization has existed. The family pattern with which present-day America is familiar consists of the husband and wife, and probably several children. Not so long ago, the family group was larger and embraced grandparents and perhaps other relatives, what has been termed a kinship group. In some countries today, the family is a large group into which the sons bring their wives and children, forming a large well-knit unit working together. But this is rarely seen in our culture. Young married couples have tended to be independent, to emancipate themselves from their family when married and set up an establishment of their own.

Traditionally the family has had several functions to perform, most of which are still the responsibility of the family, even though community agencies may share some of them. First, the family is for

---

*The writer is indebted to Professor Robert Habenstein of the Sociology Department of the University of Missouri for suggestions in the development of this chapter.

procreation; second, the family is the social institution which inducts children into the way of their culture, providing ethical and moral values for the child; third, the family is the economic unit of society, and each family head is expected to support his family; and, fourth, the family gives a setting and identity to the children in which they are nourished and become a part. Although many claims have been made that the family is losing its place as a social institution and is showing signs of instability and decay, the family today is still strong and still assuming the chief burdens for the functions as stated. Evidences of disorganization may be noted, however, particularly in the large divorce rate.

Almost everyone agrees that the family is the best institution for procreating the race. Generally cultures have been monogamous and the practice has worked well. The fourth function of providing the child with a background, so that he is known as the Jones boy or one of the Jacksons, as the case may be, at once gives the child an identity and status in the community which he achieves by virtue of his family and does not have to strive for. Conversely it might be something he would have to counteract. But there is a strong sense of belonging and that is a sense which has been found necessary for children. These two functions the family still serves well. But the family as an economic unit and as a purveyor of the mores of culture has been yielding to other institutions.

In earlier years, before the Industrial Revolution, for example, the family carried on more all-inclusive economic functions, suited to the culture of the day. Food was cultivated and prepared, not purchased in cans or frozen in packages; the yarn was spun, cloth was woven. With the invention of the plow and the domestication of animals, handicrafts became more highly developed. Families were very largely self-sustaining. The individual family usually performed such tasks as grinding grain, making soap and pottery, tanning leather, and making furniture and even preparing medications. The coming of the machine age and the growth of cities as industrial centers changed the family from a producing to a consuming unit. The family is still responsible for supporting itself although no longer an economic unit. City workers are mainly wage earners. Activities carried on in a rural household still may require the help of all members to support the family economy. The educational function of the American family is today shared with the church, school, and sometimes with recreational organizations. The child, however, is subject to the family for his knowledge of right and wrong, for the acquiring of his value system, for his ethical standards, before he ever goes to a church or a nursery school. The more formal education of the three "r's," the teaching of housewifely skills of cooking and sewing, or the training of a boy for a vocation have been assumed by most school systems. Schools, too, share with home and playmates in the socialization of the child. The church, through its Sunday Schools and church services, helps in shaping spiritual values and the fundamental religious faith which every child needs.

LEGAL STATUS OF THE FAMILY

Responsibility for the family to perform some of these listed functions is specified in laws. These laws recognize not only the family as a unit but also the individuals composing the family, and they seek to specify and regulate the activities of the members. The laws revolve chiefly around relationship of the parents to each other and the relationship of the parent to the child. In the United States most laws vary so much from state to state that there is no useful purpose served in trying to discuss specific laws. Laws regulating the relationship between husband and wife are laws of marriage and divorce. Laws specify the age at which two persons may marry without consent, whom they may marry (certain states have laws prohibiting marriage between cousins, members of different races), health requirements, sharing of property. Divorce laws, providing for dissolution of marriage, similarly specify on what grounds divorce may take place, whether it be cruelty, adultery, or some other act which can legally prove one of the marriage partners has been wronged. Other laws specify the property which must be settled on the woman, and if there are children, who will have their custody. Further laws regarding the husband-wife relationship are in regard to the disposition of the property when one of the partners dies.[1]

Laws pertaining to parent-child relationship are numerous. Most of these specify parental duties toward a minor child. Rarely does the law attempt to enforce an obligation of an adult to his parents. But the minor child, who has no legal status in his own right, must be protected. The regulations are negative rather than positive, indicating certain prohibitions or punishments if parents do not fulfill specified obligations toward the child. These include supporting the child, send-

---

[1]This material is taken from the pamphlet Legal Status of the American Family, Women's Bureau, U. S. Department of Labor, 1948.

ing him to school, keeping him healthy, not abusing or neglecting him, and not allowing him to work under exploitive conditions. Certain privileges, such as control of a child's earnings or property, may also be mentioned. Since the child is a minor, provisions for guardianship in lieu of the natural parents are quite specific, as well as delineation of conditions by which a child may be adopted. All these provisions it has been necessary to write into law.

Some dissatisfaction has been volubly expressed in the exercise of law over many of these matters of family relationship. In two situations notably has it been difficult to apply the law helpfully when it is stated in terms of opposing parties, one of whom must be right and the other wrong. In the juvenile court, and to some extent in family relations courts, the modern approach considers the situation a problem in maladjustment. This requires study and treatment directed toward rehabilitating the individual, rather than directly with punishing. In cases where parents are neglecting their children, and also in divorce cases, the separation of parent and child or of husband and wife many times seems the only answer, although in reality it may not be the best solution. Desirability of a more therapeutic approach to cases of family discord has been voiced by many. As Judge Paul Alexander of Toledo says:

> The question in the juvenile court is: What is best for the individual child? What are we going to do *for* the child, not *to* the child. Why can we not apply that same logic, same philosophy, same diagnostic and therapeutic approach, to the family when the family comes to court? Why can we not ask what is best for this family, diagnose the case, find out what caused the rift, and then apply all the skills of all the professions we can bring to bear on the problem? It is not going to make divorce easier or make divorce harder. It is going to stop divorces that should not be granted, and if, from a sociological viewpoint, the divorce must be granted, the court will act without the necessity of a public trial. We will not harass the parties by forcing them to accuse each other and, consequently, do damage to themselves and the children.[2]

[2]Alexander, Paul W.: A Therapeutic Approach, Conference on Divorce, University of Chicago, Law School, February, 1952, page 54.

CHANGES IN THE CONTEMPORARY AMERICAN FAMILY

That contemporary society has been and is constantly in a state of flux is frequently charged by the sociologists. Many vital changes have occurred in our culture patterns. These changes in family life are due to mechanical inventions, to urbanization of our culture, to changing economic factors, depressions, wars, increased mobility, and so forth. These changes may be enumerated as:

1. Change in size of family.
2. Change in family composition.
3. Change in place and type of residence.
4. Increased mobility of family.
5. More working wives and mothers.
6. Increased importance of interpersonal relationships.

The nurse must remember that in speaking of these changes no implication or inference can possibly be made that the family is disappearing. Indeed there are more families than ever before. During the twentieth century there has been an increase in persons marrying, an increase which has fluctuated considerably. During the decade ending in 1949 there were 17,400,000 marriages; 1946 represented the year when the number of marriages reached its peak.[3] The lowest number since 1900 occurred in 1932 when the depression apparently acted as a brake in marriage contracts. But the advent of the war and increasing prosperity have resulted in a great increase in the numbers of our population either marrying or remarrying. It can be expected that the rate will recede for a while, since the lowered birth rate of the decade 1930 to 1940 will mean fewer persons of marriagable age available for a few years. But then it can be expected to soar.

CHANGES IN SIZE AND COMPOSITION OF FAMILIES

The family unit is undoubtedly smaller than in our parents' and grandparents' day. If one takes a poll in any school class as to the number of children in the immediate family, the family of one of the parents, and the family of the grandparents, inevitably the present-day size is smaller. Statistically this is demonstrated by the census which shows that the average family today is smaller than in 1910. Differences

---

[3]U. S. Bureau of Vital Statistics, 1949.

exist between the size of the family in the urban and rural areas, families in rural areas having consistently more children than urban families.

Part of the increase in marriages is due to the fact that couples are marrying at earlier ages, so that we have young and perhaps immature families.   In 1910, for example, the median age at marriage for men was 25 years, in 1949 it was not quite 23 years; for women

Most children are now in urban areas

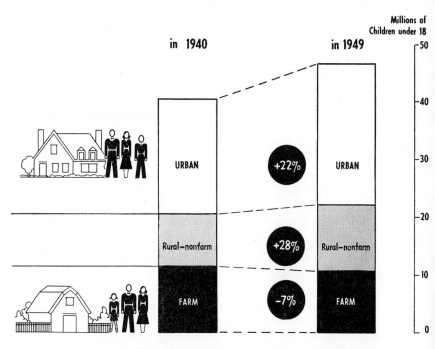

Fig. 2.—(From A Chart Book—Children and Youth at the Midcentury, Midcentury White House Conference on Children and Youth, 1950.)

the median age was 22 as compared with 20 years today.   The Midcentury White House Conference findings tell us further that men in low income groups are likely to marry earlier than those with more established salaries.[4]

These facts may raise questions as to whether these young couples become a part of the parental group of one of them to form a larger

---

[4]A Chart Book—Children and Youth at the Midcentury, Chart 8 and discussion.

family group. The development of the family in America, despite many consolidations of family groups due to housing needs, has tended to be an independent unit. That is, it is a two-generation family only as pointed out above. The young couple steps out of the parental home and starts its own establishment and then begins the rearing of children. Although contact with parents and relatives is maintained, the large family kinship group jointly operating and discussing family problems together is rarely found.

> Since these are the structure and operating rules of the predominant American family, young people can be left free to choose their marital partners with little or no counsel from their parents and relatives. There is no "great family" to be harmed by indiscretion in this respect, no loss of anticipated income, no family honor at stake. Romantic love can therefore be the basis for marriage, and personal relationships the keystone of family life. Each generation makes its own decisions, and tradition in regard to rights and duties and prescribed roles does not count for much, since the control of an interlocking kinship system is lacking.[5]

CHANGES IN RESIDENCE

The economic system is credited with influencing increased mobility and changes in residence. Occupations as demanded by the industrial system today practically require freedom of movement geographically on the part of the wage earner. Jobs are scattered about the country. Many large concerns move their personnel from one regional office to another. Industry is localized and the man moves to the job. Thus in choosing the more varied occupational opportunities offered, the small family unit is required to follow the husband and father to his place of employment.

Margaret Mead, the well-known anthropologist, comments on the cultural changes as moving so fast that the children have a hard time keeping up with them. No longer is the child born into the home in which generations of his forebears were born. The function of the home has changed to be a "launching platform" for the children to go out into the world, not to come back to. The modern family is the most mobile that we have known and during one year, 1948-1949, some

---

[5]Witmer, Helen, and Kotinsky, Ruth: Personality in the Making, New York, 1952, Harper & Brothers, page 183.

8 million children moved from one home to another, many from rural areas to the city.[6]

Thus we see the one-family unit of father, mother, and children, moving around in response to the father's occupational calling. While ties of kinship are present and respected, the parents of either husband or wife usually do not live with their children. The programs of Old Age and Survivors Insurance and Old Age Assistance provisions, discussed subsequently, may make this independence of the old couple more possible. But independence is the pattern at the present time.

Change from the rural to the urban areas has been a marked trend in American life today. With the development of the American frontier, there were always large farms and rural areas being developed. Farms have changed somewhat in their formation and many large farms are found in contrast to more smaller farms. The number of farms has been decreasing since 1935. Mechanization of agriculture, greater scientific knowledge of crops and soils, have made farming more prosperous and have decreased the need for farm labor. The United States Census shows the rural population of 1950 to be 40 per cent. In 1850 it was 85 per cent, and in 1940, 44 per cent.[7] As a result of the increasing movement to the cities, more children now live in urban areas than in rural areas. In 1950 the increase of all children living in urban areas was 22 per cent over 1940 and those in nonfarm rural areas, that is, small villages, increased 28 per cent. The farm population lost 7 per cent of its children. Other changes in our economy, such as automobiles and good roads, have tended to facilitate this change. It is still true that the families on the farms are larger, however.

Actually what a family does and much of the movement may depend on family income. Problems surrounding insufficient income are discussed in the chapter on economic dependency. The type of home in which families live has changed and many more apartment houses serve as homes than ever before. Since World War II, there has been an increase in home building, readily visible in many sections of the country. But apartment house units, housing projects in many cities have provided shelter for many families.

---

[6]This material is taken from the address by Margaret Mead, "The Impact of Culture on Personality Development in the United States Today," as reported in Children and Youth at the Midcentury—Official Conference Proceedings, 1951, pages 84-86.

[7]Raper, Arthur F.: A Graphic Representation of Rural Trends, Washington, D. C., Bureau of Agricultural Economics, 1952, pages 3-9.

INCREASED NUMBER OF WORKING WIVES AND MOTHERS

Back in the preindustrial economy of England and early United States, the father was responsible for the running of the farm, overseeing the crops and any industry on the place, while the wife provided food, managed the household and servants, and cared for any of the workers on the place in event of illness. A wife who was a good housekeeper and manager was much sought after. Actually today the smaller households and changes wrought by industrialization have reshaped these roles. The husband is still the chief provider and usually earns the major income for the family. His status is recognized by the fact that the family usually moves with him. His role of disciplinarian, however, has changed. His position around the house has changed. Because of the greater freedom which the wife enjoys, the father many times has adapted his situation to accommodate hers. Some husbands share in household tasks, in caring for baby and children.

The status of the wife, however, has undergone marked changes. She has achieved great freedom in the twentieth century in many ways. She has more status legally in management of property, less subjection to the will of her husband, opportunity to participate in politics, more chances for employment, and more leisure for the pursuit of hobbies or recreation. She has been freed from household tasks by the change in economy, progress in inventions, establishment of service industries, such as laundries, delicatessens, packaged and canned foods. Many farm women have the advantages of electricity and labor-saving devices. This progress in mechanical invention has raised the standard of living, however, so that families have increasing wants. Furthermore, living costs have risen sharply. Thus more and more wives have been working to supplement the earnings of their husbands.

Perhaps the greatest change in the family today is the increased number of wives and mothers working. Some married women work because by so doing they achieve a higher economic level and get "extras" otherwise denied. However, most of them, especially those with young children, work because their husband's wage is constantly inadequate, or they are heads of a broken family and must shoulder the burden of support. Many single women also are supporting dependents in addition to themselves.

Women have been pouring into industry since the middle of the last century, but more particularly during World War II because of needs of defense plants and induction of men into the Armed Services.

Women have also entered nearly all occupations and professions. In the 1950 U. S. Census, 1,556,891 women over fourteen were reported working, 28 per cent of the female population of the same ages. Figures are not available as to how many of these are supporting dependents. A report, released by the U. S. Womens' Bureau, summarizes some facts regarding women workers' dependency responsibility from a number of previous studies covering thousands of women workers. In brief the results show that in the last ten years from one-third to nine-tenths of the women studied have been supporting one or more dependents. Nurses represented the group claiming the smallest responsibility for support of others and women war workers reported the greatest dependency load. Single women were usually supporting parents or members of an older generation; married women were supporting children. Married women likewise reported slightly more dependents than did single women.[8] The Midcentury White House Conference on Children and Youth report nearly 25 per cent of married women living with their husbands working outside the home in 1949. Also 20 per cent of mothers with children under 18 years of age worked outside the home; about 37 per cent of these working mothers had children of preschool age.[9]

The large number of women workers with preschool children means that a community must be prepared to furnish day care centers for young children, and presumably some provision for the supervision of school age children after school. Provisions include day nursery centers, foster day care facilities, and a variety of independent arrangements with relatives and neighbors. Most cities support, either through public or private funds, nursery care for children of working mothers. The Lanham Act furnished federal funds for this purpose during World War II. Foster day care is sometimes provided by private agencies, assuring a licensed and supervised home where children can be left by the day. In all instances where community facilities are available, mothers are encouraged and expected to pay something toward the care of the children.

[8]Pidgeon, Mary-Elizabeth: Women Workers and Their Dependents, Washington, 1952, U. S. Women's Bureau Bulletin, No. 239.

[9]A Chart Book—Children and Youth at the Midcentury, 1950, Chart 12.

INCREASED IMPORTANCE OF INTERPERSONAL RELATIONSHIPS

Many sociologists today emphasize that the institutional character of the family is declining. As has been seen, some of the functions traditionally assumed have been undertaken by other social institutions. Inevitably this affects the roles of family members, that of the father particularly is less sharply defined. The father is no longer the sole supporter, authoritarian, and arbiter of family life. A greater sharing of all these responsibilities with the mother has been noticed. With the decrease in importance of fixed role, interpersonal relationships between family members becomes more important. Those of parents toward the young child have been specifically discussed in the preceding chapter. Satisfaction in interpersonal relationships should supplant the diminishing importance of the institutional character of the family, for the family now relies on these relationships for its strengths.

One can readily see that institutional and cultural traditions of family solidarity have served to maintain the family and give it stability. If the family substitutes emotional relationships between family members and these are conflicting and unsatisfying, family relationships disintegrate, divorces and separations result. Under these conditions, the modern family becomes a dynamic influence on personality development because of the importance of the interpersonal relationships and not the control of tradition or culture. Through these relationships, love, response, jealously, recognition, loyalty, are continually responding, in the interaction of everyday living.

All of this discussion is to emphasize not that the family is growing less important, but that its importance to its members is changing. One can consider the family today, not as an institution, but as a complex of individuals, each with his own personality. Sound personality development, furthermore, calls for recognition of individual differences, of emotional ties and drives, and of facilitating satisfying experiences in accordance with individual needs, not shaping the personality to fulfill specified and well-defined roles.

CHARACTERISTICS OF FAMILY LIFE

Although it has been pointed out that the two generation family is a well-recognized family pattern in the United States today, from a sociological standpoint there are many influences which create variations in family standards and practices. Since, as has been seen, the family is the primary group contact for the children and the family is still retaining its function of inculcating standards in the very young, the factors most influencing characteristics of family life are income levels and occupational status, and race and nationality customs.

Sociologists point out that our society is a class society and that one can recognize in most social situations members of the lower, the middle, and the upper class. While mobility is great, that is, a child in a certain class can marry out of his class or move up and down with far greater ease than in some societies, as India for example, still the evidences of social classes are quite marked and identifiable. Furthermore, patterns, habits, and ideals of these classes are quite diverse. Class structure depends a great deal on the income level of the family group, the lower class being invariably those with inadequate earnings, dependent for a considerable period of time on social agencies for subsistence; the middle class, usually subdivided into two, being the great bulk of wage earners and professional persons; the very wealthy and those with a venerable lineage at the top.

Space does not permit a full discussion of some of these differences, but it is important for the nurse to realize a few of them. Goals and standards of lower class children according to Dr. Allison Davis of Chicago are very different from middle class children. Most teachers, he claims, come from the middle class and frequently encounter great difficulty in understanding lower class children. The same may well be true of nurses. Thus the nurse, too, must needs be aware of some of these differences.

Oversimplified, the basic goals of the middle class are competition and conformity. Middle class parents hold up definite and perhaps rigid standards to which the child must conform. Middle class children work harder to gain approval in their desire to succeed and attain, they avoid physical conflict, but, says Mr. Davis, "middle-class children are more worried—they suck their thumbs and show other anxiety symptoms much more (3 to 1) than do lower class children".[10] Lower class children show more anxiety over food and shelter. Their families have been unable to budget profitably because of uneven earnings. They are in fear of eviction. Their behavior is also very aggressive and physical conflict is indulged, because this is learned and accepted in the

---

[10]Davis, Allison: Socio-Economic Influences Upon Children's Learning, Proceedings of the Midcentury White House Conference on Children and Youth, 1951, pages 78-79.

family group. They see and hear bad language, consequently use it. These tendencies are sources of distress to most middle class persons.

Middle class families emerge as the most stable according to Dr. Hollingshead. The aristocratic upper class family usually remains firm as a unit and more of a kinship group than any other class. But those who have achieved upper class status more recently because of wealth often exhibit considerable instability. Among working class and lower economic groups are found the greatest numbers of divorced and separated families. To quote, "Community studies indicate that from one-fourth to one-third of working families are broken by divorce, desertion, and death of a marital partner, after a family of procreation had been started but before it is reared."[11] On the other hand, lower-class families are far more numerous than any of the other classes.

Differences in family living standards of other races and nationalities are fairly well known. When immigration was less restricted, certain sections of large cities would assume foreign characteristics, reminiscent of the place from which the immigrants came, "Greek town," "Little Italy," "Chinatown." On festive occasions, costumes, folkways, and perhaps art of the countries are exhibited to further the understanding of different cultures. Customs of the past and the adaptations which may be made to the American culture patterns affect the family structure. In some cases conflicts between parents and children have developed over acquisition of American ways. The family life of the Negro has been subject to the prejudice and laws of a white population. Other effects may be generated in a family by certain imposed restrictions as on the Japanese Americans during the last war, the refusal to let families live in certain areas, discriminatory and segregation practices. These must be understood to enable one to understand that all practices and standards are not middle class white American.

THREATS TO FAMILY STABILITY

Although complete stability indicates a status quo from which perhaps vitality has fled, the greatest strength of this basic social institution has lain in its ability to pass on from one generation to another the learning, traditions, ethical standards, and religious values to the off-spring. Certain factors are always menacing this family

[11]Hollingshead, August: Class Differences in Family Stability, The Annals of the American Academy 272:44-45, November, 1950.

stability. The first and foremost is divorce, or the dissolution of the marriage. Other threats are economic—cost of living, lack of jobs, world situation, wars—and any factors which may keep the family from successfully operating as a partnership.

The increase in the divorce rate among Americans has been viewed with alarm for some time. Many have seen in it the disintegration of the family and have pointed out other attendant disruptions in the life of society and in the personal adjustment of marriage partners and children. Divorce, to be sure, represents a legal dissolution of the marriage bonds and indicates a completely broken home. Homes in which there is continued strain and tension with hostility between members may produce the same unhappy effects on parents and children, which many claim for divorce. In fact in some instances divorce may be a help to all parties involved.

The number of divorces, however, are the only tangible evidence for assessing the number of broken marriages. In the United States, and for that matter, in many countries today, the actual numbers and the rates of divorce have been increasing. Divorces since World War II in this country have risen sharply, probably due to hasty marriages during the war. Table I gives the rates of marriages and divorce compared to the total population. This table indicates that there has been a downward trend both in marriages and divorces since the high point of 1946. The lowest recent rate was during the early years of the

TABLE I

MARRIAGE AND DIVORCE RATES IN THE UNITED STATES 1935-1950

YEAR	NO. OF MARRIAGES* PER 1,000 POPULATION	NO. OF DIVORCES† PER 1,000 POPULATION
1935-1939	10.7	1.8
1940-1944	11.4	2.4
1945	11.5	3.5
1946	16.2	4.4
1947	13.8	3.4
1948	12.4	2.9
1949	10.6	2.6
1950	11.0	2.5

*From: Recent International Marriage Trends, Statistical Bulletin, Metropolitan Life Insurance Company, June, 1951, p. 2.
†From: Postwar Divorce Rates Here and Abroad, Statistical Bulletin, Metropolitan Life Insurance Company, June, 1952, p. 7.

depression. In any one year there are about 25 divorces for every 100 marriages.

Grounds for divorce and causes for divorce are two completely different concepts; the former are stated in the law and indicate the legal basis on which divorce will be granted. Grounds vary widely from state to state. New York, for example, recognizes only one ground, adultery. Many states allow cruelty, but this must be proved in court with witnesses. Cruelty and desertion are defined in different states in a variety of general and specific terms. It is difficult to phrase legal terminology to cover causes of personality clashes, for example, between marriage partners.

Other factors in state laws which vary are the length of residence required before an application for divorce may be made in any state, whether collusion in divorce evidence has taken place, or whether or not the injured spouse has condoned the action prior to bringing suit. On the residence angle, Nevada leads the states in the lowest requirement, of six weeks, and Reno has made its name as a place for easy divorce. In summarizing the legal angle, Phelps and Henderson have had the following to say:

> There are nearly fifty different grounds for divorce, but no one state recognizes all of them. The most frequently cited legal reasons are adultery, cruelty, desertion, drunkenness, neglect to provide, conviction of felony, impotency, insanity, imprisonment, incompatibility, mental incapacity, pregnancy before marriage, and voluntary separation. Their interpretation also varies considerably among the different states. No court expects to grant decrees of divorce for other than these legal fictions.[12]

As to causes for divorce, they are a different matter. Persons married young, immature and dependent, may not be able to make their marriage work. Persons marrying because of so-called "romantic love" of the Hollywood version find too little in common after their passion has subsided. Persons of different temperament find nothing but constant friction in their life together. In all these cases real divisive feelings exist between the marriage partners. But it is not enough for the law that these feelings be recognized unless one partner desert, beat up the other, commit adultery, and the like. That is why

---

[12]Phelps, Harold, and Henderson, David: Contemporary Social Problems (copyright 1932, 1938, 1947, 1952, by Prentice-Hall, Inc., New York) page 418, quoted by permission of the publisher.

some lawyers have pleaded for a therapeutic approach to the problem, whereby skilled counselling could be offered the family before legal action occurs.   In such cases many times the marriage would be preserved.   Some courts have engaged persons to give marriage counselling. Marriage counselling bureaus have also been set up under private auspices and many social agencies offer help in this area.   The reader must realize that these bureaus in no wise supplant the legal action, but skilled counselling before legal action often saves some marriages and helps clarify the feelings of the partners before divorce takes place.

The victims of divorce are more frequently the children than either the husband or wife who is seeking to be rid of the other.   The court is obliged to review the problem of the children and award their custody to one of the contending parties.   The general practice is to give the children to the mother, although there may be privileges accorded the father by way of visiting his children or having them with him for specified periods of time.   Many of today's dependent children are in divorced families.   Since divorce frequently takes place among working class and lower income families, the problem of support of these minor children is a serious one.   In a study of the children of divorce made in Cook County, Illinois, during the decade 1940 to 1950, divorces involved 172,000 children.   Approximately 70 per cent of these children were under ten years of age.   This means that they will be dependent on someone for at last ten more years.   The mother had the custody of the children in 86 per cent of the cases, and in 57 per cent of the cases support for the children was fixed at less than fifteen dollars per week.   In 33 per cent of the cases, no support was ordered; the reason was not stated except that many mothers did not ask for support.[13] One can see the problems faced by the mother in attempting to rear the children as well as to bear the burden of financial support.   Of course the provisions of the Social Security Act (to be discussed later) are available to help a mother with minor children who is unable to get support from her husband.

There exists, however, a tendency for the divorced persons to remarry, so that the results are perhaps not as serious as might be seen at first glance.   Also there are methods of families breaking up other than by divorce so that divorce should not receive too severe condemnation for instability in family life.   These are death, desertions,

---

[13]Robson, Edwin A.:   The Law and Practice of Divorce, The Judge's Point of View, Conference on Divorce, University of Chicago, Law School, February, 1952, page 4.

annulments, and legal separations. The effect on the family life may be similar to those resulting from divorce, except that in case of desertion and separation, the marriage partner cannot remarry.

Of the economic assaults on family stability, more will be said later. Obviously a family must support itself or be supported to survive, and the first elements of survival lie in food and shelter. The federal and state governments have recognized the value of family life and have provided financial help to preserve families in economic need. The family is most threatened economically by the loss of the wage earner. His earnings and support may be lost not only by death, but by a handicapping condition, long illness, prolonged unemployment. It is to plug loopholes in these situations that some of our current measures of social security are devised. If one takes a long-range aspect, one realizes that certain jobs will always be low paid and that perhaps the wage earner needs more vocational help and training so that he will not enter a blind alley job. In some instances prejudice by race or nationality prevent certain job openings for members of the race or nationality group. Thus, those factors in our economic life which prevent the wage earner from supporting his family are certainly threats to the maintenance of that family.

THE UNMARRIED MOTHER

One family group needing considerable help is that of the unmarried mother and her child. Because birth out of wedlock bears so much stigma in our society today, the pregnant young woman who is about to bear a child out of wedlock is often a confused and anxious person needing skilled help from a competent source that she may make satisfactory plans for herself and the baby. This problem is further discussed in Chapter 19.

The number of infants who are born outside of wedlock has been increasing in the last decade and has reached the number of approximately 142,000 in 1950 or a ratio of 127 per 10,000 unmarried women. These figures are not entirely accurate as all states do not record the fact that a child is illegitimate. Some falsification of birth data exists also, but the chief deficiency is incomplete data. Of these illegitimate children, 54 per cent are born to Negro and nonwhite mothers and 47 per cent to white mothers. Somewhat over one-fourth are born to girls seventeen years of age and younger.[14] In any case many of the mothers are quite young.

The problems confronting the unmarried mother are many. Prior to the baby's birth is the problem of prenatal care and of where the mother will live. Many young women prefer to go to a town other than their own where they will not be known. Most large cities have maternity homes where girls may get health care and find a place to live both prior to and after delivery of the baby. These homes have been changing policies in recent years to offer a more adequate program, including skilled social service to assist the mother in planning the future. Some homes have their own medical facilities, but many have an arrangement with a nearby hospital. All have doctors and nurses on the staff. The Salvation Army and The Florence Crittenton League have maternity homes in many cities in the United States and are noted for the careful care given to unmarried mothers.

In addition to the maternity homes, hospitals will give mothers care through outpatient departments. Other social agencies, such as a family or children's agency or the public welfare department, stand ready to help the mother in planning for her child.

Probably the nurse will also know of many commercial maternity homes where mothers may go. Many of these give excellent physical care to the mother and child but do not give the same careful social service help which the mothers need. The commercial homes usually stress confidentiality of the matter and some promise adoption of the child. Most of these are licensed but sometimes commercial homes operate illegally and are virtually what has been termed "baby farms."

The nurse is certainly more aware than the public at large of the urgent need for the unwed mother-about-to-be to get adequate prenatal care. Every child has a right to be well born and the illegitimate child shares in this. Yet in many cities records show that the unwed mothers do not seek medical care until the seventh or eighth month of pregnancy and some not until the child is about to be born. This failure to plan in advance shows the turmoil of the mother and her refusal to recognize the reality of her situation. This also shows that the mother is confused and upset emotionally and in no way ready to make plans for her child. Many mothers in this situation ask to have the child adopted and then regret the action and seek to have their child returned later.

---

[14]A Chart Book—Children and Youth at the Midcentury, Chart 14.

The plans which the mother can make are really two. She can take the baby with her, or she can give it up either temporarily, or permanently for adoption. Many mothers return home or never leave the parental home and the child is then brought back into the family group with them. Financial assistance through public welfare agencies is available for needy mothers and their children. Sometimes a mother takes the child with her and seeks to work, leaving the child in someone's care during the day. These arrangements are frequently less satisfactory. If the mother decides she and the baby cannot remain together in a family unit, she may place the child in a foster home until she can make a permanent plan. Many times she feels that the father will marry her and they can establish a home. Many times she feels she will marry someone else, but she always has in mind establishing herself in a home. Inasmuch as many unwed mothers are not skilled women and command a low wage, this struggle is often very painful. They need the most skilled help available in making decisions for their future.

The unwed mother has a right to receive some support from the father of the child. This is sometimes obtained through private arrangements. The mother can take her case to court and through a civil or criminal action seek to have the alleged father adjudicated the father of her child and liable for support. Many times it is not easy to prove. Even if paternity is admitted, little support for the child may be contributed by the father. Many child welfare workers feel that the fathers of illegitimate children should be encouraged to take more responsibility for support and for recognition that these children are theirs. A child has a right to know who his parents are, and, if adoption is to take place, hereditary factors should be known if possible to help in placing the child. Sometimes fathers prove very responsible in supporting mother and child.

STRENGTHENING OF FAMILY LIFE

As with many other aspects of our life today, efforts at helping the family unit to become stronger and function more effectively have been directed, (1) toward furnishing counsel and help to the already existing family unit experiencing some symptoms of uneasiness or maladjustment, and (2) toward preparing persons to become better parents. Since financial worries and inadequacies are perhaps quite threatening to the security of the home, public and private agencies provide a means of keeping a family together by supplementing the income. As the Children's Charter of 1930 stated, no child should have to be removed from his family by reason of poverty alone. In the chapter on economic dependency, problems which arise and efforts which have been established to mitigate these are described in some detail. Other services offered mainly through private sources and less widely available to families throughout the United States are counselling and case work provided by family service agencies, marriage counseling bureaus, and the like. Many ministers and physicians are called upon by the members of their congregation and clientele to help people, either before or after marriage, with various phases of family life. Theological schools, in particular, give some training to their students so that they will understand the deep feelings in human relationships and be able to offer assistance to troubled parents coming to them. The status of work in this area of helping troubled husbands and wives to get aid in resolving their problems, which may result either in separation or continuation of the union, is still limited and resources are mainly in urban areas.

In most large cities legal aid bureaus exist to give low cost legal service to families needing it and unable to pay. This service includes obtaining of divorce when that seems necessary and helping with a variety of other legal matters which threaten a family, such as eviction notices, garnisheeing of wages. Loan agencies to aid families at little or no interest are also available.

Family service agencies should always be able to help families beset with a variety of difficulties. The family social worker understands that family malfunctioning stems from a number of problems and that, where a real desire is present on the part of the adults concerned, they can be helped to work out their difficulties. The techniques of the case workers are to listen to the difficulties, help the client focus on the basic troubles, give him some insight into the problems, support the client in working through his difficulties, give information regarding community resources, and, where there are some environmental pressures which are heavy, help relieve these. If this help is to be real and meaningful, obviously it must be done by professionally trained persons who understand human behavior and are well acquainted with the resources of the community. The fundamental philosophy on which this work is based is the belief that the individual has strength to help himself in his difficulties, once he has been helped to see some reasons for his unhappiness, and his role in modifying his behavior patterns.

The other large scale attack on the problem of preventing family breakdown is education for marriage and parenthood. That romantic love is not enough to face the practical problems of earning a living, of keeping house on a limited budget, of rearing children has long been recognized. The fact that so many young persons marry and set up independent establishments means that they should be well fortified to work out together the many problems which will inevitably arise. This movement has been termed "family life education," and many institutions and organizations have attempted to provide it. Among these are churches, schools and colleges, family service agencies, agencies serving young people such as the Y.M.C.A. and the Y.W.C.A., and some agencies variously organized for that specific purpose. Similarly P.T.A. groups seek to strengthen family life and assist in better understanding of children, school, and home life.

In general, efforts at education for marriage and family living have been to provide courses in marriage and the family, to offer lectures or a series of talks on various phases of the subject, and to provide counselling service for individual problems. Some colleges and high schools give courses for which credit is given. In a comprehensive survey of colleges in 1948-1949 it was found that almost half offered some courses in the family or marriage education and about 2 per cent of the students were enrolled. This same study notes that there was increasing interest, and a problem was noted of finding qualified teachers. Courses for training teachers are also being established with increased enrollment.[15]

Family life education courses at the high school level have been on more of an experimental basis, but several courses of study on an elementary level have been formulated indicating some of the problems of family living. With this spade work appreciation has been gained of what can be done at this level and where suitable material can be found. The Social Hygiene Association as well as school systems and social agencies usually have speakers available who will be able to speak to groups in the community desiring such talks. Film strips and some moving pictures are available for distribution.

If one might hazard some summary of the trends which are taking place in this field, one might say that the focus is turning to problems in human relationships, to emotional and social aspects of living together in a family group, to a recognition of the symptoms of malad-

---

[15]Bowman, Henry A.: Collegiate Education for Marriage and Family Living, *The Annals of the American Academy*, November, 1950, pages 148-155.

justment, to a search for underlying causes for these symptoms, to include fathers more and more in the family picture, and to a positive interpretation of what constitutes sound and happy family life. The ball is being carried especially in this field by the National Council on Family Relations established in 1938 for this purpose. Emphasis is also being placed on training leaders in the field.

Finally it would be fitting to close with some recommendations of the Midcentury White House Conference on Children and Youth, whose theme, "Toward the Healthy Personality Development of Children" stressed the fundamental part which parents have to play.

> That greater emphasis be placed by the various professions on utilizing methods and seeking new means of bringing the parents into thinking and planning with and for their children.

> That education for parenthood be made available to all through educational, health, recreation, religious and welfare agencies maintaining professional standards and staffed by properly qualified individuals.

> That elementary, secondary, college and community education include such appropriate experiences and studies of childhood and family life as will help young people to achieve the maturity essential to the role of parenthood.

> That all professions dealing with children be given, as an integral part of their preparation, a common core of experiences and studies of childhood and family life as will help young people to achieve the maturity essential to the role of parenthood.

> That all professions dealing with children be given, as an integral part of their preparation, a common core of experiences dealing with fundamental concepts of human behavior, including the need to consider the total person as well as any specific disorder; the interrelationship of physical, mental, social, religious, and cultural forces; the importance of interpersonal relationships; the role of self-understanding; and emphasis on the positive recognition and production of healthy personalities and the treatment of variations; and that lay people be orientated through formal or informal education to an understanding of the importance of the foregoing concepts.[16]

---

[16]Conference Platform, Children and Youth at the Midcentury—Official Conference Proceedings, op. cit., page 30.

STUDY QUESTIONS AND PROJECTS

1. In what ways has family life changed in the last two decades in cities, in rural areas?
2. Discuss the forces leading to family disorganization among family members, in the community.
3. Discuss divorce, separation, annulment: (a) from their destructvie aspects to the marriage partners, the children, society; (b) from their constructive aspects to the marriage partners, the children, society.
4. Examine the statistics of marriages and divorces in your community or your state from the Bureau of Vital Statistics. How do these compare with national trends?
5. Do you think the financial hazards of marrying today are greater than those which faced your grandparents? Explain.
6. Study a number of patients to show some in which family solidarity seems to be strong; give evidence; examples of parent-child conflicts; of showing symptoms of family disorganization.
7. Discuss the interrelationship of the family and the following institutions: (a) the church; (b) the school, (c) the state; and (d) economic institutions.
8. Find out, if possible, how many working women and working mothers there are in your community. What provisions does your community make for day care of children? Do these seem adequate?
9. Are day care centers, foster homes, and institutions in your state licensed by the state? If so, what are the standards required? If not, what suggestions would you have?
10. What facilities are available in your community for the unmarried mothers?
11. What facilities exist in your community for education for family living? Education for marriage? Are these widely utilized?
12. List and discuss all the agencies and projects in your community to help in family reorganization.
13. Compare laws governing marriage and divorce in your state with those of adjoining states.

REFERENCES

Angell, Robert C.: The Family Encounters the Depression, New York, 1936, Charles Scribner's Sons.

Applebaum, Stella B.: Working Wives and Mothers, Public Affairs Pamphlet, No. 188, New York, 1952.

Bossard, James, H. S.: ed., Toward Family Stability, Annals of the American Academy of Political and Social Science, Number 272, entire volume, November, 1950.

Bowman, Henry A.: Marriage for Moderns, New York, 1948, McGraw-Hill Book Company, Inc.

Brown, Muriel W.: Education for Family Living, Handbook of Adult Education in the United States, New York, 1948, Institute of Adult Education.

Burgess, Ernest W., and Locke, Harvey J.: The Family From Institution to Companionship, New York, 1945, American Book Company.

Community Service Society, The Family in a Democratic Society, New York, 1949, Columbia University Press.

Duvall, Evelyn M.: Family Living, New York, 1950, The Macmillan Company.

Folsom, Joseph K.: The Family and Democratic Society, New York, 1949, John Wiley and Sons, Inc.

Gruenberg, Sidonie: We the Parents; Our Relationship to Our Children and to the World Today, New York, revised edition, 1948, Harper and Brothers.

Harper, Fowler V.: Problems of the Family, Indianapolis, Bobbs-Merrill Company Inc. 1952.

Koos, Earl L.: The Middle-Class Family and Its Problems, New York, 1948, Columbia University Press.

Law School, the University of Chicago, Conference on Divorce, entire issue, February 29, 1952.

Levy, John, and Monroe, Ruth: The Happy Family, New York, 1938, Alfred A. Knopf, Inc.

MacKay, Richard V.: Laws of Marriage and Divorce Simplified, New York, 1946, Oceana Publications.

Morlock, Maud, and Campbell, Hilary.: Maternity Homes for Unmarried Mothers, 1946, U. S. Children's Bureau, Publication No. 309.

Phelps, Harold A, and Henderson, David: Contemporary Social Problems, New York, 1952, Prentice-Hall, Inc. chapters 15, 16, and 17.

Pratt, Dallas, and Neher, Jack: Mental Health is a Family Affair, New York, 1949, Public Affairs Pamphlet, Number 155.

Queen, Stuart A.: The Family in Various Cultures, Philadelphia, 1953, J. B. Lippincott Company.

B. COMMUNITY PROBLEMS IN THE UNITED STATES

I. Problems Affecting Total Health

CHAPTER 6

ILLNESS AS A COMMUNITY AND PERSONAL PROBLEM

INTRODUCTION

To present health and illness as two distinct entities would imply certain norms or standards by which these conditions could be measured. Too often one implies norms in judging health and forgets that each individual must be considered in the light of what is health or illness for him. The modern concept of health has been defined by the World Health Organization as "A state of complete physical, mental and social well-being and not merely the absence of disease or infirmity." The ever-increasing realization of the interdependence of social, emotional, and physical forces in causing as well as in treating and preventing disease is very significant. It is important that the modern trend is to treat each individual as a unique personality and not as an individual with a number of unrelated organs which may be diseased and causing his symptoms. Environmental pressures and personal tensions must be considered.

It may, therefore, be helpful to refer briefly to some modern concepts of disease. Disease may be considered as a conflict,[1] the signs and symptoms being evidence of conflict between a particular set of qualities in a human being and an equally particular set of adverse forces in the environment. These forces have been listed as physical violence, chemical violence, bacterial violence, and psychological violence. It is also pointed out that the constitutional approach to the study of clinical

---

[1]Draper, George: Disease and Man, London, 1930; Kegan, Trench, Truber, and Co., Ltd.

problems and the ability to recognize different qualities of personality in people gives a better understanding of the physical or psychic trauma. These differences lie in the depth of the individual constitution. It is also pointed out that it is never just one organ but the whole man that is sick.

Another definition of health[2] is freedom from physical and mental impairment from disease and from illness. Health implies a process of continuous readjustment to one's environment. Environments include all of the external circumstances both physical and social which come into reaction in the lives of human beings.

Another consideration of disease[3] is that of failure of adaptation to conditions both within and without the individual. It may be a failure to measure up to internal standards of conduct, an inadequate integration of the organism, or an integration of the individual as a social unit, but it always presents itself as inadequacy of some sort. Problems of adjustment call for redistribution of energy and new stresses resulting from this may cause disease. Disease is a form of partial activity because of lowered resistance and it is always regressive. A sick person may become dependent and infantile in his attitude and demands.

Disease may also be considered as a disturbance of life's rhythm, and health as an undisturbed rhythm.[4] When a person is sick he is isolated from normal associations and activities and "fate" is introduced into his life. Disease may be looked upon by some as making an individual inferior or by others as setting him apart in a place of preference, if not to his relatives and friends then perhaps to the doctor who may be particularly interested in his disease. Disease relieves one of certain obligations to society and to one's family which may tend to encourage some individuals to escape from the conflicts and troubles of life in illness.

The total function of medicine today must be considered as including not only the diagnosis, treatment, and prevention of disease, but the maintenance of health and acquiring all relevant knowledge in health conditions. The total patient and his total environment must be considered. No longer is it adequate to treat the disease or care for the

---

[2]Sydenstricker, Edgar: Health and Environment, New York, 1933, McGraw-Hill Book Company, Inc.

[3]White, Wm. A.: The Meaning of Disease, Baltimore, 1926, Williams & Wilkins Company.

[4]Sigerist, Henry: Man and Medicine, New York, 1932, W. W. Norton & Co., Inc.

patient adequately while he is in the hospital. Total health is referred to by Halliday[5] as "a healthy person in a healthy society."

THE INDIVIDUAL'S REACTION TO ILLNESS

The physical effects of illness may be the temporary or permanent disturbance or loss of function in some part of the body. Since the body normally functions with a tremendous physiological reserve, changes due to illness or accident may take place and the body may still function quite satisfactorily. The individual may not even be conscious of the loss or change in function. Many operations on internal organs change the original anatomical structure without interfering with fairly normal activities. For instance, if one kidney is removed the other kidney can do the work of the two.

> A man is healthy not when his organs are built according to a definite formula which may be worked out mathematically, but rather when they work together without friction so that the organism is equal to the demands placed upon it by life and may adjust itself with sufficient rapidity to changes within certain limits.[6]

In addition to physiological reactions due to illness or physical handicap, illness invariably changes the relation of the patient to those immediately about him and often changes his relation to the community as well as his position in the group.

In order to study adequately and to draw any conclusions from the attitude of any patient to his illness, investigation must be made of his accustomed reaction to life's problems. It is important to study his background, his personality, his habits of work and play, his interests and ambitions, and to understand his family picture as a whole. Many investigators have pointed out the relationship between the physical and emotional side of health and illness. Changes in personality may be due to the patient's interpretation of his physical condition and perhaps to the adjustment he has to make. In every illness a psychic factor is present in addition to the organic disturbance. The patient's desire to come back to a state of health may depend upon what is awaiting him on his return to normal life. This psychic outlook will be influenced by the individual's past experiences, and thus the outcome of the illness

---

[5]Halliday, James L.: Psychosocial Medicine, New York, 1948, W. W. Norton & Co., Inc.
[6]Sigerist, Henry: Man and Medicine, New York, 1932, W. W. Norton & Co., Inc.

may be determined more by nonmedical conditions than is apparent at the outset. Disease always tends to bring about a certain amount of regression. The patient may become dependent and childlike for a longer or shorter period, depending upon his personality, background, and total life satisfactions.

Feelings of inferiority and of being different from one's family adds much to any physical handicap. Fear of the disease may be accompanied by fear of death. The constructive attitudes of courageousness reasonableness, hopefulness, faith, and optimism stand out in sharp contrast to destructive attitudes of anxiety, fear, depression, indifference, skeptical belief, pessimism, hopelessness, and rebellion. The way in which an individual reacts to illness depends to a great extent on his personality as his previous life and environment have shaped it. The responses made may also depend on the life circumstances of the individual at the onset of the illness, as well as on his past experiences and the way they have enabled him to face problems and make adjustments.

Probably the majority of patients found in general hospitals today are either in the acute or in the beginning stages of disease. Hospital experience often creates and fosters anxieties and fears for the patient by its strangeness and by the seeming indifference of the medical and nursing staff in their great preoccupation with other activities away from the bedside of the patient. Steps are being taken to emphasize to all nurses the importance of their personal relationship with the patient and his family as an important part of therapeutics. The patient may also be concerned because of shortages in medical care and lack of adequate personnel in hospitals or clinics.

A study of the mental attitudes of patients in the hospital showed rather interestingly the following mental states:

1. Fear, anxiety, distrust: Predisposing causes for these are strange and harsh surroundings.
2. Worry: Predisposing causes are unsettled, unsatisfactory or unknown home conditions, or social conditions with which the patient is powerless to deal.
3. Ennui and loneliness caused by the monotony of surroundings in the hospital; the lack of mental and physical occupation; the loss of accustomed pleasures; separation from family and friends.
4. Depression caused by the uncertain future outlook; the long duration of the illness; the lack of religious consolation.

5. Shame caused by lack of privacy in the hospital ward; disclosure of poverty; disclosure of physical defects and "shameful" disease.
6. Disgust caused by exposure to evil sights and smells; the careless preparation and presentation of food; the monotonous menu.
7. Irritation caused by annoying sounds from within and without the hospital; disagreeable neighbors; delayed service; favoritism.[7]

These attitudes may be greatly accentuated if the disease is of long duration. The adjustments that must be made, not only by the patient but also by his family, to tuberculosis, to diabetes, or to the loss of a limb depend to a great extent on the strengths in that family group. The interference with normal family life over a period of months, or even years, may result in strains and emotional anxiety that will tend to undermine the most normal individual.

On the other hand, an individual who has difficulty in adjusting himself to his environment when in good health may seek relief consciously or unconsciously in the form of continued illness. Thus sickness may become a satisfactory and socially approved way of escaping from an intolerable or unsolvable situation.

Miss Marcus[8] discusses three accompaniments of illness as follows: first, the loss of physical adequacy reduces one's confidence in one's ability to meet the future; second, serious physical conditions transfer control of the patient's personal destinies to the physician or the case worker, and this reinforces existing tendencies to emotional dependency; third, the patient may get so much satisfaction from the sympathy and attention given during his illness that he may not wish to give up this passive satisfaction for the more constructive satisfaction of independent effort, and the successful carrying on of responsibilities.

In dealing with sick people the ultimate goal of "normality" must be constantly kept in mind. To achieve this it may be necessary to remove strains in the patient's environment, or help him to overcome them by a more complete understanding of himself in relation to his environment. Thus, as Miss Emerson so aptly points out:

---

[7]Goldwater, S. S.: Faulty Mental Attitudes in Patients and How to Correct Them, Modern Hospital **34**:49-52, 1930.

[8]Marcus, Grace: Some Aspects of Relief in Family Case Work, New York, 1929, Russell Sage Foundation, page 82.

It is important to remember that what is of vital interest to the patient is neither his disease nor its treatment in itself, but the effect that his illness will have on his work and how soon he can resume it.[9]

The point has been made that a patient's reaction to illness depends not only on the disease and treatment, but also on the kind of an individual he is. Successful treatment demands of the patient sacrifices, cooperation, the facing of unpleasant truths, the taking of family or friends into one's confidence, or perhaps a reorganization of daily life and work.

Individuals sometimes fear that they have a disease. This may be due to superstitious beliefs regarding their symptoms, or because some relative died of that disease, or from a variety of reasons which fixed the fear in their minds. Sometimes this fear or phobia is so fixed in an individual's mind that no amount of persuasion or scientific proof on an intellectual level will dislodge the idea. Such individuals may wander from doctor to doctor and clinic to clinic, seeking treatment to allay an imaginary disease. Such diseases as cancer and tuberculosis often figure in these phobias. This fear may be encouraged more if the individual has some slight symptoms pertaining to the supposedly diseased organ. For instance, such an individual may have gastric ulcer, or even only slight stomach discomfort, and be fearful that he has cancer of the stomach.

A patient's reaction to disease may be colored by society's attitude toward that disease. The social disgrace connected with cancer, tuberculosis, or mental disease is not nearly as great as it used to be. The traditional attitude to the venereal diseases on a moralistic level, for example, has done much to prevent an adequate program of treatment and prevention from being carried out in many communities.

Illness may result temporarily or permanently in changing the individual's role and status in the family. For instance, changed roles in the family may result in changed relationships. If the wage earner loses his accustomed position in the family, either temporarily or permanently, he is likely to lose status. He may feel inferior because he can no longer provide for his family. He may resent the fact that his oldest son, who has to assume the position of wage earner, has also taken over the authority that his father had before his illness.

---

[9]Emerson, Ruth: Social Service—An Important Asset in the Nurse's Training, Modern Hospital **24:**72, 1930.

Therefore, to appreciate and to attempt to understand any patient's reaction to disease, it is necessary to know what illness means to that individual. His fears and prejudices must be understood; to him they are real. The patient's reaction to illness depends on his ability to adjust himself to the limitation or changes in his mode of life brought about by the illness. These changes may be temporary or permanent. Disease may mean surrender or a fight to the individual.

THE ECONOMIC EFFECTS OF ILLNESS

These are the concern not only of the patient and his family but also of the community. The patient, if he is the wage earner, may at first be concerned primarily with the duration of the illness, or how long he will need to be off the job. He may also be concerned with the outcome, that is, will he be able to resume his old work or will he be physically incapacitated because of the illness? The welfare of the community, of course, depends on the welfare of individuals and their families. If the patient has a communicable disease which may menace the health of other members, certain precautions are taken to prevent the spread of the disease. The economic loss to industry because of disease and physical handicaps must be considered in studying the economic effects of disease in the community. The loss to the community because of premature death or handicapping illness can hardly be estimated in dollars and cents.

In addition to the direct cost of treatment to the patient, he may be faced with the loss of wages during all or part of his illness. This may be followed by reduced wages when he returns to work. A direct economic loss to the patient and his family is the use of savings or insurance in order to meet the expense of medical care. When the patient has no financial resources or insurance to pay for his illness he may, in most communities, get medical and nursing care free at municipal clinics and hospitals, but the expense of treatment here must be met by the community. The patient and his family may become dependent on the community's social agencies for financial aid because of illness.

Other results to the family economically may be a reduced standard of living, which may result in inadequate food, shelter, and clothing. This condition, if prolonged, may mean lowered resistance to disease in other members of the family. Some effects of these economic changes in the family may be changed roles, as well as changed relationships among its members. If the wage earner is ill, his wife or children may temporarily or permanently need to assume the role of wage earner. Unless an acceptable substitute for the homemaker is available, such as a relative or close friend, children may be neglected and develop both physical and emotional problems. If adolescent boys and girls are forced to assume the positions of wage earners, they may resent the break in their accustomed mode of life.

Illness of the homemaker, while not often affecting the family's income in wages, does affect expenditures. The cost of medical care, the absence from the home if hospitalization is indicated, carfare to and from the clinic, must all be considered. A substitute homemaker may not spend the family income wisely, and the cost of paying a substitute is a financial drain on the family income. In many cities, when the family income cannot meet the cost of paying for a substitute homemaker, housekeeper service may be supplied by a social agency. This shifts the cost of the illness again from the family to the community.

If the family seeks financial help from a social agency, it may gradually develop dependency on the agency, particularly if the illness is of long duration. Because of changed roles and relationships, personal and family disorganization may develop. Sometimes help from a social agency, on an intensive case-work level, may help the family to adjust to the problems which have become accentuated by or which have developed as a result of the illness.

The economic aspects in illness may often overshadow the other aspects of the social component. It is often impossible, however, to separate them into cause and effect. There are cases where lack of income has resulted in such low standards of living that because of inadequate food, shelter, and recreation the health of the family may be impaired. There are also cases where the cost of medical care has taken all the financial reserves of the family. Individuals may even have lowered their standard of living to provide medical care.

Illness of the wage earner may mean an abrupt stop in all income unless sick benefit or insurance exists. Because of prolonged illness of the wage earner, the mother may have to work outside the home, perhaps at the cost of her own health. When the homemaker works outside the home, it is important that she have a substitute to care for the children physically and emotionally during her absence. If the children are neglected, serious physical or behavior problems may result.

THE REACTION OF THE FAMILY TO ILLNESS

During a period of illness family traits, either constructive or destructive, may become accentuated. Conflicts which were present before may become exaggerated. This, fortunately, is not always the case. In many illness situations, after the first fears have diminished and the family have made certain adjustments, the family do all they can to encourage and support the patient until he is well again. In the well-adjusted family group the illness situation may be met with very little disruption. However, if, because of the illness, economic insecurity develops and the family needs to get help from relatives, friends, or social agencies, more complicated problems of adjustment may follow. An interesting study[10] of families pointed out that illness was the single, most important contributing factor in family trouble. This did not necessarily mean illness of the wage earner but included problems developing when the wife became ill and the problem of managing the home had to be undertaken by other members. Illness in any home is disrupting and not necessarily economically or because of lack of medical care. Fear of doctors and hospitals has been found present even today in many families. The home may be broken during the illness of the wage earner or the homemaker. Temporary or permanent homes may need to be found for children, placing them with relatives, friends, or in some instances in foster homes through a social agency. Adolescent boys and girls may have to work either part or full time. This may mean that school and normal recreation is interrupted. In other words, illness of any member may disrupt the accustomed functioning of the family. Tensions and anxieties are likely to increase as normal outlets and satisfactions diminish.

It is important that the nurse study the individual situation and try to understand what the illness means to the patient and to the patient group. While it may be the patient who suffers most physically, the family is likewise concerned. The bonds of sympathy between him and the members of his family may react emotionally on them. The economic bonds may be broken and the financial dependency shift from the patient to another member of the family. This disorganization of the family's normal reactions and routine because of illness is very significant. If the illness is acute, of short duration, or if the patient and his family can be reasonably assured that in a short time he can resume his normal activities and that no physical handicap

---

[10]Koos: Families in Trouble, New York, 1946, King's Crown Press.

will remain after the acute stage is over, the necessary adjustments can often be made. If financial aid is necessary for a short period, either from relatives or a social agency, the reassurance that the period of stress and strain is likely to be a temporary one may help the patient and his family to face the necessary adjustment. However, if the condititon is chronic or leaves the patient physically handicapped, the family's reaction may be quite different.

Prolonged illness places as great a strain on the varied human relationships comprised in a family as any other factor. The parents become such a burden to the younger generation, that, after a while, the children welcome any means that will enable them to be rid of them. Not infrequently it is the son-in-law or the daughter-in-law who will not tolerate the presence of the invalid in the home. The patient himself may be so exacting in his demands and so self-centered that home care becomes impossible even when the relatives are considerate and willing. Among the poor with a large family forced to live in a few small rooms, the situation often becomes intolerable. Quite aside from the financial burden, the constant presence of the invalid, who may be querulous and exacting, and who must often be tended at night, is a constant drain on the vitality of the members of his family. Night after night, a mother, a father, a daughter, or a son may have his sleep interrupted by the calls of the patient; the whole atmosphere of the home becomes subdued, the children lose their spontaneity, and life assumes a dull and drab color. A daughter, or more rarely a son, may be compelled to postpone marriage for years because of the burden of the sick parent. A common result of chronic illness in a married person is infidelity of his mate, leading to complete rupture of the family ties. When the patient is forced to remain a member of the family group, an almost unbearable situation sometimes develops.

Because of all of these factors, we see family after family disorganized, with shattered morale and resulting destitution. These ill effects are not confined to the patient and to his family alone, but are a drain on the community resources as well. Various social agencies are called on to give relief. There is no organization doing welfare work, be it family welfare, social service, or district nursing groups, no hospital, dispensary, or home for the aged or incurable, that is not called on daily to solve problems arising from the immediate effects and by-products of chronic invalidism . . . .[11]

---

[11]Boas, Ernst P.: The Unseen Plague, Chronic Disease, New York, 1940, J. J. Augustin, Publisher, pages 30 and 33.

Outline for Studying the Individual and Family's Reaction to Illness.—The following outline may be helpful to the nurse in making detailed studies of the family and the patient in the illness situation.

1. Identifying information : name, age, etc.

2. Medical data :
   (a) Medical history—past.
   (b) Medical history—present, including medical plan and prognosis.
   (c) Health problems of other members of family.

3. Social history and situation at time of clinic or hospital's first contact with patient, including the family set-up before illness, economic data, etc.

4. General economic adjustments to illness by the patient and his family :
   (a) Providing adequate care in the hospital and at home: cost of diet, medicines, etc.
   (b) Loss of wages—temporarily or permanently.
   (c) Loss of insurance, property, etc., because of inability to keep up payments.
   (d) Family resources.
   (e) Community resources.

5. Adjustments in the home due to the illness :
   (a) Moving :
       1. Cheaper rent desired.
       2. Different environment desired for patient.
       3. Convenience to medical facilities.
   (b) Changes in the role of wage earner or homemaker.
   (c) Relatives living with the family either to help pay the rent or to help care for the patient.

6. The patient's emotional reactions to the physical illness :
   (a) Reaction of individual to diagnosis and treatment prescribed; confidence in doctor, social worker, hospital, or clinic.
   (b) Fear, discouragement, shame (especially in relation to certain diseases).
   (c) Reaction to educational or work adjustments.
   (d) Loss or gain of status in the family.
   (e) Reaction to separation from family due to illness, especially during period of hospitalization.
   (f) Development of emotional dependency.

7. Attitude of family to the illness of the patient :
   (a) Lack of understanding of diagnosis and treatment necessary, e.g., influencing patient against operation or treatment.
   (b) Dissatisfaction with medical attention and attempts to substitute quack remedies and patent medicines.
   (c) Attitude toward such diseases as cancer, skin diseases, tuberculosis, venereal and mental diseases, etc.

(d) Oversympathetic.

(e) Understanding and use of community resources for care and treatment of illness.

When patient is a child consider in addition the following points:

1. Attitude of adults to patient—oversolicitous, pampering, display of overemotionalism.
2. Attitude of other children to patient—jealous, overconcerned, fearful of disease, etc.
3. Development of behavior problems in child.
4. Effect of interruption in education.
5. Effect of changed recreation and lessened activity.

It may be instructive for the nurse to make some studies on patients under her care according to the suggestions on the outline. She might select several different types of conditions and note the different social problems which emerged and how the patient and his family met them.

COMMUNITY REACTION TO ILLNESS

Health care for the American people has been receiving increasing attention for the past twenty-five years. In this particular aspect of our society, there is evidence of culture lags. Technological inventions in the field of medicine have advanced much more rapidly than the social organization necessary to keep pace with the utilization of new inventions. There is still a certain discrepancy between the amount and kind of medical and health care available in the city and in the country. Social organization has developed to a greater extent in urban areas so that the benefits of medical science are found to a greater extent than in rural areas.

Much information has been accumulated in the past twenty-five years on the quality and quantity of medical care and on the health conditions in this country. Some of these studies are those of the Committee on the Costs of Medical Care, 1928-1931; the National Health Survey, 1935 and 1936; The Nation's Health, a Report to the President, 1948; the reports of the United States Public Health Service; the Social Security Board; the American Medical Association; the Bureau of the Census; the Department of Agriculture; and various other Governmental and voluntary agencies have accumulated much information in the health field. Probably the best known of these are the surveys made by the Committee on the Costs of Medical Care and the National Health Survey. The National Health Survey based its conclusions on information obtained from a house-to-house canvass of more than 700,000 homes in eighty-three cities and twenty-three rural areas in eighteen different states. This survey was taken in 1935 and 1936. The National Health Survey was concerned with finding out the general condition of the nation's health, the duration of illness, kind of illness, medical care received, the economic and social factors resulting from the illness, and chronic and debilitating illnesses and accidents which kept individuals from work or from school.

A more recent study presented to President Truman by Oscar R. Ewing, Federal Security Administrator in 1948, namely, *The Nation's Health, A Ten-Year Program,* analyses the resources available for health and what should be done to provide better facilities in every community.

Statistics show that the average American spends more for his automobile, movies, tobacco, and alcoholic beverages than for medical care. The question immediately might be raised, could he have apportioned a part of his income for medical care if he had considered it as important as going to the movies, having his tobacco and alcoholic beverages? In considering adequacy of medical care, the distribution of facilities and personnel must be considered. Most hospitals, and consequently most doctors, nurses, and other health workers are in large urban centers. The problem of medical care in many rural areas includes many other aspects of living than simply the medical. For example, proper supervision and protection of water, milk, food supplies, adequate sewage disposal, fly and mosquito control would decrease the incidence of many diseases found more frequently in rural than urban areas, particularly in certain sections of the country. Public health facilities operating as efficiently through all rural areas as through large urban centers would undoubtedly reduce the incidence of many diseases and the need for as much medical care as now exists, so that the big problem is a general socio-economic one rather than strictly medical. Just sending doctors and nurses into an area would not immediately solve the problem. These areas need health officers and sanitary engineers as much or more than they need doctors and nurses, and many counties cannot afford to employ the specialized personnel needed. Help from the Federal government through state and local units is necessary in many instances. According to the United States Public Health Service, about 5,000 communities need new water systems; 7,700 communities with a population of about nine million need new sewage systems; and about 2,800 incorporated communities with a population roughly of about twenty-five million have no sewage facilities at all.

Another aspect of the adequacy of medical care to be considered is the education of the people in matters of health. Public health nurses and health officers are well aware of the fact that often people do not know of health facilities available, or if they do not know they may be superstitiously afraid to use them or will not follow out the instructions given because of ignorance. Opportunities for free vaccination, free x-ray, free blood tests, and certain treatments are sometimes not utilized adequately by the general public.

Through mass communication, much health education is now being carried on. But there is still evidence of culture lag between existing knowledge and the use of this knowledge. In every community the health of individuals and groups has become a matter of major importance. Tax-supported institutions have gradually been extended and public health services developed to bring them within the reach of all individuals without regard to economic ability to pay for these services. Voluntary organizations, professional, medical, and health associations have also been working to improve health in all of our communities and the cooperation between voluntary and tax-supported organizations in the community is more evident than ever before in our history.

CONCLUSION

Because of the close contact between the patient and the nurse, the latter may be asked questions regarding the outcome of the patient's illness. Worries and fears may first be expressed to the nurse who will often get information which may help explain his reaction to the hospital or the clinic. She may be the first to know that his physical progress is being retarded because of worries of home conditions, financial or otherwise. What action the nurse takes and how she uses this information will depend on the particular situation in which she is working. If she is in a hospital or clinic, it may be that a conference with the doctor or the medical social worker is indicated. It may be that reassurance and explanations by the doctor and nurse will meet the situation. Often, however, these expressed worries and fears are the symptoms of deeper concern, unrest and insecurity and may indicate the need for medical-social treatment by the professional medical-social worker.

The nurse in the public health field who is faced with such problems, either financial or emotional, or more involved adjustment situations in relation to her patient and his family, will often need to use resources in her community which from experience she knows are suited to help with these particular problems. She may start by studying the information obtained from the Social Service Exchange about the patient and his family. Social agencies that know the patient now or knew him in the past will be better equipped to help in his present difficulty. From her detailed analysis of the patient and his present situation, and from her knowledge of the functions of existing social agencies in the community, the nurse will be helped to decide where help for the present problem can be most satisfactorily obtained.

Thus it is important for every nurse in the hospital as well as in the community to know what resources are available and to understand how she can cooperate with other professional workers and with agencies for a better working-out with the patient and his family of his present problems and difficulties.

STUDY QUESTIONS AND PROJECTS

1. Discuss in detail the economic aspects of illness (a) to the patient; (b) to his family; (c) to the community.
2. Is ill health chiefly due to cultural maladjustments or to the maladjustment of the human organism and nature?
3. Why are the economic aspects of illness so complex and why are they so difficult to solve?
4. Discuss the various points of view toward disease presented in this chapter. Try to illustrate by individual and community attitudes to disease.
5. Select one patient for special study. Consider in detail his social and personal aspects as well as nursing problems. Show how these are interrelated.

REFERENCES

Bartlett, Harriet: Emotional Elements in Illness, The Family **21**:39-47, 1940; reprinted from Medical Social Worker.

Blustone, E. M.: Social Medicine Arrives in the Hospital, Modern Hospital, August, 1950.

Ewing, Oscar R.: The Nation's Health, A Ten-Year Program, A Report to the President.

Halliday, James L.: Psychosocial Medicine, New York, 1948, W. W. Norton & Co., Inc.

Koos, Earl Lomon: The Sociology of the Patient, New York, 1950, McGraw-Hill Book Company, Inc.

Robinson, Canby: The Patient as a Person, New York, 1937, The Commonwealth Fund.

Rothstein, Mildred G.: Individual Personality Factors in Illness, Journal of Social Casework **27**:313-320, December, 1946.

Sigerist, Henry: Man and Medicine, New York, 1932, W. W. Norton and Company, Inc.

Sydenstricker, Edgar: Health and Environment, New York, 1933, McGraw-Hill Book Company, Inc.

Thornton, Janet, and Knauth, Marjorie Straus: The Social Component in Medical Care, New York, 1937, Columbia University Press.

Upham, Frances: A Dynamic Approach to Illness, New York, 1949, Family Service Association of America.

White, William A.: The Meaning of Disease, Baltimore, 1926, Williams and Wilkins Company.

CHAPTER 7

THE SICK CHILD

INTRODUCTION

The sick child like the sick adult has an individual personality shaped by the interrelationship of his heredity and his environment. The child's reaction to illness is dependent on his physical, intellectual, and psychological status at the onset of his illness. It is dependent also on the nature of the illness, the acuteness, type, severity, duration of treatment, and convalescence and the prognosis in terms of complete recovery. The needs of the sick child, like the needs of any other patient, must be considered during his illness—that is, the need peculiar to his age, his education, his recreation, his emotions—particularly during the period of his illness when there is an abrupt break in the meeting of these needs in the normal way and if he is removed from his accustomed environment. These needs must be considered to an even greater extent. (See chapters 19 and 20 for discussion of child development.)

EMOTIONAL ASPECTS OF ILLNESS IN CHILDREN

The emotional response of a child to his illness and convalescence depends on many factors. These might be grouped as follows:

1. The physical, mental, and emotional development of the child at the onset of his illness. This depends to a great extent on his family and school contacts and influences. Economic, educational, and emotional factors in the family will influence the health, the child's ability to resist disease, and his reaction to treatment.
2. The illness itself considered in terms of type; duration, acuteness, length of convalescence, prognosis must all be considered.

The child will, of course, be conditioned mainly by the attitude of adults in his family, school, recreational groups, as well as by the experiences of other children in illness situations.

The sudden break in education may result in destructive attitudes in the older child. If the illness is prolonged he may want to give up school rather than have to drop behind his classmates. If the disease is crippling or disfiguring he may shun the association of his contemporaries. Many hospitals make provision for children to continue with their studies as soon as the individual child is able to do so. Every nurse now has some knowledge of child psychology and due consideration should be given to the fundamental factors motivating all behavior. The need for obtaining much information about the child's background, the family situation, his status in the family as well as in school and recreational groups, will be most valuable to her in helping the child adjust to the hospital and to the illness situation.

While it is true today that many children have been conditioned favorably to hospitals and health centers because they have been taken to these centers as long as they can remember, the educational program of postnatal care, well-baby clinics, school health programs, physical examinations in preparation for camps and recreational activities are becoming a familiar pattern in every community. The following situations may point out the significance of environmental influences on the reaction of children:

(1) Mrs. J., aged 35 years, the mother of four children, is sitting in the clinic waiting "her turn," with Mary, aged 5, and Tom, aged 3. Mary is obviously ill. Her face is flushed and there is a profuse nasal discharge. Her breathing is somewhat noisy and her neck appears swollen. It was necessary to bring Tom because there was no one to leave him with. The two older children are at school and Mr. J. is at work. Tom is a well, normally active child and cannot understand why he must "just sit" with his wraps on.

Mrs. J. is very tired. She has been up many times during the last few nights to take care of Mary. This morning after the rest of the family left the house, she hurried to get herself, Mary, and Tom suitably dressed for the clinic visit. The result is still not pleasing as she sits on the bench waiting. Mary has perspired a good deal the past two days. Mother was afraid to bathe her as she was sure that Mary would catch more cold. The clothing of all three looks grimy and poorly kept. Obviously a bath, shampoo, and clean clothes are needed for each. Mother is acutely aware of this situation which makes her even more shy and retiring. Bathing facilities are very inadequate in her home, and she is so hopelessly tired all of the time. Tom insists upon playing on the clinic floor where he picks up more dirt. Mrs. J. does not visibly object since he is at least quiet.

The clinic is hot and stuffy. Mother has not removed her wraps or those of the children. It takes such a lot of energy, and things may get lost. Perhaps the doctor will see her soon. Anyway, she is too tired to bother. She used fifty cents of her fast dwindling household fund to take a taxi as she did not feel equal to managing the two children on a crowded streetcar. Perhaps she should have come on the streetcar, and used the money for food. Her mind is on her untidy house, the unmade beds, the stack of dirty dishes, the laundry waiting to be done. She is worried about Mary. Tom whimpers and pulls at her skirts. He needs to be taken to the toilet. Mary has fallen asleep on her lap. She seems so heavy and mother's arm is tired. She planned to get to the clinic early so that she would be seen first and would not have to wait long. She arrived at quarter after nine and found several people already waiting. The hands of the clock now point to ten. Time drags on. No one tells her how much longer she will have to wait. By twelve o'clock the other children will be home for lunch. Supplies and funds are low. What can she prepare quickly when she reaches home? She hasn't spent very wisely of late—but she has been too tired to shop carefully and plan ahead. Mrs. J.'s shoulders droop still more. Physical weariness, illness, worry, and low income have left their mark.

How could the nurse make Mrs. J. more comfortable? She could see that the room was properly ventilated. The children's wraps could be removed. Mary could be placed comfortably in a bed or on the examining table in one of the cubicles with her mother seated beside her. She could supply the mother with a drink of water for the child, paper handkerchiefs, and a newspaper pocket for their disposal. Tom could have his wraps removed, be taken to the toilet, and then provided with play material. Through casual conversation with Mrs. J., the nurse could learn many things which would give her a better understanding of the home circumstances. Many parents are hungry for conversation. They want to tell you about the family and ask advice on many matters. The nurse can learn much if she will but show an interest in the patient and his family. Some questions may seem trivial but they are very important to the mother. Incidental conversation while Mary is made comfortable, her temperature taken, and the clinic chart started will help the mother feel more at ease.[1]

(2) James, a likeable 4-year-old, was taken by his parents to their private physician. Father remained at home from work today to accompany the family. Preparation for the visit to the physician had been a rather strenuous ordeal. James had not been feeling well for several days. He was usually a good-natured child, but now suddenly objected to everything that was being done. In the first place, he did not want to get dressed and go to the doctor's office. He very dramatically told his mother so. He was finally dressed and taken against his will. He consistently objected to all procedures in the office. He kicked and cried when his temperature was taken. Why all the fuss and flurry at home to get dressed only to be undressed again? This sudden turn baffled the parents. The mother pleaded and coaxed. Upon questioning the parents, the physician discovered that James had not acted quite normally for several weeks. His appetite was poor. There had been considerable weight loss, and the child looked generally pale and tired.

The physician decided that James should be admitted to the hospital for a few days to permit a more thorough examination. Laboratory tests and care-

---

[1]Benz, Gladys: Pediatric Nursing, St. Louis, 1948, The C. V. Mosby Company, pages 236-237.

ful observations could then be made to assist in determining the best plan of treatment. When James heard the word "hospital" he noisily objected with a great display of temper. The mother was almost at the point of asking permission to take the child home and to attempt to bring him to the hospital at a future date. After all, he did not seem acutely ill. However, she decided the physician must know best. She had always had great faith in him. She ardently wished she had done something during the past year to prepare the child for a possible hospital experience. It was too late now. Her uncertainty and tension were also transmitted to the child.

James was accustomed to a rest period in the afternoon while mother read or told him a story. He had his shoes off during this time and lay on his bed under a snuggly blanket. Sometimes he even dropped off to sleep for a little while. Then he and mother had their afternoon milk or fruit juice before he went out to play. All this had been omitted today. Now, at four o'clock in the afternoon, the family of three had arrived at the hospital physically exhausted and nervous. What would await them here? Would James cry to go home? Would the nurse understand that he was ordinarily a "good" child but that the recent experiences had been very wearing on him?[2]

These situations could be duplicated many times. It is very important that the nurse and all the personnel in contact with the child and his family in clinics and hospitals consider each child and each family in its own unique situation. It may seem easier to consider these things when the worker visits the child in his own home. Here, however, she must be very careful to consider the pressures and stresses of the home situation and not project her own ideas of what the mother and father and other members of the family should or should not do until she has carefully considered the total family setting in the community. (See chapters 10 and 15 for special disease conditions affecting children.)

COMMUNITY PLANS AND PROGRAMS

Reduction of disease and early treatment has been the keynote of all work with children. Beginning with the mother, through prenatal and postnatal care, improved obstetrical facilities, educational programs in the importance of health for all children, in the school health program, families and the community are becoming aware of their responsibility for every child's health. Service for crippled children under the Social Security Act emphasizes that each child should be given adequate medical care.

---

[2]Benz, Gladys: Pediatric Nursing, St. Louis, 1948, The C. V. Mosby Company, pages 239-240.

The education of the crippled child is now provided for in most public school systems. The Social Security Act provides grants-in-aid for each state that has submitted and had approved by the Children's Bureau plans for "locating crippled children, for providing surgical, corrective, and other treatment and facilities for diagnosis, hospitalization and aftercare for children who are crippled or who are suffering from conditions leading to crippling." When children reach sixteen years of age provision for vocational training is made available from funds provided jointly by the state and Federal governments.

The National Foundation for Infantile Paralysis is an organization interested in every phase of this disease. In 1941 a grant was made from this fund to the National League of Nursing Education for the purpose of establishing a joint orthopedic nursing advisory service with the National Organization for Public Health Nursing. Through this grant, scholarships are offered to prepare nurses for work in this field. Study has also been made of available places where special study in orthopedic nursing may be carried out, and pamphlets on different aspects of the subject have been published.

Many neglected types of crippling diseases of children are now being studied. For example, The National Society for Crippled Children and Adults has made a special study of the cerebral palsy problem. In many localities these children have been neglected because of ignorance and lack of facilities for treatment and education. The attitude of communities is tending more and more to an interest in all crippling conditions and causes. Communities are also beginning to provide medical, nursing, educational, vocational, and recreational facilities for all crippled children.

Many states now include some schools for the handicapped child as part of the general program of education. As pointed out above, some provision for the crippled child is made in the Social Security Act. It is interesting to note that in the White House Conference on Child Health and Protection the handicapped child was considered under the following groups: the deaf, and hard of hearing, the visually handicapped, and the crippled. There are many privately supported as well as tax-supported organizations interested in this phase of social endeavor.

The education of the deaf is highly important, because many individuals deaf from birth can be taught to speak. Those who can speak can be taught lip reading, and the skill of some of the deaf in lip reading is very remarkable. The Gallaudet College in Washington, D. C., offers collegiate work to the deaf. Many cities and states have special schools for the deaf as part of their public school system. From all reports it is estimated that about ten million persons in this country suffer from defective hearing to such a degree as to interfere with their education, their vocational adaptation, and their social adjustment.

Sometimes the home environment is not adequate for the constructive guidance the handicapped child needs for many years. There are also residential schools in this country for handicapped children. In these schools children are taught according to their individual problems, and if they are capable of assuming such responsibility, they are given vocational training and guidance so that as many of them as possible may be able to contribute economically to their support. The United States Office of Education has a series of bulletins relating to the education of handicapped children. The list of these publications may be obtained from the Superintendent of Documents, U. S. Government Printing Office, Washington, D. C. The reader is also referred to the list of agencies found in the Appendix. Many of these specializing in work with children give free and inexpensive material in their fields.

STUDY QUESTIONS AND PROJECTS

1. What is the attitude in your community toward the sick child? Are the needs of sick children adequately met by existing facilities in your community?
2. Describe in detail from your own experience (a) how a child has reacted to illness; (b) how his family has reacted to his illness.
3. Show how medical progress has changed the type of care needed to meet the needs of sick children today.
4. What normal needs of all children should be considered in planning care for (a) the acutely ill child; (b) the child with chronic illness?

REFERENCES

Benz, Gladys: Pediatric Nursing, St. Louis, 1948, The C. V. Mosby Company.
Berg, Roland H.: Polio and Its Problems, Philadelphia, 1948, J. B. Lippincott Company.
Blakeslee, Alton, L.: Polio Can Be Conquered, Public Affairs Pamphlet, No. 150, 1949.
Buchanan, J. J.: Rehabilitation of the Patient With Chronic Poliomyelitis, Journal of the Association for Physical and Mental Rehabilitation 3:8-11, October, 1949.
Carlson, Earl, R.: Born That Way, New York, 1941, John Day Company.

Cohen, Ethel: Social Planning for Children with Rheumatic Heart Disease, The Child, January, 1941, pages 164-167.

Cottrell, Lillian: Understanding the Adolescent, American Journal of Nursing, **46**:181-183, 1946.

Easby, Mary: Rheumatic Fever and Rheumatic Heart Disease, The Family, January, 1946, pages 340-347.

McBroom, Elizabeth, and Froelich, Ursel: Interpretation of Physical Disability to Children, Journal of Social Casework, April 1949, pages 154-159.

Midcentury Conference on Children & Youth, Proceedings: Washington D. C., 1951, Raleigh, North Carolina National Health Institute.

Ribble, Margaret A.: The Rights of Infants, New York, 1945, Columbia University Press.

Senn, Milton: Emotional Aspects of Convalescence, The Child, August, 1945, pages 24-28.

Taylor, Eugene J.: Help at Last for Cerebral Palsy, Public Affairs, Pamphlet No. 158, 1950.

Upham, Frances: A Dynamic Approach to Illness, New York, 1949, Family Service Association of America.

CHAPTER 8

ACUTE CONDITIONS AND CONVALESCENT CARE

INTRODUCTION

The general discussion presented in Chapter 6 covering the patient, his family, and community reaction to illness are applicable in situations where the disease is acute, always considering the deviation inevitable in the disease situation to a particular individual. Many traditional acute disease situations no longer exist or, if infection is present, the whole course has been changed by chemotherapy and antibiotics. For example, protection including both general public health and medical measures against many of the acute diseases means that the individual does not contract the disease or if it does develop, it is in a very mild form. The long-drawn out illnesses, such as pneumonia, and respiratory infections, are being reduced with modern discoveries particularly in the field of chemotherapy and antibiotics. Many individuals are not acutely ill for as long a period, therefore the convalescence is not as lengthy. Early ambulation in surgery and the modern approach to maternity care has also changed the convalescent period. The surgical patient who does not stay in bed for days or weeks after an operation does not have to face the problem of getting his muscles and general physical condition back to normal again. In spite of all these modern developments, illness, either acute or chronic, is always a shock to the individual organism from both an emotional and physiological viewpoint.

SOME SPECIAL SITUATIONS

In surgical situations, health workers should anticipate certain rather common patient reactions, such as the general fear of hospitalization or fear of the anesthesia. Many patients are afraid that they are not going to "wake up" again. Some patients are afraid the doctor will do things not specified in presurgical conversations and are afraid of taking a general anesthetic. He wants to know what is going on, as he says. In acute situations, as in many diseases, the patient may be worried about finances and fear for his ultimate recovery and his ability to take his place in the community again. Confidence in the doctors, nurses, other health workers, and the institution will do much to allay these fears. Pre-operative preparation includes psychological conditions as well as physical considerations. Patients who are afraid, who are emotionally upset about the operation are not likely to make as quick or as good a recovery as those individuals who are confident and would not have unnatural fears.

Accidents are always sudden occurrences. It is interesting to note that most accidents occur in the home which is assumed by many individuals to be a relatively safe environment. An accident is always accompanied by a sudden break in the individual's activity often meaning a complete change in his affairs or activities over a longer or shorter period of time. Industries are aware of the accident factor among their employees and safeguards are set up to prevent accidents and to protect workers. Many of these safeguards are required by law. Most modern industries also have health supervision and facilities available and some type of first-aid routine is necessary in both industry and home. It is particularly important that children be instructed as to what they should do when an accident occurs when the parents are away from home. Even very young boys and girls can assume certain responsibilities when these unusual and unlooked for events take place. It is interesting that in various group activities and in schools, children are taught what to do in accident situations and something about the fundamentals of first-aid. Parents should supplement this by some particular instructions applicable to their own home situation.

The attitudes of families to health protection and health education is very significant in the prevention and treatment of both acute and chronic conditions. Many conditions can now be prevented or controlled or the period of illness shortened if known instructions are followed.

CONVALESCENT CARE

Convalescence may be described as a temporary condition when an individual is neither wholly sick nor is he completely well. It is usually considered as that period between the acute illness and when he has recovered so that he can resume his accustomed mode of life.

Convalescence is usually considered different from chronic illness in that convalescence has an end and usually is considered to be that period following an acute illness, while chronic illness is a much longer period of disability, perhaps when the individual never completely recovers from the illness. The convalescent period is very important because on the care given depends the patient's recovery and may often determine whether his illness passes from an acute to a chronic state. Good care during acute and convalescent period in many conditions may prevent chronic conditions from developing. It must be remembered, however, that during convalescence the patient is likely to show fatigue, emotional instability, and even some neurotic tendencies. Constructive help during convalescence will do much to prevent destructive emotional situations from developing and help the patient to recover much more quickly. The feelings of boredom, irritability, and frustration which develop as a result of his weakened physical condition and the change in his accustomed daily routine can be alleviated by the modern approach to convalescence.

Many hospitals for the acutely ill are now equipped with libraries, occupational therapy departments, and various other facilities, such as beauty parlors, barber shops, and drug stores where patients can get relief from boredom. Many hospitals also provide recreation for their patients, such as radio, television, movies, and recreational units where patients can gather and play games and visit. The isolation of patients in individual rooms and cubicles, unless it is necessary for medical reasons, is in many instances not good for the patient emotionally.

In the majority of instances, patients are discharged to leave the hospital before they have completely recovered. This is for several reasons. The cost of hospital care is so great that patients and families do not want to assume that economic burden any longer than is necessary. There is also in most communities a scarcity of hospital beds and this results in patients being sent home just as soon as their physical condition permits. There is also the psychological fact that some individuals may become depressed and emotionally upset during their convalescence if they are in too close contact with individuals who are physically ill. The question then arises, where should the patient be until he recovers completely from his illness? In modern urban communities the apartment may not be the best place for convalescence, particularly if the individual has few relatives or friends. During convalescence he may be confined for days to an apartment with very little if any contacts with other individuals or with the outside world. Unfortunately, adequate institutions for convalescent care are not available in all communities. Efforts are being made in many instances to provide convalescent homes or hospitals. These are very much needed today for many reasons. First of all, they will relieve the hospitals for the acutely ill of many patients whose needs can be met in convalescent homes; and secondly, they will insure a more rapid and lasting recovery to many individuals who are transient, homeless, or for various other reasons cannot get the best environment in their own homes.

Preparing the patient for leaving the hospital is a very important function of all hospital personnel. This very often falls mainly to the nurse. She should have learned enough about the patient's background and home life in her contact with him in the hospital to evaluate the home situation in regard to convalescence. It may be necessary to consult with other members of the family to work out some plans for his convalescence. Provision should be made for certain recreational activities, and for visiting by friends while he is still confined indoors. In many instances, facilities in the community can be utilized and often the services of the social worker can be used cooperatively to plan for the patient when he returns home. It is pointed out that good hygienic conditions, economic security, and the assurance that the individual's role and status has not been permanently interfered with will do much to help during the convalescent period. During convalescence and illness, some individuals may tend to regress and develop conflicts about getting well and facing the realities of their situation. Satisfactory interpersonal relationships do much to minimize these attitudes.

STUDY QUESTIONS

1. What conditions in an acute disease or accident situation may be especially difficult for the patient to accept?
2. Study the attitudes of patients in the surgical department (a) to the anesthesia; (b) to the operation.
3. What is convalescence? What are the needs of patients during this period of an illness?
4. What are the facilities in your community for convalescent care? Are these adequate? If not, what plans are being made to improve them?

REFERENCES

Cherkasky, Martin: Hospital Service Goes Home, Modern Hospital **68**:47-8, 1947.

Cooley, Carol H.:   Social Aspects of Illness, Philadelphia, 1951, W. B. Saunders Company, chapter 7.

Gardiner, Elizabeth G., and Thomas, Francisca K.: The Road to Recovery From Illness, A Study of Convalescent Homes Serving New York City, Hospital Council of Greater New York.

Jensen, Frode, Weishotten, H. G., and Thomas, Margaret A.: Medical Care of the Discharged Hospital Patient, New York, 1944, The Commonwealth Fund, pages 9-55.

Mills, Alden B.: Convalescent Unit, Special Services in the General Hospital, Modern Hospital, March, 1952, pages 62-66.

Upham, Frances: A Dynamic Approach to Illness, New York, 1949, Family Service Association of America, chapter 4.

CHAPTER 9

CHRONIC ILLNESS

INTRODUCTION

Increasing recognition of the importance of chronic illness is evident in medical and nursing circles by the increase in the number of papers on this subject in medical and nursing journals and in discussions given at meetings. There can also be noted a great increase in the interest of the community in studying this whole problem and in working with professional and administrative groups to provide better care for the chronically ill. The Commission on Chronic Illness has defined chronic illness as "Any illness of three or more months' duration." However, this definition should not be adhered to in a strictly rigid sense. Neither is it wise to associate chronic illness and the aged too closely in our minds; it is found in all age groups. It has been pointed out that modern science has given us the techniques for controlling epidemics and for reducing infant mortality and thus made it possible for more individuals to live and contract chronic illnesses.

As modern medical science has wiped out many acute diseases common to mankind in the past, the chronic diseases remain as a major individual family and community problem. Chronic diseases, like old age and unemployment, affect the individual and family security. Boas[1] refers to chronic diseases as the "Unseen Plague" or the "Modern Plague."

The attitude to long-term illness, or chronic illnesses, is often one related to incurability and hopelessness. The reactions of the individual and his family are often a reflection of this community attitude. Doctors, nurses, and social workers today are trained to approach this problem from the more positive attitude of studying each individual patient and his potentialities in terms of his illness and its effects on his activities or his mode of life.

[1]Boas, Ernst P.: The Unseen Plague—Chronic Disease, New York, 1940, J. J. Augustin.

The whole field of chronic illness shows more clearly than in many other areas the lag which exists between discovery and application in medical science. For example, many chronic illnesses are the result of the lack of or inadequate medical care for acute conditions. Adequate treatment of all illnesses and more thorough and complete application of all health knowledge in the fields of sanitation, housing, vaccination, nutrition, and general healthful living will do much to reduce the incidence of chronic illness in all age groups and particularly for the increasing number of individuals who live to be over fifty years of age. In addition to improving the physical environment, the mental and emotional environments are now being considered more important than in the past. The stresses and strains of modern industrial living are contributing factors in causing certain chronic illnesses. Tensions are more likely to wear down the individual's resistance and chronic conditions such as heart disease, rheumatism, gastrointestinal disturbances may develop at the individual's weak points.

STATISTICS

Many community, regional, and some national studies have been made in the last twenty-five years and more accurate knowledge of the prevalence of chronic illness has been gained. One can refer to the National Health Survey taken by the United States Public Health Service in 1936. Since then many communities and states have been surveyed and have added to the statistical information in this field. It has been pointed out that between 50 and 70 years ago only one death out of three was due to chronic illness.[2] Today two out of every three deaths are caused by one or another of the prevalent chronic diseases. It has been assumed by many individuals that chronic diseases are mainly found in the aged group or at least in individuals over fifty. Figures show that one out of every six individuals with chronic illness is under twenty-five and about 50 per cent of those affected are under forty-five. Cerebral palsy, rheumatic fever, polio, tuberculosis are most commonly found in children and young adults.

As causes of death, the leading chronic diseases are heart diseases, cancer, arteriosclerosis, high blood pressure, and nephritis. The most prevalent chronic diseases are rheumatism, heart diseases, arteriosclerosis, and high blood pressure, hay fever and asthma, and as causes of

---

[2]Yahres, Herbert: Something Can Be Done About Chronic Illness, Public Affairs Pamphlet, No. 176.

CHRONIC DISEASE IS LEADING KILLER OF AGED
DEATH RATES PER 1,000 PERSONS, 1949

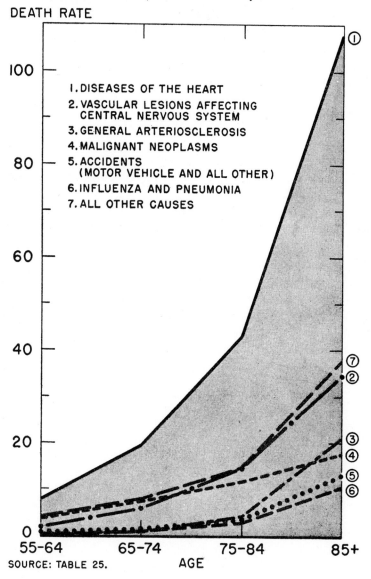

Fig. 3.—(From Fact-Book on Aging, Federal Security Agency. Committee on Aging and Geriatrics, 1952, Washington, D. C.)

disability nervous and mental diseases, rheumatism, heart diseases, tuberculosis, arteriosclerosis, and high blood pressure. Chronic diseases are leading causes of death in the older age group. Heart disease, for example, is responsible for about one-half the deaths of persons sixty-five and over. Other important causes of death in this group are cancer, cerebral hemorrhage, and arteriosclerosis.

SOCIAL AND ECONOMIC IMPLICATIONS

Medical and nursing concepts of chronic diseases will not be discussed here. The reader is referred to nursing and medical books in various clinical areas for such information. It has been pointed out that any illness is likely to disrupt the patient's accustomed mode of life. It is apt to bring changes not only to the patient but also to his family and sometimes to groups with which he has been associated. When the illness is acute and of short duration, adjustments can often be made satisfactorily. Chronic illness which implies that the disease continues over a long period of time often involves constant and expensive medical care. This may necessitate adjustments in the patient's economic status bringing implications which may be difficult for the individual and the family to accept.

Included in the direct cost of the illness is the expense of making the diagnosis, long-continued treatment often involving hospital care, clinical visits, visits to doctor's offices and home care. In certain conditions, such as cancer, the patient may go from one clinic to another, from one hospital to another, seeking another diagnosis or better treatment.

Chronic illness is more common in the low income groups; that is to say it is more frequently found among those who can least afford medical care. Individuals in the lower income groups suffer more from chronic illness not only because they cannot afford adequate treatment but also because such diseases as tuberculosis, rheumatic fever, and arthritis are found more frequently among those who live in overcrowded dwellings and in unsanitary environments including insufficient diet. Therefore the problem of adequate diagnosis and satisfactory long-term care can seldom be met satisfactorily by these individuals, and the community must help them to get adequate treatment and to regain as much as possible of their ability so that they can again become contributing members of the community.

The problem of chronic illness can be satisfactorily solved only by teamwork. In many communities medical, nursing, and social workers are working together as a team in its detection, treatment, prevention, and rehabilitation. Because of the expense involved in adequate medical treatment, social agencies are often drained to give the patient and his family means whereby they can eke out the bare necessities of life often without doing very much to remedy the condition.

Physical deterioration accompanying chronic illness results in the curtailment and often in changes in the individual's activities. This may result in a temporary or permanent state of hopelessness or helplessness. Rehabilitation, based on a complete study of the individual and his environment, aims to restore each individual to as full functioning as possible. This often involves changes in the individual's accustomed mode of life including his employment, recreational, and other daily activities. Since this means change and since change is often difficult to accept particularly when it seems to involve the individual's security and status, many persons need time to adjust to it. Group work between all professional workers, doctors, nurses, social workers, rehabilitation workers, does a great deal to help the individual and his family make satisfacory adjustments.

REHABILITATION

Rehabilitation has been referred to by Dr. Rusk as the third phase of medicine. Much of our thinking in this field has been limited to rehabilitation of the physically and mentally handicapped. Today, however, the concept has been broadened to include rehabilitation of all patients. Any person who is ill, even for a short period, has to make certain adjustments in order to assure his complete recovery. All workers in contact with sick persons very soon recognize that individuals differ greatly in their recovery, and in their ability to assume responsibility for themselves following their illness. Emotional maturity has a great deal to do with the individual's cooperation, initiative, adaptativeness, determination, and enthusiasm, all of which are needed during any illness and convalescence.

Rehabilitation, if it is to be effective, means a continuous, uninterrupted, and interrelated series of services necessary to meet the needs of individuals and patients and aimed to help each patient return to his accustomed social and economic life as quickly and effectively as possible. This process is divided into three major parts:

1. *Medical rehabilitation,* the curing or treatment stage. This means the study of the individual physically and mentally and vocationally by a team of specialists: doctors, psychiatrists, social workers, physiotherapists, occupational therapists, nurses, educators, and any other professional workers who can contribute. A total evaluation of the patient in terms of his potentialities is considered. This phase is usually carried on in the hospital or rehabilitation center.

2. The *conditioning phase* of rehabilitation is concerned with those services having to do with preparing the way for the patient's return to his family and the community. At this phase, there is concentration of post-hospitalization period and the rehabilitation team described above continues to work and as the patient recovers physically and mentally his economic and vocational possibilities are studied in detail.

3. *Vocational adjustment.* This is the final stage when the individual is ready to take his place as a contributing member of the community.

Rehabilitation starts or should start when the patient is in the acute stage of his illness. Therefore, it is important for the hospital nurse to know fundamentals of rehabilitation and the various techniques employed. She is an integral part of the rehabilitation team and her mastering of these techniques is a vital part of clinical instruction. The nurse is the liaison between the doctor and patient. She is responsible often for interpreting the doctor's instructions, for helping him in the activities and exercises prescribed. It is interesting that modern concepts of rehabilitation including early ambulation in surgery and greater activity and early ambulation for the obstetrical patient are sometimes resisted by individuals and their families who feel that nurses should "do" more "things" for them when they are ill. A great deal of interpretation is necessary in many instances so that self-help is emotionally acceptable to certain individuals and their families. Rehabilitation is important in its physical aspects; that is, retraining of muscles, etc., but equally and often more important is the psychological effect in that the patient feels that he is doing something for himself. Constructively applied rehabilitation will do much to shorten the period of dependency often noticed during illness. Greater details about rehabilitation will be found in the chapter on the Physically Handicapped.

PLANNING FOR THE CARE OF THE CHRONICALLY ILL

Since diseases in this group involve medical and often social help and supervision over a long period of time, the individual and his family often need help. Traditionally, hospitals in this country are organized and administered to care for the acutely ill. Until recently the chronically ill were not welcomed in many hospitals and if institutionalization was necessary it was sometimes more custodial than therapeutic. Patients may often need hospital services during the diagnostic and initial therapeutic stages. Before and following that, care in the out-patient clinic, associated with medical and nursing services in his home, may be adequate. It is important for every community to study all available medical and nursing sources and see how they can be better correlated and integrated in meeting the problem of adequate care. Many communities have made surveys and are planning community programs with this end in view.

Home care involves not only the giving of actual bedside nursing when indicated, but also, and more important, teaching some member of the family to assume responsibility for these necessary activities and also teaching the patient to care for himself. The activities of public health nurses in meeting this particular problem are very important. When institutional care over long periods of time may be indicated, communities are now planning hospitals for the chronically ill with all the modern diagnostic, therapeutic, and rehabilitation facilities which may help many individuals leave the institution for more effective functioning in the community than would have been the case a decade ago.

Since many patients with chronic diseases are medically indigent, social resources as well as the economic resources of the individual and his family must be carefully studied by the social worker. The patient may have some type of insurance or may be eligible for certain benefits under Social Security. All of these possibilities should be explored. The social worker will know what sources are available in her community either through private or public agencies and will utilize these resources and interpret them to the patient and his family as indicated.

Many communities are developing central services for the chronically ill, the first being established in Chicago in 1944 by the Institute of Medicine and the Council of Social Agencies now called the Welfare Council and the Community Fund. The purpose of such a central service may be described briefly as follows: First, to serve the total problem of chronic illness in the area; second, to refer chronically ill persons and their families to existing agencies best able to serve them; third, to make plans to expand facilities for the chronically ill as needed in the community; and fourth, to stimulate community interest in this problem.

In line with community interest in this field, the Commission on Chronic Illness was founded in 1949 by the American Hospital Association, the American Medical Association, the American Association of Public Health, and the American Public Welfare Association. This is an independent national agency to study the problems of chronic disease, illness, and disability, and it already has done a great deal to awaken community interest and to help formulate plans and programs. The goals stated by this Commission are as follows:[3]

Goal 1: Define the problems arising from chronic illness in all age groups.

Goal 2: Pave the way for dynamic programs to: '
prevent chronic illness
minimize its disabling effects
restore its victims to a socially useful and economically productive place in the community.

Goal 3: Clarify the interrelationships of the many professional groups and agencies working in the field.

Goal 4: Coordinate the separate programs for specific diseases with a general program designed to meet more effectively the needs common to all the chronically ill.

Goal 5: Stimulate in every locality a well-rounded plan for the prevention and control of chronic disease and for the care and rehabilitation of the chronically ill.

Goal 6: Modify society's attitude that chronic illness is hopeless.

The Commission on Chronic Illness is supported financially by the American Medical Association, the National Tuberculosis Association, the American Cancer Society, the American Heart Association, the National Society for Crippled Children and Adults, the New York Foundation and the National Foundation for Infantile Paralysis. This Commission shows the modern approach to integrated community action in dealing with an important community problem.

---

[3]Commission on Chronic Illness, 615 N. Wolfe St., Baltimore 5, Md.

CONCLUSION

It is being pointed out today that adequate care of the chronically ill cannot be planned for apart from good general medical care and that the inadequacies in this area show the need for better integration of community services and better utilization of existing knowledge. In other words, there is evidence here of a culture lag. Much more knowledge is available than communities and individuals use either because they do not know about the existing facilities or because they are not willing to change their accustomed ways of doing things in order to accept programs that would be beneficial. Nursing service is an important part of any program for the chronically ill. Much of this nursing service will be given in the patient's home. Therefore, the nurse must be aware of the total overall needs of the patient and the total facilities available in her community for anything that the patient or his family might need that would be helpful in any particular situation. In this area the great importance of knowing the community and of being equipped intellectually and emotionally to be a member of the team in the diagnosis, treatment, and rehabilitation of the patient is absolutely necessary.

The integration of services and facilities as presented by the first cardiac conferences in 1950 may well be considered in planning for all chronic conditions. It was pointed out that the definition of integration implies the effect of working together in continuing community effort of all the interests that can contribute to the prevention, treatment, and control of disease. The importance of the local community as a focal point of interest was pointed out because in the local community the individual patient and his family are the units of integration efforts, and all community organization is involved in securing the best results for the individual and his family. In the total planning all individuals and groups affected by the problem should be represented. Some of the obstacles to integration lie in the complexity of these community health problems and in the unrelated and variety of facilities necessary to deal with the different problems. The determination of omissions and gaps in necessary community resources must be studied and steps taken to develop essential missing resources. In dealing with many of these community health problems, assistance from national organizations, both private and public, can be secured. In fact, local branches are being formed in many communities. Not only the complexities of chronic illness, but also the long-term nature involving continued treatment and rehabilitation places a great strain on all community facilities.

STUDY QUESTIONS AND PROJECTS

1. Why is the total problem of chronic illness receiving more attention today than ever before?

2. Present several patients known to you showing different reactions to chronic illness.

3. Why is rehabilitation so important in treating the chronically ill?

4. What types of medical, nursing, and social care are needed by the chronically ill?

5. Discuss some national plans and programs to meet the needs of this group.

6. Is your community participating in these plans?

7. Are facilities in your community adequate to meet these needs? If not, what is being done about it?

REFERENCES

Alvarez, Walter C.: Chronic Illness and the Constitutionally Inadequate, Medical Clinics of North America, March 1949, W. B. Saunders Co., Philadelphia, pages 427-434.

Blustone, E. M.: Planning for Long Term Illness, Medical Clinics of North America, March, 1949, W. B. Saunders Co., Philadelphia, pages 587-597.

Boas, Ernst P.: The Unseen Plague, Chronic Disease, New York, 1940, J. J. Augustin.

Breslow, Lester: Multiphasic, Screening Examination, An Extension of the Mass Screening Technique, American Journal of Public Health, March, 1950, pages 274-278.

Brightman, I. Jay, and Hilleboe, Herman E.: A Joint Attack Upon Chronic Illness, Public Health Nursing, January, 1951, pages 21-44.

Cherkasky, Martin: The General Hospital Is The Place for the Care of the Chronically Ill, Modern Hospital, July, 1952, pages 98-102.

Chronic Illness: Digests of Selected References, Public Health Bibliography Series, No. 1, Public Health Service, Federal Security Agency.

Commission on Chronic Illness, 525 North Dearborn Street, Chicago, Ill. Pamphlets and reports are available.

DeBuck, Roger W.: Development of New Community Facilities for Care of Long Term Patients in Hospitals, Hospital Council Bulletin, January, 1947, pages 15-16.

Editorial: Chronic Disease as a Public Health Problem, American Journal of Public Health, April, 1950, pages 470-472.

Fazekas, Joseph: The Total Patient Approach to Chronic Illness, Public Health Reports, May, 1952, pages 421-425.

Hilleboe, Herman E.: Chronic Disease Prevention—A Community Job, Chronic Illness News Letter, August, 1951.

Hilliard, Raymond M.: Chronic Illness, Major Cause of Dependency, Survey Midmonthly, November, 1947, pages 306-316.

Hilliard, Raymond M.: Cost of Chronic Illness, Public Health Reports, February, 1952, page 133.

Levin, Morton L.: An Approach to the Problem of Long-Term Care, Modern Hospital, November, 1950.

McLester, James S.: Dietary Needs in Long Term Illness, Medical Clinics of North America, March, 1949, W. B. Saunders Company, Philadelphia, pages 561-572.

Marsh, Edith L.: Nursing Care in Chronic Illness, Philadelphia, J. B. Lippincott Company, 1946.

Merrill, A. P.: The Hospital Can Help the Nursing Home, The Nation's No. 1 Health Problem, Chronic Disease, Modern Hospital, January, 1952, pages 51-54.

Murdock, Thomas P.: Diseases in Middle Life and Beyond, Public Health Nursing, December, 1947.

Nicholson, Edna: Long Term Illness Must Be Fought on Two Fronts, Modern Hospital, July, 1945.

Nicholson, Edna: The Role of the Central Services for the Chronically Ill, Hospital Council Bulletin, January, 1947.

Randall, O. A.: The Chronically Ill Who Live in the Community, Jewish Social Service Quarterly **25**:524, 1949.

Reeve, Irma E.: Nursing the Chronically Ill, Public Health Nursing, December, 1947.

Rogers, Edward S.: Chronic Disease—A Problem That Must Be Faced, American Journal of Public Health, April, 1946, pages 343-350.

Schless, Bessie: Achieving Maximum Adjustment in Chronic Illness, Journal of Social Casework **27**:320-325, 1946.

Steps Toward Prevention of Chronic Disease, Health Publications Institute, Raleigh, N. C. (Summary report.)

Upham, Frances: A Dynamic Approach to Illness, New York, 1949, Family Service Association of America.

Vilter, Richard W., and Thompson, Carl: Nutrition and the Control of Chronic Disease, Public Health Aspects, May 18, 1951, pages 630-636.

Wall, E. Lucille: Public Health Nurses Are Interested in the Chronically Ill, Public Health Nursing, January, 1942, pages 24-25.

Waterman, Theda L.: Care of the Chronically Ill, American Journal of Nursing, June, 1951, pages 391-393.

Yahraes, Herbert: Something Can Be Done About Chronic Illness, Public Affairs Pamphlet, No. 176.

CHAPTER 10

HEART DISEASE

INTRODUCTION

Because of increased morbidity and mortality, heart disease is being recognized more and more as a community problem, particularly in the preventive and rehabilitation aspects. Cardiac patients are similar to those with many other chronic conditions in which physical activity is limited and some medical and at times nursing supervision is necessary over a long period of time. More individuals are living past forty years of age when certan types of cardiac and other degenerative diseases are prevalent. As the patient with a chronic disease gets older, he is less able to provide for himself economically and in many instances his earning ability may decrease rapidly if his physical condition is neglected. As in other chronic conditions, institutional care for cardiac patients over long periods of time is not available in all communities. In many instances the individual with cardiac disease may be living in the home of a married son or daughter and when additional care is needed the home situation may become more complicated.

As in all chronic diseases, prevention is very important. Prevention of heart disease goes back, of course, to a study of its causes. Rheumatic fever and venereal disease cause some cardiac conditions. Various forms of degenerative heart diseases seemed to be caused partly by the stresses and strains of modern living. Better diagnosis and more adequate treatment for rheumatic fever, venereal disease, and certain other infections are a necessary part of the program for prevention of heart disease. Better adjustment between the individual and the stresses in his environment is necessary to reduce the incidence of certain other types. Prevention also includes doing everything possible to stop early heart disease from developing any further. It is often pointed out that such patients may be more willing to accept instructions, since there is in many individuals an emotional fear of heart diseases. If an individual suspects or knows he has heart disease, he

Table II

Ten Leading Causes of Death in New York City, 1875-1946*

(In Order of Frequency)

1875		1885		1905		1946	
All causes[1]	28.25	All causes	24.75	All causes	18.32	All causes	10.1
T.B.[2] (pulmonary)	373	T.B. (all forms)	392	Pneumonia	246	Heart diseases	389.9
Diarrhea (under 5)[3]	316	Diarrhea (−5)	257	T.B. (all forms)	238	Cancer	180.7
Diphtheria	294	Pneumonia	247	Nephritis	147	Accidents	50.8
Pneumonia	242	Diphtheria	146	Diarrhea (−5)	145	Cerebral hemorrhage	46.2
Smallpox	124	Heart diseases	123	Heart diseases	144	T.B. (all forms)	41.7
Violence	99	Violence	95	Violence	109	Diabetes	39.2
Heart diseases	93.5	Nephritis	87	Cancer	73	Pneumonia	37.7
Nephritis	59	Cancer	51	Diphtheria	38	Nephritis	34.5
Scarlet fever	54	Scarlet fever	45	Typhoid fever	16	Diarrhea (−5)	32.2
Cancer	41	Typhoid fever	27	Scarlet fever	12	Liver and gall bladder	20.7

*Published by the American Heart Association, "Diseases of the Heart".
[1] Death rates from all causes are per 1,000 of the population.
[2] Death rates from tuberculosis and other causes except diarrhea are per 100,000 of the population.
[3] Death rates from diarrhea under five years of age are based on the population under five.

may be more willing to listen to the instructions of the doctor than if he is not aware of any symptoms. The different health workers in the community, particularly those who are advising individuals in general health of the need for periodic examinations, can do much to instruct individuals and their families about prevention of heart disease.

It is pointed out that the two main reasons why the death rate from heart disease is so great are, first, the reduction in other causes of death, particularly in the acute communicable diseases of childhood, and, second, the increase in the length of life whereby increasing numbers of individuals live to be over fifty-five years of age when diseases of the heart are the most frequent causes of death.

ADJUSTMENTS TO HEART DISEASE

The adjustments which cardiac patients may face have been well described by Queen and Mann as follows:

> Knowledge of the fact that they have defective hearts brings forth quite different attitudes in different people. Some become "prisoners of fear," over-sensitive to their surroundings and constantly worrying about their condition. They display a tendency to excessive introspection and "moodiness." Some are inert and lack initiative. They are overcautious. Often this is due to the sheltered life and the restrictions made necessary by their handicap. Others seem never to be able to face the fact of their limitations, refuse to reorganize their mode of living and eventually pay the penalty.
>
> The question of whether a cardiac patient should marry is of importance, especially in the case of a woman. It is not a matter of heredity so far as we are aware, but of ability to meet the obligations of married life. "If marriage is to bring increasing anxieties and added physical burdens to a patient who is barely holding her own under the protection of her parents, the venture is probably unwise. If it is likely to bring added comfort and less physical and mental strain, the verdict might be reversed." This is not simply a question of "to marry or not to marry." There are numerous complicating factors to be taken into account. First of all, enforced celibacy may seriously affect the physical and mental health of the cardiac cripple herself (or himself). There is likely to be already a sense of inferiority, deprivation and exclusion. When to this is added repression of the sex impulses, the health hazards may be greatly increased. Second, assuming that marriage is entered upon, there is the further question as to the wisdom of pregnancy.

This last problem is perhaps the most difficult of all. A physician may advise in a given case that pregnancy is unsafe. But celibacy within marriage may be more disturbing to one's emotional make-up than celibacy outside of marriage; and this may be true of either the man or the woman or both. Shall the patient and her husband refrain from intercourse? Shall they use contraceptives? Or shall the woman's life be risked against the advice of her physician? But rarely is there "free choice" of these alternatives. The couple, or one of them, may belong to a religious sect which frowns upon birth control. What shall they do? Evidently it is not easy to effect such an adjustment of relationships between husband and wife as not only to avert child-bearing, but also to guard against emotional upheavals which so often follow upon interference with the sex life.

Indeed, there are many problems which have to be faced by the cardiac "housewife," whether she be married or not. Woman's work in the household is often heavy, imposing both physical and mental strain. It is difficult to make the work easier and hard to make some women give it up. But when a heart disease appears, a change must be made; and to change working and living conditions for the housewife it may be necessary to change the living arrangements of the entire family. These adjustments may include sending children away so as to give the mother a partial rest, sending her on a vacation, seeing that she has fewer stairs to climb, sending out the washing, hiring help in the home, securing better paid work for the husband so that he can pay for these added necessities. If the woman is a wage earner herself, it may be necessary to provide light home work to take the place of outside employment. In general, heart disease in the housewife calls for a reorganization of her own scheme of life and often for a reorganization of the life of the whole family.

For the workman with a heart disease one of the hardest trials is likely to be giving up a trade with which he is familiar and in which he takes pride. Along with it will probably go the loss of congenial associates. He may have to seek new employment among strangers and accept a job in which he has little interest beyond the earning of his living. If he is an older man, he may have to give up a skilled trade and try some form of unskilled labor. If he is younger, there is the problem of securing training for a new vocation in which he can take pleasure and through which he can earn a respectable income as well as guard against overstraining his heart. Besides these vocational adjustments, the worker may have to give up active participation in trade union or other group life. When working hours are over he may have to go home and rest instead of romping with the children, attending the movies or talking politics with the neighbors. All this may produce a sense of futility and inferiority. If so, demoralization has begun.

When the patient is a child, there is the same problem that adults face of learning what to do and what to avoid. There is the equally difficult problem of bringing it to pass that others may understand his limitations. Some people seem to regard heart disease as an imaginary affliction "adopted as an excuse to get out of doing one's honest share of the day's work." Others go to the opposite extreme, become sentimental over the "poor little sufferer" and fret lest he overdo. Either attitude is bound to react unfavorably upon the child. The first may make him into a discouraged little introvert; the second may render him egocentric, selfish, demanding more and more attention, enjoying exaggerated pity. Heart disease may reduce the educational opportunities of children in two ways; first, by the family's excessive fear that school attendance may involve overstrain and hence ready acquiescence in the child's desire to stay away; second, by absences due to actual physical incapacity. This is a very serious matter, for the cardiac patient cannot depend on brute strength to make his way in the world. He must make special adjustments; he must find opportunities for work and recreation which conform to his capacity for physical exertion. Hence he needs education quite as much, if not more, than the average healthy child.

The economic aspect of heart disease has been well summarized in the following words: "Diphtheria is a matter of days; typhoid, of weeks; tuberculosis, of years—heart disease may run for decades. No other diseases (except perhaps some of the mind) handicap their victims for self-support so persistently and so long as those of the heart. The task before us is not merely to keep the cardiacs alive, but to help them walk the narrow path between dependence and overexertion; to find work that will mean self-support and the meeting of family responsibilities without jeopardizing the wage earner's dearly won hold on life."[1]

Cardiac patients are similar to those with many other chronic conditions in which physical activity is limited and some medical and, at times, nursing supervision is necessary over long periods of time. More people are now living past forty years of age, when cardiac and other degenerative diseases are more prevalent. As the patient grows older he is less able to provide for himself economically, and, if he has some chronic disease, his earning ability may be decreased

---

[1]Queen, Stuart A., and Mann, Delbert M.: Social Pathology, New York, 1925, Thomas Y. Crowell Co., pages 502-505.

sooner. The provision for old age assistance in the Social Security Act has become necessary as there are more older people in our contemporary society.

As with all chronic conditions, cardiac patients may become depressed and apprehensive about themselves. It is very important, therefore, that all individuals, medical, social, or vocational advisers, maintain as good rapport with the patient and his family as possible and be constantly aware of the need to boost his morale and to develop in him as constructive an attitude toward his own particular condition as possible.

THE CARDIAC PATIENT AND HIS JOB

Since most individuals have some job to do in our society, it is very important to evaluate the ability of the individual cardiac patient and advise him about his activity. Emotional tension may develop because he is afraid he will not be able to support himself and his family or that his wife will not be able to carry out her accustomed activities in the home, or the child will not be able to continue with his education. Thus the modern approach to all such conditions is the constructive one of finding out the total abilities of the individual and helping him to adjust to any limitations his physical condition may place upon him. A study of the whole situation for each individual is important. At the beginning, it is necessary to determine the amount of the restriction that needs to be placed upon him. This, of course, can be done only after complete and careful diagnostic work by the doctor. Standards have been made by the American Heart Association classifying individuals according to what they should be able to do without further injury to the heart.

The five classes that have been set up are as follows:

Class A. Patients with cardiac disease whose ordinary physical activity need not be restricted.

Class B. Patients with cardiac disease whose ordinary physical activity need not be restricted but who should be advised against unusually severe or competitive efforts.

Class C. Patients with cardiac disease whose ordinary physical activity should be moderately restricted and whose more strenuous physical efforts should be discontinued.

Class D.   Patients with cardiac disease whose ordinary physical activity should be moderately restricted.

Class E.   Patients with cardiac disease who should be completely confined to bed or chair.

It is pointed out that each individual should find an occupation, recreation, and other activities which will place less strain on the heart than he is able to carry, so that the possibility of overtaxing would not be as great. Nurses and social workers are cooperating with teachers and vocational workers in helping these individuals prepare for and choose an occupation. Sedentary occupations are often the best suited for most cardiac patients. Sometimes individuals have not had the necessary educational background or vocational training for the type of job which will be best suited to more limited ability. In these instances the nurse or social worker may get help from the vocational education division of the public school system. Lists of suggestions of suitable occupations have been compiled through the cooperation of the American Heart Association and the New York State Bureau of Rehabilitation and may be obtained on request.

It is most important that the individual be well-adjusted and feel happy and secure in his work; therefore, every effort should be made to find the most suitable occupation and to help him become as well qualified as possible, so that he may have the satisfaction of doing a good job even with rather limited ability.

THE CARDIAC CHILD

Two types of heart disease make it a most frequently found chronic condition among children. These are congenital heart disease and rheumatic heart disease. The congenital malformation of the heart accounts for only about 5 per cent of the total cardiac conditions in children. Therefore, the major problem is one of rheumatic heart disease. As the result of modern surgical technique, one type of heart disease called "patent ductus arteriosus" may be successfully treated. Rheumatic heart disease, however, presents an entirely different situation because it involves treatment of the acute infection, a rearrangement of the child's activities in accordance with the damage that has been done to the heart, and medical supervision over a long period of time to prevent recurrence of the disease and thus prevent further damage to the heart. Nurses are taught in their clinical studies the importance of complete treatment for the acute respiratory infections and the importance of taking seriously stories of "growing pains" which should be thoroughly investigated.

A child with rheumatic fever usually faces a long time in bed and often in a hospital. He will miss his parents and home surroundings. This is demonstrated by the following case:

Tony R., seven years old, was found to have rheumatic fever. He was taken from his busy, active, warm family life with seven brothers and sisters living in a few rooms in a crowded tenement. Tony had never been away from home before entering the hospital. He had never slept alone. He had never eaten on a tray, nor been exposed to a diet such as the hospital provided. He was fearful about what would happen to him. He missed his mother very much and she could come only infrequently to see him because of the distance. Nor was his mother able to write to him for she could barely write her name, but his sister did send him a few notes. He was somewhat comforted by the children in nearby beds and by the nurses who made much of him.

After several months in the hospital Tony was sufficiently recovered to leave. He wanted to go home, and his family wanted him back. But the crowded rooms were on the third floor. Little light and sun streamed into the rooms. Tony's mother, while giving warmth and security to her children, seemed unable to understand the need for Tony's further rest, and felt it would be impossible to keep Tony in bed and quiet at home. So he was moved to a convalescent home where he could get the proper care, the right food and a judicious balancing of rest and activity.

But Tony did not want this care. He begged to go home. After much interpretation to him and his family, they were able to wait for his recovery. The family, too, had worried about the expense of the care until the availability of the Crippled Children's services was explained.

Parental reaction to illness and handicaps differs widely. In addition to inadequate physical arrangements, and lack of understanding of treatment, parents may overprotect a child or neglect him because of his handicap. A little blind boy was so protected by his mother that he had virtually lost the use of his muscles and was afraid to venture anywhere alone. That was before he attended a school for blind children.

Some of the later problems in considering the cardiac child are obviously in the fields of education and recreation. Many communities now have special schools or special classrooms where children with limited ability are taught.

Such factors as the size of the class, the amount of unassigned time, and the amount of pressure that is put on the child are all taken into consideration in planning his education. When the child's condition is such that he must be at home or in a hospital at certain periods, visiting teacher service is often available. The cardiac child needs special vocational guidance and teamwork between all professional workers is necessary, so that all of the child's potentialities and community resources can be utilized to the full. Intelligent cooperation from the family is very essential in dealing with all cardiac children. The ideal of normalcy shoud be kept in mind and every effort made to help the child lead as normal a life as possible in his recreational activities as well as in his education.

When possible, environmental patterns should be studied with a view to their improvement. Such would include for a cardiac child adequate housing, adequate diet, good family relationships, and family adjustments to the stress and strains of daily living.

THE ADULT CARDIAC PATIENT

The individual in middle life discovering that he has heart disease may at first suffer severe emotional reaction. Depending upon his condition it may or may not mean changes in his home, recreation, and work. Total medical care during the initial attack is, of course, essential. At this time his complete diagnosis has been made and, if all known therapy has been applied, the doctor and the patient are in a position to plan the future life for the patient. Often the patient may continue his accustomed mode of life and occupation with very few, if any, restrictions. A feeling of confidence in the doctor and in his instructions and the need for his instructions is a first constructive step to living with heart disease.

If the patient is a homemaker, some very minor changes in her activities or in her working environment may be all that is indicated. For example, the elimination of heavy laundering may relieve the individual of enough strain so that she can satisfactorily continue with her other household activities. Help is available for these patients and there has been developed through the combined efforts of the American Heart Association and certain technical and utility services the "Cardiac Kitchen," a kitchen planned for the cardiac so that she can carry out her activities with a minimum of effort. For the adult cardiac, the question of reeducation or retraining for another type of work may have to be faced. Again, teamwork is necessary. Many facilities are available now for reeducation and retraining of handicapped individuals. The nurse and social worker must be aware of community resources in this field and often through the local office of vocational education much help can be obtained. It may be that a more protected type of job is indicated. Again, through employment agencies working with vocational rehabilitation groups the types of jobs and the industries in the community willing to employ handicapped persons can be studied.

The individual with heart disease must never feel that all the joy has been taken out of life and that he is prevented from participating in recreation because of his heart condition. Many, many activities involving little if any stress on the heart are available, and when the nurse and social worker know what the patient's recreational interests are, he can be directed into those which will place least strain on his condition. Such, of course, would include first of all radio and television, and all kinds of handicraft; and games such as checkers and chess.

In the adult group of women, those of child-bearing age must be considered. In many cases, particularly for women, the sheltered and quiet routine of married life may not be injurious if the individual does not have too serious a heart condition. The commonest form of heart disease found in young women is chronic rheumatic heart disease. According to a leading authority,[2] a young woman with rheumatic heart disease might expect the following: (1) if she is able to lead a reasonably normal life without symptoms showing her heart is overworked (a reasonably normal life means such ordinary things as light housework or office work, or both may be undertaken) she has fifty chances to one she will be alive after one year if not pregnant and she has better than forty chances to one she will be alive after one year after starting pregnancy and about eight chances to one that her baby will live; (2) if her heart is affected so that she cannot do these things without cardiac symptoms or if she has some other serious disease in addition to heart trouble, her chances for being alive in one year are sixteen to one if she is not pregnant and six to one that she will be alive after the beginning of pregnancy and a little better than an even chance that she will have a living child; (3) if she has an irregular heart beat; that is, auricular fibrillation, she has eight chances to one of living a year if not pregnant and only two chances of living a year after the beginning of pregnancy and a little less than an even chance of having a living child. Dr. Hamilton indicates that the chances for successful motherhood are slightly better if the woman is between 23 and 35 years

---

[2]Hamilton, Burton E.: Heart Disease with Pregnancy, American Heart Association.

of age.   He points out that the young woman with heart disease has a chance of living for a long period only if she lives as she should and that during pregnancy she should certainly have expert medical care and supervision.   He points out that the chances of having a successful pregnancy depend on her availing herself of modern medical care and of following conscientiously all instructions given.   In such situations it is very important that other members of the health team, particularly the nurse and social worker, avail themselves of all community facilities needed in such a case and interpret to the patient and her husband the need for following all instructions given.

THE AGED CARDIAC PATIENT

Statistics show that heart diseases rate highest in the cause of death in the older age group, and, since the numbers in this group are increasing, more individuals are going to be alive to die as old cardiacs. The individual who develops cardiac disease after he has retired may not constitute such an economic problem as one in the middle age group, because he may have some retirement or insurance benefits or is eligible for old age assistance.   However, if he is living with younger relatives, the fact that he is a semi-invalid may place an extra burden on his family.   Institutional care is often the best solution for this group and many communities are developing suitable homes for aged persons, including those who have such chronic conditions as heart disease.

Modern rehabilitation has done a great deal to help one of the disabling conditions of this older age group, namely apoplexy resulting in hemiplegia.   Under modern techniques, efforts are made to prevent deformities from developing and to help the return of function of the extremities, to teach the patient to care for himself and to walk and talk again.   This is in sharp contrast to the past when such individuals were often considered by their families and the community as hopeless invalids, bedridden and incompetent, and a constant burden to those looking after them.   Today, this modern regime may often be carried out in the home under the supervision of a physician trained in these methods and working with a nurse, a physiotherapist, a social worker, and members of the family.   The keynote to his rehabilitation is detailed examinations, physical and mental, to determine his physical and psychological condition.   It has been the experience of such large centers as the New York University Institute of Physical Medicine and

Rehabilitation that under such a program of rehabilitation, many hemi-plegic patients may learn to care for themselves, to walk, and to return to some type of gainful employment.

COMMUNITY PLANNING FOR THE PREVENTION AND CONTROL OF HEART DISEASE

The community has become vitally interested in all phases of heart disease and because it now leads in the cause of death, lay persons as well as doctors, nurses, and social workers are vitally interested in joining in plans for detection, prevention, therapy, and rehabilitation. Since 1947 the American Heart Association, a privately supported organization, changed from being a professional organization to include laymen in its organizational activities with a greatly increased budget and program including financial aid for research. This organization works on a state and local level with groups organized in major areas, urban and rural. Today, it carries forth a comprehensive program of research, education and community service and includes laymen, physicians, and scientists among its members. Many leaflets and booklets are published by the American Heart Association and may be obtained through the local office. The National Heart Institute of the United States Public Health Service in Bethesda, Maryland, was established by Congress in 1948. Thus, federal as well as private funds are available for the control of this disease. The National Heart Institute program includes research, training, and community activity.

Another organization, the Life Insurance Medical Fund, organized in 1945 is spending a great deal of money each year on research in heart disease. Many insurance companies, like the Metropolitan Life Insurance Company, have valuable material which can be obtained free or for very little charge for both patients and professional workers.

Consultant services and materials can be obtained from both the American Heart Association and the National Heart Institute. Since a certain number of individuals with heart disease are children, the importance of including the teacher on the team for the detection, prevention, and supervision of cardiac children is emphasized. Lay education which is so necessary in the prevention of heart disease aims first to develop community interest in the problem and stimulate the desire to do something about it. The interested communities then need interpretation from experts in the facilities available and how these facilities may be used. Any such program should study the local situation and try to make plans so that every patient will get the necessary skills, techniques, and facilities for diagnosis, treatment, and general supervision of his condition. Any such program for training and supervision for cardiac patients should be integrated with the total community health program. This would include a study of the medical services and facilities in the community, including hospital and outpatient services as well as doctors, and laboratory facilities. Mobile diagnostic units are being provided for in some communities. The community services would also include consideration of medical practices in local industries and the school health program. Nursing services available in the community would, of course, include not only the services available in the hospital and outpatient department, but the nursing services available for home nursing through Visiting Nurse Associations, and the nursing services provided through industry and municipal or state organizations. For cardiac patients, as for many other chronic patients, the total nursing services available would include, of course, practical nurses, attendants, as well as professional nurses. The social services necessary in terms of personnel would include medical-social workers, trained in all the skills to study the patient with heart disease and to help him to adjust. It would also include the general social workers in the community and the importance of interpreting the needs of the cardiac patient to the general social workers. In the modern consideration of heart diseases, the importance of rehabilitation services has been emphasized. Many of the necessary rehabilitation services, such as job appraisal, vocational rehabilitation services, and education, are not yet completely developed in every community. However, the community should know that rehabilitation is a necessary part of total treatment, medical as well as social, and help to include this in the total program.

A consideration of community educational facilities in addition to the special schools and supervision of cardiac children would also consider the educational program for both children and adults in the home and vocational training for all cardiac individuals if indicated. Recreational facilities in the community should be studied and all professional workers should know what services are available so that recreation can be planned for the patient and adjusted to his emotional, mental, and physical capacities.

Certain environmental adjustments may be necessary for this type of patient. Some of these are transportation for the cardiac patient to and from school, to and from his work, to and from the clinic or hospital or the doctor's office. Housing for the cardiac patient should be adjusted to his need, the amount of space, and the convenience of the facilities he will use in the home in relation to his condition. Sometimes if the cardiac patient is a homemaker, housekeeping services may be necessary. Some communities are working out plans whereby housekeeping services are available for cardiac patients. The importance of simplifying all housework through such studies as those that have been done by the American Heart Association and have resulted in the development of a cardiac kitchen are particularly significant.

Sometimes for cardiac children foster home care, temporary or permanently, may be advisable. This, of course, needs to be worked out on the merit of the individual situation. Also for the aged cardiac, if he cannot be cared for in his own home, the question of institutional care must be considered in the light of his needs and limitations and what the community can offer.

One very important aspect of all community facilities in this, as in all other conditions, is based on teamwork and on the integration of these services so that together agencies and workers plan a program for the patient whereby he benefits most from the facilities available.

STUDY QUESTIONS AND PROJECTS

1. Discuss the effect of the modern medical diagnosis and treatment of heart disease on community and individual reactions to this condition.
2. Describe in general the adjustments usually needed when the cardiac is (a) an adolescent; (b) a middle-aged man; (c) an elderly woman.
3. Discuss the activites of the American Heart Association. Does your community participate in this program? Describe these activities on a local level.
4. How have advances in the field of communicable disease and public health affected individual and community needs for the cardiac?
5. For what types of work might a young cardiac be advised to prepare?
6. Discuss the activities of the federal government for this type of patient.

REFERENCES

American Hospital Association, Blue Cross Guide; A summary of group enrollment benefits, rates, and regulation of nonprofit Blue Cross Hospital Service Plans, Chicago, Ill., The Commission, 1951.

Blakeslee, Howard: Know Your Heart, Public Affairs Pamphlet No. 137, 1950.

Crosby, Alexander L.: Your Blood Pressure and Your Arteries, Public Affairs Pamphlet No. 168, The American Heart Association, Inc.

Facts About Rheumatic Fever, State Programs for Care of Children With Rheumatic Fever. U. S. Children's Bureau, Federal Security Agency, Washington 25, D. C.

Hamilton, Burton E., Heart Disease With Pregnancy, American Heart Association, Inc.

Heart Disease in School Life, Occupations for Those with Heart Disease, American Heart Association, 1790 Broadway, New York 19, N. Y.

Heart of the Home (Picture edition—work simplification for the housewife with heart disease) American Heart Association, 1790 Broadway, New York 19, N. Y.

Marvin, H. M., Jones, T. Duckett, Page, Irvine H., Wright, Irving S., and Rutstein, David D.:   You and Your Heart, New York, Random House, 1950. (Ordered through the American Heart Association or its affiliates).

Proceedings, First National Conferences on Cardiovascular Diseases, 1950, American Hospital Association, New York, N. Y.

Rheumatic Fever in Children; Its Recognition and Management, Metropolitan Life Insurance Company, 1 Madison Avenue, New York 10, N. Y.

Yahraes, Herbert: Rheumatic Fever—Childhood's Greatest Enemy, Public Affairs Pamphlet No. 126, Rev. Ed., 1951.

CHAPTER 11

CANCER

INTRODUCTION

Cancer has become the second most frequent cause of death. It is found often in middle-aged and older people, although it does occur in children and young people. In considering the increased incidence of this disease, three important reasons must be considered; namely, improved physical diagnosis; more people are living longer and more are subject to cancer; and through medical research the death rate from other diseases has been lowered faster than that of cancer. Much emphasis must be placed on early diagnosis and treatment. Experts point out that education of the public is needed for early diagnosis and treatment, and that much of this education must be done by nurses and social workers in addition to physicians. Since World War II, there has been greatly intensified effort in attempting to solve the cancer problem. In all programs of public health education, emphasis is placed on early detection and treatment. Greater emphasis is needed on the professional training of doctors, nurses, and social workers in this area, as well as in the diagnostic facilities available in the community.

Cancer research has been greatly stimulated by both private and public funds and has brought results; for example, a comparison of death rates for the period 1946-1947 and 1949-1950 by the Metropolitan Life Insurance Company shows reduction in fatality from malignant neoplasms among white women from twenty-five to seventy-five years of age.

EMOTIONAL REACTION TO CANCER

There are few other diseases where so much superstition, misinformation, and fear exist. Difficulties and vagueness in making diagnosis and in giving treatment have all added to the patient's fears and superstitions.   Even today when it has been demonstrated that early diagnosis and adequate treatment can often stop the further development of the condition, it is difficult for patients to accept these facts intellectually, mainly because they have been conditioned to destructive emotional reactions to cancer.   Psychologists point out that many individuals, in fear of the diagnosis or treatment, set up a defense mechanism and try to escape from facing reality.   Sometimes emotional attitudes are set up by an individual to protect him from admitting that he has cancer and from facing the necessary pain, discomfort, or death.

Superstition often affects family and community traditions in regard to many diseases.   Some people feel that disease is a punishment for sin.   This attitude, of course, develops a feeling of guilt in the patient. Cancer and mental disease are among those conditions where feelings of guilt are often present.

A real fear of cancer is present in many individuals, sometimes referred to as "cancerphobia."   A dread of the diagnosis itself, a dread of the surgery or special treatments that he thinks may be indicated and a fear of death which the patient feels may be the eventual, if not the immediate, release from his present pain, all contribute to a state of anxiety in many individuals.   Many patients fear mutilating operations; for example, many women fear the loss of a breast and delay diagnosis until it is too late for treatment.   The fear of pain, the discomfort and perhaps the embarrassment that may accompany radical abdominal surgery are very serious situations to most individuals.   In the educational campaign, fear must be replaced by hope; inadequate and wrong information must be replaced by the truth.   Most health workers now feel that the patient and his family must be told the truth about his condition.   Evasion of the truth must be avoided.   The word "cancer" must be used instead of saying the patient has a "tumor." The public sees in posters certain facts about cancer.   The word is used on the poster, articles appear in the lay press about cancer, the discussion of activities of local and national organizations is described and when the patient or his family feel that the doctor, the nurse, or the social worker are evading the truth, confidence in professional workers may be reduced.

ECONOMIC AND FAMILY ADJUSTMENTS TO CANCER

Since the diagnosis and treatment of cancer involve the use of especially equipped institutions, the patient may have to leave his home, at least until the diagnosis has been made, if adequate facilities do not exist in his community. Therefore, contacts with the nurse or social worker in the clinic or hospital are most important. The following problems may present themselves during a first interview with a cancer patient:

1. How may the homeless patient receive the shelter and care which he will require following discharge from the hospital? This is a pertinent question and should receive attention at once, because the hospital cannot keep the patient after his treatment is completed.

2. Is there any source of support for the family during the period when the patient's wages will be discontinued?

3. Who will care for the children during the mother's hospitalization and after her return home? The average mother is more concerned about the welfare of her children than about treatment for herself.

4. What plan should be made for the aged couple whose security is threatened by the illness of one of them? This responsibility may be assumed by grown children, but there are instances when outside aid is needed.

5. Is the out-of-town patient going to be able to come to the hospital often enough to insure complete treatment and adequate observation? The scarcity of institutions equipped to deal with cancer makes it necessary for many patients to travel long distances for treatment. Often financial resources are exhausted by one trip, and the question of subsequent treatment and observation has not been considered.[1]

Most patients with cancer are over fifty years of age, and the problem of adequate financial support as well as medical and nursing treatment is presented. Many communities do not have adequate facilities for the care of such chronic and terminal cases. A certain amount of daily nursing care is required, especially during the latter stages, and in crowded urban living conditions this may be difficult to provide even when the nearest member of the family is willing to assume the responsibility. The public health nurse often must help the family make plans. These involve a complete study of the family situation as well as of any available institutional care in the community.

[1]Cockerill, Eleanor: The Role of the Social Worker in the Diagnosis and Treatment of Cancer, Hospital Service 27: 558-559, 1933. Published by the Hospital Social Service Association of New York City, Inc., 200 Madison Ave., New York, N. Y.

Fortunately, the educational campaign of recent years is now beginning to bring results, and more and more patients are seeking medical attention at an early stage; thus, treatment is more successful, and the patient returns to his place in his family and often can carry on his accustomed work. While these patients are in the hospital the nurse can do much to cheer them by emphasizing the encouraging factors of their situation.

CANCER IN CHILDREN

Cancer including leukemia ranked third in the first ten causes of death in 1952. The 1952 death totals of children one to fourteen years old from accidents and the nine most important nonaccidental causes of death were:[2]

Accidents	10,278	Poliomyelitis	1,282
Pneumonia	2,907	Gastritis, enteritis and colitis	940
Cancer	2,862	Heart disease	740
Congenital malformations	2,085	Nephritis	768
Tuberculosis	1,302	Meningitis (nonmeningococcal)	584

Cancer among children differs from the disease in adults in that the disease is shorter and the tumor grows more rapidly and metastasizes early. In general, duration of the illness is brief. Many physicians point out that diagnosis of cancer in children is difficult because the symptoms may be indefinite or hidden. Therefore, he depends upon a very careful history and diagnosis. Because of this, a great responsibility is placed upon pediatricians and school physicians who examine children, so that the condition can be recognized as early as possible and therapy started. Most parents have quite an emotional reaction when a diagnosis of cancer in one of their children has been made. It is the natural tendency to protect the child against the unknown, against pain, and, since the disease may not be of very long duration, fear of death may often be present. Professional workers, particularly the nurse who may see the family more frequently, must do everything possible to establish rapport and a feeling of friendliness and understanding. Emphasis should be placed on the importance of regular physical examinations of children. The cooperation of parents and teachers in the early detection and support of com-

---

[2]Accident Facts, 1952 ed., National Safety Council, 425 N. Michigan Ave., Chicago.

munity facilities for the diagnosis and treatment of this condition should be developed. Cancer in children is a very serious disease and the prognosis is uncertain and in many instances grave. Balanced against this is the fact that early diagnosis followed by adequate and continuous treatment is the best hope, and many children are alive today due to this program.

AS PEOPLE GROW OLDER CANCER TOLL GROWS*

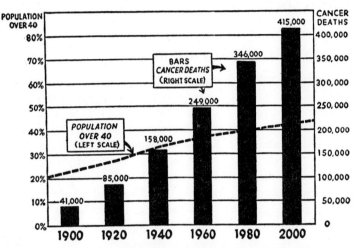

GRAPHIC ASSOCIATES FOR PUBLIC AFFAIRS COMMITTEE, INC.

* FIGURES DO NOT INCLUDE LEUKEMIA AND HODGKIN'S DISEASE.

Fig. 4.—(From Johnson, Dallas: Facing the Facts About Cancer, Public Affairs Committee, Inc., New York, N.Y.)

THE NURSE AND THE PROBLEM OF CANCER

In addition to the physician the nurse should know the symptoms that may appear early in cancer. She knows the significance of these symptoms and, because of her relationship to the patient and his family, she has a unique position in not only encouraging him to get adequate diagnostic and therapeutic help but also in allaying his fears and in helping to build his morale. Because many of these patients need home care and medical supervision in the doctor's office and clinic, the nurse is an important person in seeing that all of these instructions are carried out, and in interpreting them to the patient and his family. She should be thoroughly familiar with all such medical and nursing resources in her community and should utilize them to the utmost. Her unique position in this problem should be a challenge to her. She has an opportunity, not only of giving skilled nursing care and serving as a health educator to the patient and his family, but also of being able to interpret to social agencies the need for detailed follow-up. The American Cancer Society has pointed out the nurse's responsibilities in cancer control as follows: (1) to promote early detection through periodic physical examination, (2) to recognize early symptoms, (3) to know the newest methods of diagnosis and treatment as they affect nursing care, and (4) to know community resources for the cancer patient.

COMMUNITY PLANS AND PROGRAMS

This major health problem is now being attacked by the whole community in addition to the specialized professional groups such as doctors, nurses, research workers in various specialized and allied fields of science. If this disease is to be successfully attacked and conquered, more research is indicated. Therefore, more funds for research must be available. A recognition of the fact that early detection and adequate treatment are keynotes in the control of cancer is recognized by the community in providing funds for detection centers, specialized departments in general hospitals, and special cancer hospitals.

In 1913 The American Society for the Control of Cancer was formed. This is the best known private organization in the field. From the beginning this society included doctors and representatives of medical societies, research workers, nurses, social workers, and interested laymen. The name of this society has recently been changed to the American Cancer Society. Through its educational program, it issues a bulletin, pamphlets, newspaper stories, and radio stories. Much of the lay educational program is now carried on by the Women's Field Army organized in 1936 which conducts educational campaigns and enlistments in all states. The American Cancer Society is supported by endowment, dues, contributions, and fees from the Women's Field Army. The Women's Field Army organizes surgical dressing units often through enlisting women's clubs in the community.

Recognizing that education would be necessary to solve this problem, the American Cancer Society has recently developed a service division. The purpose of the service division of the American Cancer Society is to work with both national and local medical groups in establishing, maintaining, and improving all types of service to the cancer patient. All of the plans of this service division have been approved by the American Medical Association. The projects suggested for this division include, first of all, a survey of local and state needs, detection, diagnosis, and treatment, including the support and organization of these facilities as needed. A minimum standard for hospitals and for cancer clinics has been set up by the American College of Surgeons.

Voluntary organizations in this field laid ground work for more economic support from the community through the stimulation of community interest. In support of this, Congress in 1937 established the National Cancer Institute within the United States Public Health Service. Under the National Cancer Institute Act, a National Advisory Cancer Council was created consisting of six members from leading medical and scientific groups, specializing in this field. The Surgeon General of the United States Public Health Service acts as chairman of the council, ex officio. This Council is authorized by the Act to (1) aid field research for projects or programs submitted to or initiated by it relating to the study of the cause, prevention, or methods of diagnosis and treatment of cancer; (2) collect information as to studies that are being carried on in the United States or any other country as to cause, prevention, or methods of diagnosis or treatment of cancer and make such information available through appropriate publications for benefit for public or private health agencies, for physicians or other scientists and for the information of the general public; (3) review applications for many university hospital laboratories or other institutions whether public or private or from individuals for grants-in-aid, for research in projects relative to cancer and certifying through the Surgeon General for approval of the grants-in-aid of the projects which show promise.

In 1939, the cornerstone for the National Cancer Institute was laid in Bethesda, Maryland. In 1946, Congress increased cancer research appropriation from $490,000 to $1,772,000 and in 1950 Congress appropriated $8,900,000 for the Institute plus contract appropriations of $6,000,000 for facilities. The American Cancer Society in that same year raised $13,934,000. In the year 1946, Congress began appropriating funds to State Health Departments specifically for cancer control. Beginning in 1947 the National Cancer Institute appropriated funds to medical schools for education in cancer control programs. Grants are also given to dental schools for this purpose. Postgraduate training for doctors and nurses has also been initiated. Because the nurse is such an important person in this whole program, the National Cancer Institute has developed nationwide educational programs. Regular courses in cancer nursing and cancer control have been established in several universities all over the country. The first centers to establish such courses were the University of Minnesota, Columbia University and Yale University. The nursing section of the National Cancer Institute has also developed aid for nursing schools such as films and manuals.

The importance of visual aids in adult education is recognized and in cooperation with the National Cancer Institute, the American Cancer Society has produced a series of films, some for professional groups and some for the lay public.

As a result of increased funds available, great strides have been made in research, both at the National Cancer Institute and at many centers all over the country. Other organizations interested in this problem are the Damon Runyon Cancer Fund and many private endowments given to the universities and hospitals for research.

CONCLUSION

In discussing all community problems, teamwork is emphasized. In few other fields is it so evident that teamwork is necessary as in this field. No one scientist or community health worker can function independently when confronted by this problem. Psychological adjustment and financial burdens have to be met by the family. A sympathetic understanding of human relationships, a knowledge of all community resources, and constructive guidance are necessary to help the patient and his family solve his problem.

STUDY QUESTIONS AND PROJECTS

1. What is the background for the attitude of some individuals to cancer? What changes have been taking place, in general, in these attitudes?

2. What facilities exist in your community for the diagnosis and treatment of cancer? In terms of modern scientific knowledge, are these adequate?

3. Present in detail several patients with cancer. Try to contrast situations showing the results of early diagnosis, treatment, and constructive patient and family adjustments as contrasted to more complicated situations.

4. Why is the part played by the nurse of special significance in this condition?

5. Discuss plans and programs in your community for the diagnosis and total care of cancer patients. Describe the program of both governmental and voluntary agencies.

6. Show how programs of individual and community health education have contributed to lessening the incidence of certain of these conditions. Could these same techniques be used for helping to treat or prevent other community problems?

REFERENCES

A Cancer Sourcebook for Nurses, American Cancer Society, Inc., 1950, 47 Beaver Street, New York 4, N. Y.

Cameron, Charles S., Progress in Cancer Research, American Journal of Nursing, Vol. 50, No. 4, April, 1950, pages 209-211.

Cancer Diagnosis with Isotopes, The Cancer Bulletin, Vol. 3, No. 4, July and August, 1951.

Cockerill, Eleanor E.: The Cancer Patient as a Person, His Needs and Problems, Public Health Nursing, February 1948, Vol. 40, pages 78-83.

Doherty, Beka: Cancer, New York, 1949, Random House.

Editorial: Treatment of Cancer, Journal of the American Medical Association, Vol. 149, No. 15, August 9, 1952, pages 1400-1402.

Facing the Facts About Cancer, Public Affairs Pamphlet, No. 38, 1951, American Cancer Society and National Cancer Institute.

Grant, Lester: A Teaching Guide to the Challenge of Cancer, Superintendent of Documents, U. S. Government Printing Office, Washington 25, D. C., 1950.

Haagensen, C. D.: Self-Examination of the Breasts, Journal of the American Medical Association, Vol. 149, No. 4, May 24, 1952, pages 356-360.

Oberling, Charles, and Woglum, William H.: The Riddle of Cancer, New Haven, 1944, Yale University Press.

Patterson, Mary G.: The Care of the Patient With Cancer, Public Health Nursing, July 1950, pages 377-384.

Sokoloff, Boris, Unconquered Enemy, New York, 1940, The Greystone Press.

Soller, Genevieve: Children Get Cancer, Too, Public Health Nursing, December, 1950, pages 638-643.

Terminal Care for Cancer Patients, The Central Service for the Chronically Ill, Chicago.

U. S. Fights Cancer, The Government's Program, National Cancer Institute, Bethesda, Md.

CHAPTER 12

SOME IMPORTANT MEDICAL CONDITIONS

ARTHRITIS

INTRODUCTION

Arthritis and associated conditions often grouped together under the name of rheumatism affect a very large portion of the population. A recent survey[1] totaled an estimated 10,104,000, or 9.3 per cent of the total population, as having arthritis or rheumatism. Of this number about 2,500,000 persons, or 2.3 per cent of the population, were not seen by a doctor, while about 7,500,000 people, or about 6.9 per cent, were given some kind of medical supervision. The incidence among females is considerably higher than that among males and a sharp increase of diagnosed arthritis and rheumatism with age was also noted. The great majority of individuals with arthritis are adults; that is, they are in the productive years of life. Since more women than men are affected with the disease, many housewives and mothers are handicapped. Arthritis seldom kills but often cripples. It is one of the most common of chronic diseases. Therefore, the whole discussion which has been given about chronic illness is applicable for this particular condition.

Recently medical science has contributed greatly to the control of this disease in the new drugs of cortisone and ACTH. In many instances these drugs have prevented the advance of the disease and have reduced the pain, making it possible for the individual to lead a much more active and comfortable life. The importance of physical rehabilitation for these patients is being emphasized today. As for all chronic conditions, medical care and health supervision reaches beyond care given while the patient is institutionalized, but the continuing treatment for his total needs when he returns to the home is necessary.

---

[1]Woolsey, Theodore D.: Prevalence of Arthritis and Rheumatism in the United States, Public Health Reports, Vol. 67, No. 6, June, 1952.

As with most other chronic conditions, the discouraging thing to the patient and his family is the treatment, exercise, and other health restrictions that must be continued for months and years sometimes when very little progress is seen.

SOCIAL AND ECONOMIC CONSIDERATIONS

Because of the crippling condition, arthritis frequently requires that the patient change his mode of life. The arthritic patient, like the cardiac, must learn to live within his physical limitations. Unlike most cardiacs, he has to adjust to pain over a long period of time. In this respect, however, the modern medicines have done a great deal to help the patient's morale in reducing the pain. The arthritic patient may be faced with the need of changing his vocation. In evaluating the needs of the individual patient, teamwork is essential. All resources in the community, medical and health, social welfare, educational, vocational, counseling and guidance are often necessary. The loss of time from the job by arthritic patients as well as the loss to the community when individuals are not employed at all is very great. Medical treatment for these patients is expensive. Detailed diagnosis, therapy and rehabilitation costs money. Therefore, the economic aspects of this disease weigh heavily on the individual patient and his family and must be seriously considered by every community. The patients are likely to become emotionally upset partly because of the economic aspect, partly because of the indefinite and seemingly endless duration of the disease, partly because of the pain and the total feeling of frustration which accompanies the condition. This mental state is not conducive to successful recovery. All workers must be aware of this and do everything possible to boost the morale of the patient and to interpret his needs and feelings to the family so that they can cooperate in the necessary emotional rehabilitation.

One economic aspect of the disease is that it is more prevalent in the lower income groups. Better personal hygiene, including adequate diet, good sanitation, adequate housing, good working conditions do much to prevent this condition from developing. If the patient is a homemaker, certain adjustments may have to be made in the home, such as moving to a one-story house and adjusting the home facilities so that she can carry out her activities with as little effort as possible.

The arthritic patient like the cancer patient often wanders from one clinic to another, from one doctor to another, seeking a different diagnosis or more dramatic results.   All workers on the team must be aware of the possibility of this situation developing and do everything to secure the patient's confidence in the total health program that is being worked out for him.   Integration of available services and co-operation between all workers for the greatest benefit to each patient are essential.

COMMUNITY PLANNING FOR ARTHRITIS

While there are few if any hospitals or health agencies in this country devoted entirely to treatment of arthritis, many institutions are making special studies of arthritis, and hospitals for the acutely ill are more willing to admit arthritic patients now than formerly.

The American Committee for the Control of Rheumatism, meeting first in 1928, and the American Rheumatism Association formed in 1933 are doing important work.   The Arthritis Foundation is a voluntarily supported national organization of physicians and laymen formed to eradicate arthritis and rheumatism by means of research, increased professional education, improved facilities for treating sufferers, and rehabilitation of those disabled.   This Foundation publishes valuable material in this field.   (See references.)   In addition, many general health and welfare organizations are interested in the problem of arthritis, particularly organizations dealing with chronic illness and rehabilitation.   Publicly supported organizations in these fields also can contribute greatly to the prevention, treatment, and rehabilitation of arthritic patients.   The reader is referred again to the chapter on Chronic Illness for certain general principles which are applicable for this special group.

DIABETES

INTRODUCTION

It is estimated that at least a billion people in the United States have diabetes, and for every known case there may be three cases unrecognized.   Two contrasting situations should be considered in approaching the community problem of diabetes; namely, most persons having this disease can keep well and lead normal useful lives if modern medical and health facilities are utilized.   In contrast to that, in addition to the high death rate of diabetes, neglect of the condition is responsible for the general impairment of health and many disabling complications. That is, that while diabetes is typical of a disease which will be with the patient always, it is not necessarily disabling and should not prevent him from functioning as a normal individual in his community.

SOCIAL AND ECONOMIC CONSIDERATIONS

The patient who recognizes and adjusts himself to the limitations placed on him by diabetes may live a satisfying life in his emotional, vocational, and recreational activities. Good medical care for the diabetic must be supplemented with careful study of his environment and interpretation of the condition to him, his parents, teachers, employers, etc. It is being recognized now that many other factors in the life of the diabetic are quite as important as the food he eats, and that often problems exist in the home which interfere with successful treatment.

Diabetes is not curable. The disease is always with the patient, but it is seldom disabling. This often involves not only interpretation, but school and work adjustments. An individual's ability to adjust to this limitation may be judged by his inherent personal and mental make-up, and the way in which he has reacted to the other problems in his life. The extra financial burden including special diet, insulin, visits to clinic or doctor's office must be considered. The prevention of obesity and periodic health examinations to get the disease under medical supervision as early as possible are definite steps in controlling diabetes. The need for constant, good medical supervision and the danger of "quacks" should be emphasized to all patients.

In diabetic children school exceptions should be made only when absolutely necessary. These children should be taught to live as normal lives as possible and should not be set apart from the others. Diabetes, as a lifelong disease, will show clearly the use an individual makes of his disease: whether he uses it to get what he wants, to remain on an immature, dependent level; to shun responsibility; or to accept his limitation on a mature level. The adolescent, in his reaction to all authority, is likely to go through periods of breaking diet and routine. An understanding of the adolescent is necessary for the nurse dealing with these patients. The education of a "key" person in the family when the patient is a child is important. However, the child should be taught as soon as possible to assume part of the responsibility and take over more and more as he grows older.

Interpretation to other individuals who have contact with the diabetic, such as teachers, employers, etc., is desirable. This must be done in such a way that fears and antagonisms are not developed. All diabetics should be taught to give good daily care without becoming emotionally obsessed by the necessary routine.

One aspect of diabetes as a community problem is that as the length of life has increased so has the diabetics'. Largely due to insulin, gains in the average length of life of diabetic patients, particularly of children, have been very great. The emotional and intellectual maturity of the diabetic play a very essential part in his ability to adjust successfully to his condition and to lead a satisfying life. Since this disease may be found at any age, in the child as well as the aged, his status in the family must be considered. As in cardiac conditions, different problems are presented when the patient is a child, an adolescent, an adult, or an aged diabetic person. When the diabetic is a child, the whole problem of the sick child must be evaluated and in line with his physical restrictions the family, with help from health and social agencies when necessary, must help condition the child to live as normal a life as possible. He must be taught from the beginning that he must adjust to his condition as well as feeling that his family and social groups must be constantly adjusting to him. During adolescence emotional instability may be exaggerated in the diabetic. The resentment of authority common to all adolescents may tempt him to break his health program, and the condition may be exaggerated. Intelligent guidance by teachers and health workers during adolescence is very essential. It is important to emphasize to patients that diabetes is the least crippling chronic disease and that, properly cared for, the individual can live a very normal life.

The American Diabetic Association emphasizes the following important points for every diabetic:

1. Honesty with one's self regarding the careful observance of diet and other restrictions which may be necessary;

2. Complete divorcement from self-pity. Other people have equally severe problems, why inflict yours upon them? This applies with equal force to loved ones and chance acquaintances;

3. Adaptation to the life of the family. There is no need for special foods, special routines, and annoying concessions. You, as a diabetic, may eat the foods that the family eats that are on your diet. You can do this by measuring the food you eat at first with scales or with ordinary house-

hold measures, such as the measuring cup and the tablespoon. Later you may succeed in training the eyes satisfactorily to do your measuring for you. You must forbid yourself extras, not torture a loved one for the responsibility for your sins against yourself. You must exercise self control; that is your first duty to your family. You, too, must adapt yourself to their mode of living so that you remain one of them. Do not become a subject of continuous inconsideration and special favor, a position that is unhealthy and unpleasant both for you and for them. By the same token, your disease gives you no special rights or privileges in your community. With an even break you should and you can achieve the same measure of success as your fellows and often with proper moderation in eating you may outstrip them in the matter of general health and vigor.[2]

COMMUNITY PLANS AND PROGRAMS

The American Diabetic Association was organized in 1940, originally by physicians interested in diabetes. This national, privately supported organization now includes laymen as well as physicians and publishes much material including a magazine, *Forecast,* which is issued bi-monthly. In recent years one activity of this organization has been through a committee sponsoring a Diabetes Detection Drive. This committee has stimulated the organization of about five hundred committees on diabetes in county and medical societies. Many lay organizations are cooperating with physicians in this valuable preventive work. In 1945 the U.S.P.H.S. added a division on Diabetes to the National Health Institute.

TUBERCULOSIS

INTRODUCTION

Tuberculosis is one of the communicable diseases where incidence and death rates have been lowered by public health measures. In the last half century, this disease has moved from first to eighth place as man's chief killer in this country. While the decline in morbidity has not been as great as that in mortality, it is true that because of educational campaigns and better health policies in schools and industry, many cases with minimum infection are discovered early. Since more than

---

[2]McGavick, Thomas H., The Diabetic, His Family and His Community, from *Forecast,* Nov. 1950, published by American Diabetic Association, p. 17.

120,000 new cases of tuberculosis were reported in 1950, it is still a serious disease in the 16-35 year age group and as the individual is in the most productive period during these years, it is a serious economic and social problem.

SOCIAL AND ECONOMIC CONSIDERATIONS

Since the young adult group is the age group most frequently affected, it is encouraging to note that there has been a steady reduction in tuberculosis mortality among American wage earners and their families. While there is great geographic variation in the incidence of tuberculosis, for example, Utah, Idaho, Iowa, and Kansas, and other states in the midwest, have very low incidence, certain states, Arizona, New Mexico, have higher than average mortality rates. High incidence in some of the southwestern states such as Arizona and New Mexico may be due in part to the migrations of people with tuberculosis seeking a better climate. The high incidence in some southern states, such as Kentucky, Tennessee, and Mississippi, may be due to poor social conditions, such as low economic status, poor diet, and lack of diagnostic and medical facilities.

The relationship between low economic status resulting in poor housing, crowded living conditions, and ignorance in poor housekeeping and unhygienic habits and tuberculosis has been pointed out. Because this disease is of long duration, the expense of adequate treatment is heavy. Many individuals who have tuberculosis cannot pay for the treatment themselves. And since the largest group affected is the young adult group at the age when they have heavy family responsibilities, their dependents may often need economic assistance. Therefore, community resources are necessary not only for the treatment of the patient but also for the economic assistance for the family. Contributing to the reduction in tuberculosis, in addition to better diagnostic and treatment facilities, general improvement in personal hygiene, better housing, improved working conditions, shorter hours of work, better food, have all been environmental factors which have contributed to the total improvement.

Nurses are taught that early diagnosis and treatment are necessary. Studies of actual cases emphasize the fact that many are discovered accidentally. Periodic health examinations including chest plates for everyone will be a great step toward early diagnosis. Most schools of nursing now require chest plates on all students at regular periods during the course and have improved their program of total health so that protection, education, and better health are given to the young adult group who are student nurses.

Rehabilitation for this group is similar in principle to rehabilitation for any individual with a chronic condition. Perhaps more encouraging factors are today presented in the tuberculosis situation since there has been a change in regard to thinking regarding physical capacities and working conditions suitable for tubercular persons. Depending upon the acute stage of infection and the individual's response to treatment, many former restrictions placed on tuberculosis patients in the past are unnecessary where the individual has begun recovery, has good personal hygiene habits, and where in his place of work he will get the reasonable protection that modern industry should give to every worker.

COMMUNITY PLANS AND PROGRAMS

Special hospitals for tuberculosis patients have existed in this country for many years and have contributed much to improving the situation by providing good care; well-trained medical and nursing staffs are essential in these hospitals. In tuberculosis, as in all community health problems, when the total patient needs are considered, progress can be made only through teamwork. Teamwork is necessary not only between doctors and nurses, during the acute stage, but with the medical social worker, the occupational therapist, the rehabilitation worker taking their parts on the team as early as possible. When an individual should be trained for a different type of work, vocational guidance should be availabe to him.

The National Tuberculosis Association was established in 1904. Through its more than 2,500 affiliated associations, it reaches into all local communities. It is financed mainly by the proceeds from the annual sale of Christmas seals. The Christmas seal idea originated with a Danish postal clerk in 1903 and was introduced into America in 1907, and it certainly has brought results. The National Tuberculosis Association carries on an active program of education through pamphlets, posters, booklets, and films which are distributed in schools and colleges and industries and many other centers in the community. Funds are also used to provide tuberculosis training for physicians, nurses, technicians, and public health workers. Research and study is sponsored by this association.

In 1944, the Tuberculosis Control Division of the United States Public Health Service was established. Many municipal and state public health departments have been very active in the control of tuberculosis and have expanded their facilities to sponsor x-ray examination on mass scale. For example, in Massachusetts, each city with a population of 50,000 or more is required by law to supply diagnostic facilities for the finding of tuberculosis.

Attitutdes toward the employment of the individual with a history of tuberculosis are being changed by the improvement of medical care and health supervision in industry. Cooperation between health workers and employers can result in more effective rehabilitation of the patient and a more intelligent understanding of his contribution to society as well as of his needs.

CONCLUSION

Almost all facts about tuberculosis and its prevention and control are on the optimistic side. It remains the responsibility of all professional workers to continue leading in this successful campaign. Improved personal hygiene, improved total environment, including good housing, sanitation, better general education, will undoubtedly continue to contribute in reducing this community health problem which used to be one of the great killers in every country. The stigma associated in years gone by with tuberculosis has practically disappeared. This is significant, because it should point to a similar encouraging situation developing in other diseases such as cancer, mental illness, and other chronic illnesses that now lead the list not only as killing but as crippling great numbers of the population.

STUDY QUESTIONS AND PROJECTS

1. In what ways have community attitudes and conditions toward cancer and tuberculosis changed in the last twenty-five years?
2. Discuss the emotional, economic, and other social effects of the so-called "miracle drugs" in the treatment of such diseases as arthritis and tuberculosis.
3. Since diabetes is a lifelong condition, discuss the emotional, educational and vocational needs of individuals in different age groups and point out special adjustments which the diabetic may have to make.
4. Make a study of one patient in each of the major disease conditions discussed in this chapter.
5. From the central office of community health and welfare agencies in your community get a list of all the agencies interested in any of the diseases discussed

in this chapter. If possible, get copies of materials published by these agencies. With which of these agencies does your hospital clinic cooperate in providing medical care and health supervision for patients having the diseases described above.

6. Are medical and social facilities adequate in your community for the treatment of these conditions? If not, what plans does your community have to provide better facilities?

REFERENCES

Aitken, A. N.: The Need for Developing Work Tolerance Following Tuberculosis, Transactions of the National Tuberculosis Association, 1942.

Blakeslee, Alton L.: Tuberculosis—The Killer Cornered, Public Affairs Pamphlet, No. 156, 1949.

Blakeslee, Alton L.: Arthritis and the Miracle Drugs, Public Affairs Pamphlet, No. 166, 1950.

Bulletin on the Rheumatic Diseases, 2-page monthly on current advances in management of rheumatic diseases; nine issues. Arthritis and Rheumatism Foundation, 23 West 45th Street, New York 19, N. Y.

Newman, L. B.: Rehabilitation of the Tuberculous Patient in the Veterans Administration, Tuberculosis Institute of Chicago and Cook County, Chicago, Ill., February 25, 1950.

Pattison, H. A.: Rehabilitation of the Tuberculous, Livingston Press, Livingston, Columbia County, New York.

The Primer on the Rheumatic Diseases, published by the American Rheumatism Association.

The Story of Compound E, Arthritis and Rheumatism Foundation, 23 West 45th Street, New York 19, N. Y.

Upham, Frances: A Dynamic Approach to Illness, New York, 1949, Family Service Association of America.

U. S. Veterans Administration: You Can Lick T B, Washington, D. C., Government Printing Office, Pamphlet 10-18, 1947.

What You Should Know About Arthritis: Arthritis and Rheumatism Foundation, 23 West 45th Street, New York 19, N. Y.

Yahraes, Herbert: Good News About Diabetes, Public Affairs Pamphlet, No. 138.

CHAPTER 13

ALCOHOLISM AND DRUG ADDICTION

INTRODUCTION

Alcoholism has at various times in the history of this country been classified as a moral problem, an economic problem, an educational problem, a problem for families, and more recently a psychiatric and medical problem. Traditionally, alcoholics have been treated according to the community attitude toward alcoholism. Sometimes they have been punished, sometimes ridiculed, sometimes neglected and hidden by society. Facilities available in many communities have been mainly the jail or the mission center. Private sanitarium care and so-called cures for alcoholism have been available to those who could afford them. It is recognized today that sociological factors play a definite part in the anxieties, hostilities, and frustrations which seem to contribute to the development of alcoholism. Alcoholism has become the subject for medical discussion as well as for community and industrial conferences. Alcoholism is to be more and more looked upon as a disease which should be studied and treated rather than as a crime and, in the discussion here, alcoholism may be defined as excessive, habitual use of alcohol resulting in intoxication and poisoning.

All health workers should be interested in the result of excessive drinking on the health attitudes and life activities of the individual, and of the relation between excessive drinking and marital conflicts, standards of living, and family disorganization, and finally the effect of the tavern in social disorganization. Statistics from insurance companies show that alcohol addiction shortens life and so increases the death rate. The relationship of alcoholism and unemployment, dependency, and poverty is well known. It is estimated that 25 per cent of families economically dependent on alcoholic addicts have to get relief from either private or public agencies. Safety campaigns have emphasized the connection between drinking and traffic accidents. In an interesting study,

"Middletown in Transition,"[1] emphasis was placed upon increasing evidence of drinking as a leisure-time activity.

CAUSES OF ALCOHOLISM

Like the other social problems discussed in this book, a search for the causes leads one to the conclusion that in few social problems can the causes be isolated and pointed out clearly. Many factors contribute to the development of alcoholism. Some of these are:

1. *Personal Inadequacy.*—Individuals get into the habit of taking a drink "to give them a boost." Such individuals may be inadequate because of inherent nervous defects; they may drink in order to escape from unpleasant reality, or because alcohol gives them a temporary feeling of importance.
2. *Relaxation.*—Individuals drink for relaxation from the nervous strain of their daily work or because their work has physically exhausted them and they are deluded by the belief that alcohol furnishes added strength.
3. *Companionship.*—Individuals drink for companionship and this is a cause contributing to the development of chronic alcoholism often pointed out in contemporary American life. It has become the fashion to drink and social pressure may be placed on one by the group to indulge.
4. *Social Conditions.*—Social conditions such as poor food, bad housing, economic uncertainty, and ignorance may all contribute to the development of chronic alcoholism.

PREVENTION OF ALCOHOLISM

Alcoholism can be prevented through a program of individual and community education by providing adequate recreation, better working conditions, better housing, and greater security. In fact, in general, it may be said that alcoholism as a social problem may be greatly reduced when individuals know more about physical and mental hygiene and when those factors contributing to personal and social disorganization have been reduced.

ALCOHOLISM AND JUVENILE DELINQUENCY

The relation between alcoholism and family dependency and disorganization has been mentioned. These factors are among those that

---

[1]Lynn, Robert S., and Lynn, Helen M.: Middletown in Transition, New York 1937, Harcourt, Brace and Co., Inc.

may contribute to juvenile delinquency and dependent and neglected children. Serving alcoholic drinks to minors is often done illegally and may lead to sex delinquency and other evidence of juvenile delinquency, especially in feeble-minded children. In homes where either of the parents is an alcoholic addict, children are exposed to nervous tensions, insecurities, physical neglect, and an irregular mode of life which may contribute to personal disorganization if not to actual delinquency.

COMMUNITY PLANS AND PROGRAMS

Programs must be developed for the treatment, prevention, and rehabilitation of alcoholics. As in all other disease situations, the individual's desire to recognize and to follow instructions for his treatment are very significant. Detailed medical and nursing treatment will not be discussed here; the reader is referred to books in this clinical area for this information. Because of the complicated social and emotional situation existing in most alcoholic conditions, some type of psychotherapy is needed in almost every instance. Almost all treatment and community plans are considering this aspect as well as the strictly medical and social. It is pointed out that up until about ten years ago, the only treatment that was being done by city or state governments was giving addicts the jail treatment. By 1952, about thirty-six states had taken action on alcoholism; nineteen had organized some kind of clinic, placing the program for the treatment of alcoholism within the state department and combining rehabilitation with treatment. A National States Conference on Alcoholism has been organized as an association of administrators and official delegates of the state agencies on alcoholism.

Perhaps the best known organization dealing with the alcoholic is Alcoholics Anonymous. This group was founded in 1934 by a "Mr. X" who found the answer to his alcoholic problem in a personal religious experience. He initiated the organization of a group of alcoholics and since then the organization has become nationwide with many local branches. Alcoholics Anonymous claim that 75 per cent of those who really try their methods recover. The therapeutic value of this approach seems to derive from a religious or spiritual force to help the individual overcome his alcoholism.

In 1944 a National Committee on Alcoholism was organized by a group of prominent citizens. It is an independent, voluntary agency with activities based on three fundamental concepts:

1. That alcoholism is a disease and that alcoholics are ill.
2. Alcoholics can be helped.
3. Alcoholism is a public health problem and therefore is a public responsibility.

This committee has become a national clearing house in education about alcoholism and has as a main purpose to tell the public and the medical profession the facts about alcoholism and to try to break down misconceptions about it. It assists communities in organizing and establishing clinics and information services. Many other centers are developing specialized clinics dealing with this subject. One was organized in 1944 at the Yale Laboratory of Applied Physiology. The so-called Yale Plan Clinic has become a model for clinics all over the country and publishes a magazine called the *Quarterly Journal of Studies on Alcohol*.

It is interesting to note that many industries are attacking this problem in the modern, constructive way. Some industries now are recognizing that the alcoholic is one of their employees and they have a responsibility to him and they are interested in developing programs of prevention and rehabilitation. A committee on the problem of drinking has been organized in the Industrial Medical Association. Industry points out that the employed alcoholic is a valuable investment wanting protection through education and treatment services if possible and that alcoholics in the community who were formerly employed represent an equally valuable potentiality when facilities for their treatment and rehabilitation are available. Industries are realizing that investment by them in educational, treatment, and rehabilitation programs will be financially sound, and that the cost of rehabilitation will be much less than the tangible and intangible factors of economic loss to the industry and to the community than by simply discharging the employee.

DRUG ADDICTION

Drug addiction is different from alcoholism in this country in that the use of alcoholic beverages in many families and at traditional social ceremonies is quite customary. The use of the opiate drugs in socially acceptable groups is not usual here as it is in certain Oriental regions. The opiates in this country have been used for medicinal purposes only and legally have been kept under strict licensure. The most important drugs usually considered as leading to addiction are opium and its derivatives (morphine, codeine, heroin), cocaine, hashish, and marijuana. Causes of drug addiction may be traced in some instances to the use of a drug to relieve pain or to the association with other drug addicts or to those in the trade. Some individuals point out that the stress and strain of modern life leads some emotionally unbalanced individuals to seek relief and escape from reality in taking sedatives, perhaps mild ones at first and then depending more and more upon opium for relief. Once the habit has been formed, the individual is no longer content to get the drug through the doctor in legal channels, but will seek illegal ways of getting enough to satisfy him.

One of the great problems in the field of drug addiction is that it is used by adolescents and sometimes they are used to "peddle" the drug. The adolescent seeking excitement, the teenager in the large city without adequate family security, satisfaction, and supervision, the high school boy and girl living in a community lacking in recreational facilities is a prey to the narcotic peddler. The teenager often starts with the marijuana cigarette usually for a thrill and soon becomes dependent upon the drug. A concerted campaign through the school with parent-teachers' organizations is the most constructive approach in case-finding and in prevention. In 1931 the Association for the Advancement of Instruction about Alcohol and Narcotics was organized at the Yale School of Alcoholic Studies. The object of this association was stated as "assisting public and private school educators to discharge effectively their responsibility to inform students concerning alcohol and narcotics. In carrying out its objects the Association shall gather and organize its information derived from research activity and classroom experience and shall relate such data to persons regularly enrolled as members." This Association is an independent one, not affiliated with any institution or agency. It plans to distribute pamphlet material as funds are available.

The United States Government recognizes this as a problem for Federal control and maintains two hospitals for treatment: one at Fort Worth, Texas, and one at Lexington, Kentucky. The shortest time for treatment at either of these hospitals is about four and one-half months. They are overcrowded and are not particularly constructive environments for teenagers, since often they are thrown in contact with older addicts. Patients and former patients from the Lexington Hospital have recently started a group, Narcotics Anonymous, based upon similar principles of group therapy and carried out so successfully by

Alcoholics Anonymous. Such groups are being organized in many of our cities.

It is important for the family to recognize that no family and very few doctors can by themselves treat a drug addict. It is often necessary that he be sent to one of these Federal hospitals specializing in the treatment of drug addicts. Applications should be addressed to the Medical Officer in Charge of the United States Public Health Service Hospital at either Lexington, Kentucky, or Fort Worth, Texas.

STUDY QUESTIONS AND PROJECTS

1. Define alcoholism.
2. Show how our culture pattern affects the individual and community attitudes to alcoholism and drug addiction as community problems.
3. In what legal ways does drug addiction differ from alcoholism?
4. Has your community accepted the modern concept that alcoholism is a disease? If so, what facilities has it provided for the diagnosis, treatment, and rehabilitation of these patients?
5. Discuss national plans and programs for dealing with these problems. Are any of these programs operating in your community?

REFERENCES

Alcohol, Science and Society, Quarterly Journal of Studies on Alcohol, New Haven, Conn. (29 lectures and discussions given at Yale Summer School of Alcohol Studies.)

Anderson, Dwight: The Other Side of the Bottle, New York, A. A. Wyn, 1950.

Blakeslee, Alton L.: Alcoholism—A Sickness That Can Be Beaten, Public Affairs Pamphlet, No. 118, 1952.

Committee on Problems of Alcohol, National Research Council, 2101 Constitution Avenue, Washington 25, D. C.

Hirsh, Joseph: The Problem Drinker, New York, 1949, Duell, Sloan and Pearce.

McCarthy, Raymond G., and Douglass, Edgar M.: Alcohol and Social Responsibility, New York, 1949, Thomas Y. Crowell.

National States' Conference on Alcoholism, 66 South Street, Concord, N. H., or c/o Blue Hills Clinic, 51 Coventry Street, Hartford 12, Conn.

Seliger, Robert V.: Alcoholics Are Sick People, Baltimore, 1945, Alcoholism Publications.

Seliger, Robert V.: The Horror of Dope, Family Circle, October, 1951, pages 21 and 42.

Straus, Robert: Recognizing the Problem Drinker in Business and Industry, The Journal of Business of the University of Chicago, pages 25, 95-100, April, 1952.

The National Committee on Alcoholism, 2 East 103 Street, New York, 29, N. Y.

Tiebout, Harry M.: Therapeutic Mechanism of Alcoholics Anonymous, American Journal of Psychiatry, January, 1944.

CHAPTER 14

VENEREAL DISEASES

INTRODUCTION

The venereal diseases are rather different from other communicable diseases in that they have become associated in the minds of most individuals with sexual promiscuity. Syphilis and gonorrhea are still major community health problems in spite of the fact that recent advances in diagnosis and treatment are doing much to bring them under control. A particularly pertinent fact is that while the highest rate of infection of syphilis is in young adult life, the aftereffects do not often show up until middle and later life. During the contagious period, the examination of all contacts is extremely important. Facilities are available to control and to a great extent to prevent venereal diseases; for example, early and adequate treatment of the mother during pregnancy usually prevents congenital syphilis in her child. The new rapid treatments which have been developed partly with the use of penicillin and sulfa drugs have led many individuals to be overoptimistic about their treatment and many being overconfident do not see the need to return for serological and spinal fluid examinations. It is extremely important that all health workers encourage individuals to return for follow-up examinations as indicated by their doctor.

SOCIAL AND ECONOMIC IMPLICATIONS

The diagnosis of any of the venereal diseases often comes as a shock to the individual and his family and may be a contributing cause to temporary or permanent family disorganization. Lack of education, poor environmental conditions, including lack of recreational facilities and unsatisfactory interpersonal relationships, often may be contributing causes to the acquisition of the venereal diseases. Schools as well as various youth organizations are contributing to prevention by sponsoring programs for better sex education and recreation.

A patient's reaction to disease may be colored by society's attitude toward that disease. The social disgrace connected with cancer, tuberculosis, or mental disease is not nearly so great as it used to be. The traditional attitude to the venereal diseases on a moralistic basis has done much to prevent an adequate program for treatment and prevention from being carried out in many communities. In these diseases an individual's reaction is often colored by the standards of society. Efforts to promote health teaching and a scientific attitude toward such diseases as syphilis, cancer, tuberculosis, and mental illness are bringing results in changing attitudes to the preventive as well as the diagnostic and curative aspects.

Because of the association with sexual promiscuity, the knowledge that one's marital partner has contracted syphilis nearly always leads to a family crisis. Family tensions are increased and disorganization may be permanent. If not, great unhappiness is likely to result if there is childlessness because of sterility or fetal or infant death due to venereal infection. The public health campaign launched by Dr. Parran, former Surgeon General of the United States Public Health Service has brought results and the community is being educated in the essential nature of these infections and the importance of early diagnosis and treatment.

Since interpersonal relationships, emotional instability, and insecurity are vital factors contributing to the cause and to the inability of the individual to follow through treatment, psychiatric as well as medical services should be available in the community and should be utilized by doctors and other health workers when indicated.

It is estimated that the annual cost of the care of the syphilitic insane and chronic patients alone will amount to $41,000,000. Reduction in the incidence of these later complications of venereal disease and of syphilitic heart disease can come only through better diagnosis and treatment through the acute stages.

COMMUNITY PLANS AND PROGRAMS

Since venereal diseases are communicable, they are reportable to public authorities for the protection of the individual and the total community. Knowledge for the diagnosis and treatment is available and the community has recognized its responsibility in this area. The National Venereal Disease Control Act was passed in 1938, at first taking the form of grants to help with local clinics for reporting and

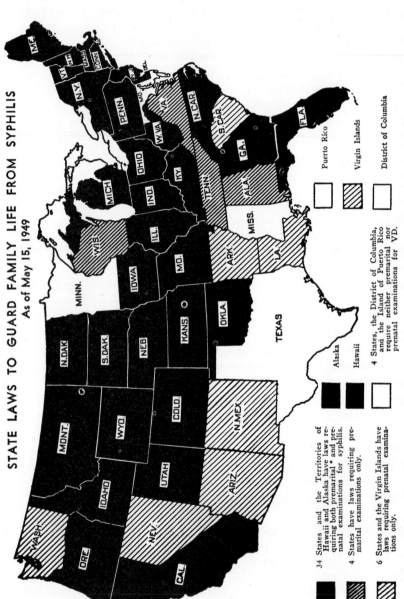

STATE LAWS TO GUARD FAMILY LIFE FROM SYPHILIS
As of May 15, 1949

34 States and the Territories of Hawaii and Alaska have laws requiring both premarital* and prenatal examinations for syphilis.

4 States have laws requiring premarital examinations only.

6 States and the Virgin Islands have laws requiring prenatal examinations only.

Alaska

Hawaii

4 States, the District of Columbia, and the Island of Puerto Rico require neither premarital nor prenatal examinations for VD.

Puerto Rico

Virgin Islands

District of Columbia

* Including examinations of both bride and groom as a prerequisite to issuance of a marriage license. The States of Texas and Louisiana require examinations of groom only, and their laws for this purpose are not included.

Fig. 5.—(From American Social Hygiene Association, New York N.Y.)

treating the condition. This program is administered by the Surgeon General of the United States Public Health Service. Legislation requiring premarital blood tests is another public health measure. By 1949, laws for premarital examination of blood had been passed in forty-six states.

The American Social Hygiene Association, a privately supported organization, has for years carried on a program of education for professional workers and laymen. Much valuable information can be obtained from this organization of the incidence, control, and prevention of these diseases.

PROSTITUTION

It is recognized that prostitutes are the most frequent carriers of the venereal diseases. There are, it is true, accidental infections from drinking glasses, towels, etc., but they are in the minority. By far the greatest number of patients become infected from contacts with other people. The eradication of prostitution would be an effective measure in preventing many cases of venereal diseases. This can be done only by a program of vocational guidance, adequate recreation, and better living conditions in the whole of society. Most prostitutes drift into that occupation because of unsuccessful and unsatisfactory contacts elsewhere. Many are mentally deficient and thus should get entire protection from society. Some are sexually promiscuous and need help from a psychiatrist. (See also Chapter 3.)

STUDY QUESTIONS AND PROJECTS

1. Show how the traditional community attitude to the venereal diseases has in the past hindered both medical and social treatment.

2. Present a study of a patient with venereal disease and show how family strengths and weaknesses were accentuated because of it.

3. Describe how effective teamwork in the community can help in prevention, treatment, and rehabilitation. To be most effective, what special groups should be represented on the team?

4. Is the control of venereal diseases a problem for governmental or for voluntary agencies? Why do you take the stand you do on this?

REFERENCES

Cooley, Carol H.: Social Aspects of Illness, Philadelphia, 1951, W. B. Saunders, pp. 219-229.

Johnson, Bascom, Gould, George, and Dickerson, R. E.: Digest of State and Federal Laws dealing with prostitution and other sex offenses with notes on the control of the sale of alcoholic beverages as it relates to prostitution activities, American Social Hygiene Association, 1942, rev. 1946.

Johnson, Bascom: Digest of laws and regulations relating to the prevention and control of syphilis and gonorrhea in the 48 states and the District of Columbia, American Social Hygiene Association, 1940, rev. 1942, 1946.

Morris, Evangeline: Public Health Nursing in Syphilis and Gonorrhea, Philadelphia, 1951, W. B. Saunders, ed. 3, rev.

Safier, Benno, et al.: A Psychiatric Approach to the Treatment of Promiscuity, American Social Hygiene Association, 1949.

Upham, Frances: A Dynamic Approach to Illness, New York, Family Service Association of America, 1949, pp. 143-157.

CHAPTER 15

THE PHYSICALLY HANDICAPPED

INTRODUCTION

Many individuals become handicapped as the result of disease or accident. Others have been born blind, deaf, or with some other defect. In planning programs for the handicapped, prevention is the first step. The interest of the state in providing adequate prenatal and postnatal programs all over the country is evidence of its interest in keeping preventable defects at a minimum. Adequate medical care for everyone in this country is another constructive modern approach. Many defects occur because some condition was not adequately treated soon enough. The nurse can often help in the preventive program by urging parents to seek medical care or by encouraging them to continue under medical supervision when they may think it is no longer necessary. Adequate medical and nursing care during convalescence will do much in the prevention of defects. The school nurse is in a very advantageous position and can often advise special care for children before parents realize that it is necessary.

The medical treatment of the handicapped and continued medical supervision of the individual are not today considered enough. Segregation of the handicapped in specialized institutions is not the modern approach to this problem. Today, handicapped individuals should be considered as members of our society and should be helped to function as normally as possible in their families and communities. Good medical care, adequate public health facilities, better educational programs, and improvement of the total environment, including housing, recreation, vocational and occupational opportunities, will do much to prevent handicaps.

In dealing with the handicapped individual in our modern democratic society, the problem is one of meeting his total needs; medical, educational, vocational, and social. Physical handicap may be the cause as well as effect of community problems, such as poverty, dependency, unemployment and delinquency. Some criminologists point out the relationship between physical defects and delinquency. Because of the handicapping conditions associated with war, interest in this field was greatly stimulated during World War II. Fortunately, that interest has remained and has been introduced into civilian medicine and public health.

The emotional shock sustained as a result of injury or illness must be considered. Fortunately most individuals do have the resistance and initiative necessary for recovery. In considering the problem of the handicapped, it must be remembered that not only does he have to recover physically and emotionally from his illness or his accident, but very often he has to work out new activities in education, recreation, and vocation which will need to replace his accustomed mode of life and which should give him the feeling of satisfaction and accomplishment.

SPECIAL SITUATIONS

Extreme handicaps such as complete blindness or deafness have been the center of much philanthropy in the past. Misdirected efforts on an emotional basis may tend to develop dependency on the part of the handicapped. National societies and agencies, both public and private, tend to approach the problem of the handicapped from the positive approach of making him a self-supporting and self-efficient individual.

The American Society for the Hard of Hearing serves as a national information center on all problems related to the hard of hearing. It gives special attention to promoting adequate education of children who, because of defective hearing, have fallen below standard in their studies and in their social attitudes.

It stimulates scientific efforts in the prevention of deafness and the conservation of hearing. It works constantly to improve educational, economic, and social conditions among the hard of hearing—adults, young people, and children. It encourages the study of lip reading. It encourages the use of hearing aids and gives information as to what aids are reliable and useful.

It gives advice on vocations suitable for the hard of hearing. It encourages and promotes the formation of local chapters and gives guidance and advice to existing groups. It aims to spread over the country a great network of organized endeavor for the betterment of the hard of hearing.

It has a special department for the heard of hearing who live in small towns or rural sections and arranges for an interchange of letters on hobbies or mutual interests. This department is called the Everywhere League. It educates the public in the need of conservation of hearing, especially in children. It is constantly striving to make the world a better place for adults and children who are hard of hearing.[1]

While blindness affects a considerable number of children, almost one-half of the blind are over sixty years of age. This is another factor which adds to the social problem of planning for this group of handicapped. Many private schools exist in different parts of the country for the special instruction of this group. The Social Security Act of 1952 contained a provision for assisting by subsidy those states giving aid to their needy blind. Since the great majority of blind are over sixty years of age, the need for pensions is evident.

Most public school systems now make some provision for the educational and vocational training of the blind. The first system of printing devised for the blind was by means of raised letters; the Braille system, however, is easier as it uses raised dots. Industrial education is emphasized for this group. Not only is this necessary in order to make the blind as economically independent as possible, but it helps in their social adjustment. The use of guides, "seeing eye" dogs, has been developed in recent years. "Talking books" which are developed on records help to extend the horizon of these individuals. As well as those totally blind, many individuals have defective vision so that they are handicapped in their school or vocational activities. These persons also must be included in the program of rehabilitation.

National organizations from which information can be secured about care for the blind are the American Foundation for the Blind, the National Society for the Prevention of Blindness, and the Braille Institute of America. The National Society for the Prevention of Blindness[2] states its objects as follows:

1. To endeavor to ascertain, through study and investigation, any causes, whether direct or indirect, which may result in blindness or impaired vision.
2. To advocate measures which shall lead to the elimination of such causes.
3. To disseminate knowledge concerning all matters pertaining to the care and use of the eyes.

---

[1] Facts About the American Society for Hard of Hearing (pamphlet), 1537 Thirty-Fifth St., Washington, D. C.
[2] 1790 Broadway, New York, N. Y.

The National Society for the Prevention of Blindness has a public health nurse on its staff who will help individual nurses and groups with problems in the field and who will also aid in the development of community eye programs. The society also publishes many articles which may be obtained for very little cost by any nurse. (See Appendix for list of agencies.)

The proper care of the baby's eyes at birth is the first step in the prevention of blindess as the result of infection during birth. Discovery of any eye defect as early as possible is important. This means that every child should have periodic eye examinations and testing of vision. Adequate lighting in the home as well as the school is stressed. The protection of children from such accidents to the eyes as may result from the careless playing with sharp-pointed articles as scissors, sticks, arrows, pea-shooters, knives, toy guns, and pistols of all kinds is urged. The use of firecrackers is now being supervised in most communities so that injury to the eyes from their improper use should diminish.

Industries are now required to install various safety devices for the protection of their workers. Goggles must be worn by those doing work dangerous to the exposed eye. Flying metal or wood is particularly dangerous; so is subjection to great heat. Eye defects which may be associated with certain diseases, particularly the acute infections of childhood, may often be lessened or prevented altogether by adequate medical and nursing care during the convalescent period as well as during the acute stage. It is cheaper to try to prevent the defect from developing than to have to provide for it after it already has occurred.

Traditionally, the physically handicapped were looked upon as individuals who were lame, who had lost a limb and were handicapped and therefore not able to adjust economically and socially. It is recognized today that many chronic illnesses which contribute to the individual's loss of efficiency should be considered also. In addition to major physical handicaps, minor physical handicaps which reduce an individual's efficiency and well-being are being studied today. The results of examinations of selectees for World War II emphasized the need for a program to reduce preventable defects such as those resulting from communicable diseases and from the lack of inadequate medical or dental care. Communities are beginning to be aware of the economic loss to industry and society as a result of neglected physical handicaps and are eager to help the individual and his family. Much is being done by industry and by legal measures to prevent industrial hazards and accidents and thereby lower the number of accidents and physical disabilities in industry. Society has also become concerned with the reeducation of the individual and with the prevention of economic and emotional dependency as well as the prevention of anti-social behavior in these individuals.

When any handicap is present, every resource should be utilized to assure as complete medical diagnosis and treatment as possible. Under modern medicine, many conditions can be cured and many others can be prevented from further developing. Teamwork in the adequate utilization of all community resources for this group is essential.

REHABILITATION

The Council on Physical Medicine and Rehabilitation has defined rehabilitation as the process of attempting to improve the health of handicapped people and returning them as useful members to society at the earliest possible moment. The dynamic approach to rehabilitation in civilian life emphasizes this need in all hospitals, health centers, and communities. It is necessary not only in situations where gross physical defects are evident, but in chronic illness, and it has become a vital factor in all convalescence. Many hospitals today are recognizing their community responsibilities in this phase of restorative medicine and have established rehabilitation and physical therapy departments as important units in their institutions. The potentialities of rehabilitative work are illustrated dramatically by statistics from the Office of Vocation Rehabilitation. In a recent survey[3] of over 43,000 persons undergoing vocational rehabilitation under this agency, 22 per cent had never been gainfully employed and nearly 90 per cent were not employed at the time they started their rehabilitation. The average annual wage of the entire group before rehabilitation was $148. After rehabilitation the annual average wage of the group increased to $1,768. Before rehabilitation the majority of these persons depended upon public assistance, not only for themselves, but for their families. The annual cost of this assistance to the community was from $300 to $500 per case. The total cost of rehabilitation averaged only $300 per case. In

---

[3]Federal Security Agency, Office of Vocational Rehabilitation, Washington 25, D. C.

every community better results will be obtained if all agencies interested in and planning for rehabilitation work together in integrating their services for the benefit of the total community.

VOCATIONAL REHABILITATION

Vocational rehabilitation is concerned with developing and conserving the working usefulness of individuals. In our country it is available to all disabled persons and it is estimated there are at least 1,500,000 men and women disabled through accident or illness to such an extent that their disabilities constitute job handicaps. In addition there are many hundreds of thousands of individuals with arthritis, cardiovascular disease, tuberculosis and hemiplegia who are not in the industrial world, but who can be helped to lead much more satisfactory lives if they are made more self-sufficient. This is in part true as far as handicapped women are concerned. Many disabled housewives are being restored to greater efficiency and emotional satisfaction for themselves and their families by the application of modern rehabilitation; for example, a booklet published by the Institute of Physical Medicine and Rehabilitation of the New York University Bellevue Medical Center called "Treatment for the Disabled Housewife" includes principles of work simplification in household operations and self-help devices. Details are included about how the home can be rearranged and rather simple appliances used which make all the difference between self-efficiency and dependency.

The Baruch Committee on Physical Medicine was established in 1943 for the advancement of the science of physical medicine. The original committee made the following recommendations regarding the chief needs in this field: (1) an adequate supply of physicians who can teach and use physical medicine; (2) more extensive basic and clinical research in physical medicine; (3) the proper use of physical medicine in relation to wartime rehabilitation and peacetime physical preparedness. Recognizing that much has been learned during the war, this committee felt that these war experiences should be translated into civilian application. Since then, this committee has been concerned with community plans and surveys, facilities, personnel, and problems and the basic needs of the community in this area. Many other privately supported agencies and medical centers are now concerned with the problem of rehabilitation. A few of these are The Children's Aid Society, The National Foundation for Infantile Paralysis,

The American Heart Association, American Arthritis Association, The Association of Amputees, Public Health Nursing Services, Tuberculosis and Health Association, the American Legion, and the Veterans of Foreign Wars.

Because of the long-term needs of these patients, public funds have been necessary and in this country there has been a program for the rehabilitation of the physically handicapped since the passing of the Vocational Act of 1920. This was under the state boards of vocational education and was financed by grants-in-aids to states. This law had limitations which prevented it from meeting the needs of all handicapped individuals. There was no provision for medical treatment, no special services for the blind were included. Federal funds could not be used for maintenance during rehabilitation, and the mentally or emotionally handicapped were not included. The services were limited really to vocational counseling, vocational training, and placement of the handicapped. Rehabilitation must be more than physical; the deeper problems of adjustment must be solved. In this program no single organization or agency, either public or private, can offer all of the services needed. The trend is toward integration and coordination of all community agencies that can contribute to the program.

Passage of the Barden-LaFollette Act (Public Law 113; 78th Congress) in July, 1943, authorized and expanded the program of vocational rehabilitation. This law authorizes federal aid to enable state boards of vocational education and state agencies for the blind to give disabled individuals all the services necessary for their rehabilitation. These include: medical diagnosis and treatment, hospitalization, nursing care, physical and occupational therapy, prosthetic appliances, vocational counseling and training, maintenance during training, occupational tools and equipment, placement in employment, and follow-up. The program also includes the mentally as well as the phyically disabled. Except for certain types of war disabled veterans, individuals receiving restorative services must be in financial need. The rehabilitation of veterans with service-connected disabilities is under the Veterans Administration. The central idea of these laws for both civilians and veterans is that any vocationally handicapped person should be enabled to enter productive work if at all possible. An attempt has been made to provide all necessary steps.

The state and federal program of vocational rehabilitation is a public service and is considered an essential responsibility of communities. The following services are provided under the Vocational Act:

1. Medical examination in every case to determine the extent of disability, to discover possible hidden, or "secondary," disabilities, to determine work capacity and to help determine eligibility—at no cost to the individual.
2. Individual counsel and guidance in every case to help the disabled person to select and attain the right job objective—at no cost to the individual.
3. Medical, surgical, psychiatric, and hospital care, as needed, to remove or reduce the disability—public funds may be used to meet these costs to the extent that the disabled person is unable to pay for them from his own funds.
4. Artificial appliances such as limbs, hearing aids, trusses, braces, and the like, to increase work ability—these also may be paid for from public funds to the degree that the individual cannot meet the cost.
5. Training for the right job in schools, colleges or universities, on-the-job, in-the-plant, by tutor, through correspondence courses, or otherwise, to enable the individual to do the right job well—at no cost to the disabled person.
6. Maintenance and transportation for the disabled person, if necessary, while he or she is undergoing treatment or training—these expenses may be met from public funds, depending on the person's financial inability to take care of them.
7. Occupational tools, equipment, and licenses, as necessary, to give the disabled person a fair start—these may be paid for from public funds to the extent that the person is unable to do so.
8. Placement on the right job, one within the disabled person's physical or mental capacities and one for which he has been thoroughly prepared—at no cost to the individual.
9. Follow-up after placement to make sure the disabled person and his employer are satisfied with one another—at no cost to either party.

CONCLUSION

Every health worker should be familiar with resources available in her community for the physically handicapped. As stated above, programs may be carried on by private agencies, or by public authorities. Many public school systems are vital agencies in the educational and vocational aspects of rehabilitation. Rehabilitation of any individual covers nine integral factors of which all or part may be required for successful adjustment:

1. Early location of persons in need of rehabilitation to prevent the disintegrating effects of idleness and hopelessness.
2. Medical diagnosis and prognosis, coupled with a vocational diagnosis as the basis for determining an appropriate plan for the individual.
3. Vocational counseling to select suitable fields of work, by relating occupational capacities to job requirements and community occupational opportunities.
4. Medical and surgical treatment to afford physical restoration and medical advice in the type of training to be given and in the work tolerance of the individual.
5. Physical and occupational therapy and psychiatric treatment as a part of medical treatment where needed.
6. Vocational training to furnish new skills where physical impairments incapacitate for normal occupations, or where skills become obsolete due to changing industrial needs.
7. Financial assistance to provide maintenance and transportation during training.
8. Placement in employment to afford the best use of abilities and skills in accordance with the individual's physical condition and temperament, with due regard to safeguarding against further injuries.
9. Follow-up on performance in employment to afford adjustments that may be necessary, to provide further medical care if needed, to supplement training if desired.

STUDY QUESTIONS AND PROJECTS

1. What types of conditions are usually considered in the broad category of the "physically handicapped"?
2. What types of physical handicaps are most common in different age groups? Because of this, what different problems are presented?
3. What provisions in the Social Security Act are found for the physically handicapped?
4. Find all the resources in your community for the physically handicapped. Note which are governmental and which are voluntary. For what conditions are the resources more adequate? Why?
5. What is a modern definition of rehabilitation?
6. Discuss the importance of rehabilitation for all types of patients with physical handicaps.

REFERENCES

A Bibliography on Employment of the Physically Handicapped, The National Society for Crippled Children and Adults, Inc., 11 South LaSalle Street, Chicago 3, Illinois.

Barton, P. N.: Adjusting the Handicapped Worker to the Job Situation, Journal of Rehabilitation **15**:20, 1949.

Bond, J. H.: Rehabilitation—American Style, Journal of Rehabilitation **16**:17, 1950.

Buchwald, Edith: Physical Rehabilitation for Daily Living, New York, McGraw-Hill Book Company, Inc.

Burling, T.: The Vocational Rehabilitation of the Mentally Handicapped, American Journal of Orthopsychiatry **20**:202, 1950.

Cooley, Carol H.: Social Aspects of Illness, Philadelphia, 1951, W. B. Saunders Company.

Davis, J. E.: Rehabilitation, Its Principles and Practice, Revised and Enlarged Edition, New York, A. S. Barnes, 1946.

Deaver, G. G.: Rehabilitation of the Hemiplegic Patient, Journal of the Association for Physical and Mental Rehabilitation **4**:9-12, December 1950-January 1951.

Dening, K. A. and others; Ambulation, Physical Rehabilitation for Crutch Walkers, New York, 1951, Funk and Wagnalls Company

Eisert, Otto: Rehabilitation of the Chronic Medically Ill, Journal of Association for Physical and Mental Rehabilitation **3**:15-20, August, 1949.

Elton, F. C.: Personality Factors in Vocational Rehabilitation, Mental Hygiene **34**:373, 1950.

Kessler, H. H.: The Principles and Practices of Rehabilitation, Philadelphia, 1950, Lea and Febiger.

Kessler, Harry, and Abramson, A. S.: The Rehabilitation of the Paraplegic, Journal of Association for Physical and Mental Rehabilitation **4**:8-12, April-May, 1950.

Krusen, F. H.: The Scope and Future of Physical Medicine and Rehabilitation, Journal of American Medical Association, **144**:727-730, October 28, 1950.

Manson, M. P.: The Dynamics of Rehabilitation, Journal of the Association for Physical and Mental Rehabilitation **4**:12-15 February-March, 1951.

Marks, Morton, and Hoerner, Earl F.: Rehabilitation, Progress in Neurology and Psychiatry, Vol. VI, 1951, chapter 34.

Neuschutz, Louise M.: The Rehabilitation of the Hard of Hearing Adult, American Journal of Nursing **44**:1055, 1944.

Porter, E. B.: What Is Rehabilitation? Journal of Rehabilitation, **16**:3, 1950.

Rusk, Howard A.: Rehabilitation, Handbook of Physical Medicine and Rehabilitation, Philadelphia, 1950, The Blakiston Company.

Rusk, Howard A.: New Program Provides Aid for the Physically Handicapped, Journal of the Association for Physical and Mental Rehabilitation **3**:9, August, 1949.

Rusk, Howard A.: Rehabilitation: The Third Phase of Medicine, Archives of Industrial Hygiene and Occupational Medicine **1**:411, 1950.

Rusk, Howard A., and Taylor, Eugene J.: New Hope for the Handicapped, New York, 1949, Harper & Brothers.

Shands, A. R., Jr.: Diagnostic Clinics for Rehabilitation, Journal of the American Medical Association **140**:937-940, July 16, 1949.

Treister, B. A.: Physical Medicine and Rehabilitation in Geriatrics, Physical Therapy Review **30**:411-415, October, 1950.

U. S. Veterans Administration, Rehabilitation of the Chronic Neurologic Patient, Washington, D. C., Government Printing Office, 1949, Pamphlet 10-29.

U. S. Veterans Administration: A New Approach to the Rehabilitation of the Blind at the Veterans Administration Hospital, Hines, Illinois, Government Printing Office, Washington D. C., 1950, Pamphlet 10-32.

Van Schoick, J. H.: Motivating the Patient in Physical Medicine and Rehabilitation, Journal of Rehabilitation **14**:14-16, June, 1948.

Van Schoick, J. H.: Their Hospital Time Can Be Learning Time: Teacher Turns Therapist, Journal of Rehabilitation **15**:11-15 February, 1949.

Vocational Rehabilitation, Federal Security Agency, Washington 25, D. C., pamphlets and reports are available.

Wilbur, R. A., and Krusen, Frank H., and Others: The Baruch Committee of Physical Medicine, Report on "A Community Rehabilitation Service and Center," New York.

Yearbook of Physical Medicine and Rehabilitation, 1949, edited by F. H. Krusen, Howard A. Rusk, and others, Chicago, 1950, Year Book Publishers.

CHAPTER 16

MATERNAL WELFARE

INTRODUCTION

The family is the central unit in our culture and the presence or absence of children has a great deal to do with the stability of the family and with its strength. The coming of children and the position of the mother has always had special significance in any culture and is surrounded by traditions and habits of the individual family and of the community. Environmental factors have a great deal to do with the welfare of both mother and child. All workers in this field must be sensitive to the attitudes and ideas about pregnancy, child-bearing and child-rearing which are prevalent in the community. They must also be aware of the psychological, emotional and physical factors which influence the behavior and attitude of the prospective parents and which may affect the welfare of the mother and child.

In few other areas of medicine have such advances been observed as in the reduction of maternal and infant mortality. This reduction is due, in part, to development in medical science, to advances in the field of public health in making the physical environment safer, and to the general rise in our standard of living, including better housing, better nutrition, better health protection for a large group of the population. The inter-relationship between poverty and illness often pointed out is, of course, evident here and it is obvious that the financial status of the family will determine its ability to obtain necessary food, clothing, housing, recreation, and medical care.

In addition, of course, one must consider the intelligence of the family and its willingness to avail itself of services that are available. Various studies made recently show that women in the lowest economic group, or those who are on relief, women living in rural areas, and multiparous women are among those who do not always receive adequate prenatal care. Difficulties and accidents during delivery and the post-partum period are also found most frequently among these groups. It is evident also that the general health standards of the community will be reflected in the care given to all pregnant women. While women in the lowest income groups have not yet fully benefited from advances in this field, the over-all picture in this country is very good. The maternal mortality rate has dropped to under 10 per 10,000 nationally and in some sections of the country it is even less than 5 per 10,000 live births. Many authorities point out that safe maternity is the result of the increasing utilization of hospital facilities and the services of the physician at childbirth. In 1935 only 37 per cent of the births were delivered in the hospital, but by 1949 the figure had risen to 87 per cent. At the same time the number of women attended by a midwife dropped from 13 per cent to 5 per cent.

During and since World War II, motherhood has enjoyed much greater popularity than in the depression of the 1930's. Record-breaking birth rates since the late 1930's has continued. It is significant that about three-fifths of the births in this country are to women in their twenties. Doctors have always pointed out the great advantage to both mother and child when the mothers are in their late teens or twenties. It is interesting to note that recent figures from the Bureau of the Census show that women in urban areas have in the last decade shown greater increase in fertility than farm wives, and for the first time in about four decades enough births are taking place in cities to maintain the urban population without relying on migration from the country. Favorable economic conditions in this country since the early 1940's have also had an influence in early marriage and larger families. Almost the same unsatisfactory social conditions react on this maternal picture as with other community health problems, namely, unsatisfactory economic and social conditions including inertia, ignorance or carelessness on the part of the woman and her family, lack of adequate funds for proper care, lack of adequate facilities and trained personnel in the community. The most frequent serious complications of pregnancy are infections, toxemias, hemmorrhages, and injuries, and, for most of these, medical science has knowledge relative to their causation, prevention, and treatment if adequate instruction and care can be given at the appropriate time.

Abortions cause many maternal deaths, and it is pointed out that these are often the result of social and emotional situations. The de-

tails of ante-partum and post-partum care and delivery, as well as patho-
logical conditions, of course, will not be presented here. The student
is referred to standard books in this clinical area.

EMOTIONAL CONSIDERATIONS

The health worker in any obstetrical situation should study the
individual family in regard to the children, the position of the parents,
the traditions and customs surrounding motherhood and pregnancy.
Pregnancy places a physiological strain on the individual and it may
place an economic and emotional strain on the family as a whole or on
certain members. Pregnancy and childbirth are often referred to as
normal processes. They are normal processes, but many normal processes have certain strains accompanying them. Some individuals are
better able to meet these strains than others. From a physiological
point of view the pregnant woman may have certain health conditions,
such as tuberculosis, diabetes, heart disease, which will mean that special
precaution should be taken during a pregnancy. In these instances it
is particularly important that adequate medical supervision be given
during the entire pregnancy, delivery, and post-partum period.

If any special disease situation exists, so that the physiological strain
will be greater, the emotional stresses during pregnancy may also
be increased due to fears, insecurities, and uncertainties as to the
outcome or the health of the mother and the child. In such cases both
of the parents should be able to get great support from professional
health workers and should be encouraged to follow all instructions
completely.

It has often been pointed out that the culture in which the prospective mother has been reared, her attachment to her own mother, the
relationship between her and her husband, may serve as constructive
and healthful environments during the pregnancy. The woman who
is emotionally immature may suffer during the pregnancy because of
her fears that she will not be able to fill this new role satisfactorily,
and it may increase her dependence either on her own mother or on her
husband. It has been pointed out that many of the emotional problems
developing during pregnancy and the post-partum period are the result of poor relationship between the young mother and her own parents. These emotional situations, if it is not possible to reduce them,
may be carried over into poor relationship between the mother and her
new child. Such emotional conflicts and poor relationships will, of

course, be accentuated in the unmarried mother. The attitudes of society to unmarried mothers will be reflected in the attitude of the individual patient. Sharing of responsibilities for the new baby by other members of the family is essential and modern approach to pregnancy includes the prospective father and gives him a much more prominent place than was so until recently. When the father is brought into proper position in the total parental situation, rivalries between father and children for the mother's affection are less likely to develop.

Acute emotional crises may develop if there is an accident during delivery, if the child dies during or soon after birth, or if the child is not normal. In the latter instance, many parents experience a sense of guilt feeling that they are being punished for some real or imagined sins in the child's defect.

For most normal women, stillbirth or the death of the newborn child arouses a feeling of futility and frustration. It is very important in these situations that emotional support be given to the parents and particularly to the mother. There may be disappointment in the sex of the child; however, with proper prenatal preparation for the child, most intelligent parents do not experience too great disappointment. In helping parents plan for the baby, it is very unwise to encourage special planning for one sex or the other or to carry on conversations about the anticipated baby as if it were already known that it were a boy or a girl.

The role and status of the grandparents and other family members must be considered in the whole emotional picture. In many urban families today, young couples are alone, often without even very close friends. For this reason it is very important that health workers, particularly nurses and social workers, give time when visiting pregnant women in their homes or in the clinic so that patients particularly those anticipating the first child have someone to whom they can talk and with whom they can discuss their problems, their fears, and anticipations.

THE ROOMING-IN PLAN

The great decline in maternal mortality has been attributed to better obstetrical practice and particularly to the fact that more deliveries have taken place in the hospital than in the home. The rapid development of specialization in all health fields has resulted in certain institutional practices. In the obstetrical field, the separation of mothers

and babies and the keeping of the father away from any contact with
his child is an accustomed situation in our modern hospital system.
It is being pointed out that this is an unnatural fragmentation of the
family during one of its important critical periods. For the last twenty
years, the coming together of experts from the fields of obstetrics,
pediatrics, psychiatry, psychology, and sociology to discuss common
problems have brought out many interesting points about the importance of early experiences in the child's life and the significance of
the different emotional stages in every child's development. One result of some of this thinking has been the development of "rooming-in"
in maternity departments. By "rooming-in" is meant the arrangement
where the mother and her baby are cared for in the same room or
cubicle. It implies and should include something beyond physical
facility, that is, it signifies a different attitude in maternal and infant
care based upon the recognition of mother and child as a unit. Rooming-in was started about 1940 in this country and since 1946 has been
developed in many obstetrical departments and hospitals.

The over-all prophylactic and psychological objectives of this arrangement have been stated as follows :[1]

1. To promote the natural, biological relationship between the
   mother and her newly born infant and to defer the independence of one from the other until there is evidence of
   biological readiness. This might be very simply stated in
   terms of the mutual comfort of mother and infant.
2. To provide facilities in the hospital for meeting promptly
   the infant's and mother's obvious needs. Promptness is
   more important for the infant, who is helpless and cannot
   understand reasons for delay. But none the less the mother's positive response and devotion to her infant is promoted
   by the genuine and timely help accorded her. This flex-
   ibility in schedule, otherwise known as "ad lib" or "self-
   demand," is appropriate for both breast-fed and artificially
   fed infants.
3. To offer natural stimulus and appropriate help to mothers
   who wish to breast-feed their babies.
4. To allay anxiety of the mother who in the absence of her
   baby worries about what is happening to him.
5. To provide opportunity for the mother, before she goes
   home from the hospital, to observe and learn her baby's

---

[1]From Family Centered Maternity and Infant Care, Supplement 1 to Problems of
Infancy and Childhood, Transactions, Fourth Conference, 1950, Josiah Macy, Jr.
Foundation, New York City.

reactions, to learn how to take care of him, and to have instruction in changes to be expected in the forthcoming weeks. This goes far in preventing such fear and anxieties as are reported by mothers who have gone home without close knowledge of their babies or experience in handling them.

6. To develop a maternal response by offering the mother appropriate occupation during the lying-in period; by providing opportunity to develop trust in her own observation, feelings, and judgment; conversely, to decrease situations which encourage mothers to feel sorry for themselves like helpless children under authoritarian control.

7. To provide opportunity for the father to share acquaintanceship of their newborn child with his wife and to learn the essentials in taking care of the baby. This starts the new members of the family under cooperative supervision, allays the father's feelings of exclusion, rejection, and jealousy, and is a positive help to the mother in assuming her responsibilities on returning home from the hospital. (The wholehearted participation of fathers in rooming-in projects is breaking down the tradition that it is unmanly for a father to participate in the care of his infant.)

8. To restore in some degree continuity of medical supervision for the mother throughout pregnancy, labor, puerperium, and postnatally at home. Continuity is important for the mother's feelings of confidence. It was lost in part with the development of specialization. A substitute for continuity may be achieved through close inter-departmental association and consultation of the professional staffs responsible for maternal and infant care, both in and out of the hospital. The ideals of a program that embraces maternal, infant, and family welfare convey a sense of continuity when they are consistently represented by all attending nurses, obstetricians, and pediatricians and when collaboration between these groups and individuals is genuine and apparent. Some actual extension in continuity of care is being variously achieved through prenatal interviews of mothers with the same pediatricians who will subsequently look after the baby in the hospital, at home, or in well baby conferences, as well as through parents' classes (community, clinic, and private) in the conduction of which hospital-staff obstetricians, pediatricians, child-psychiatrists, and nurses are collaborating, and so forth. The aim of a collaborating continuum of maternity services is to offer parents a beneficient and consistent consultative service and to avoid their exposure to the bewilderment of contradictory, authoritarian advice.

Some nurses may resist this development in maternal care since it interferes with accepted patterns of hospital routines. However, it must be emphasized that the professional nurse has a much greater responsibility to her patient and her family than that of giving technical and personal services. In few fields are the interpersonal relationships so necessary as in the obstetrical area.

MATERNITY AND WORKING WOMEN

The protection for pregnant women who are working outside the home has increased in significance as the number of married women has increased. It is pointed out that more than one-half of the women in the labor force are married. With the high marriage rate and high birth rate, problems relating to the employment of pregnant women and maternity benefits are a concern to the community in general and to industry in particular. In the United States, according to the report of the Women's Bureau Bulletin No. 240, 1952, the only national legislation giving industry-wide benefits to pregnant employees is a 1946 amendment to the Federal Railroad Unemployment Insurance Act that provides insurance for sickness and specifically includes pregnancy and maternity disabilities. In about one-half of the states, pregnancy disqualifies a woman from unemployment insurance. It is interesting to note that maternity protection in this country has not been achieved through legislation but through private industry and organized labor. Many union contracts provide for maternity leaves of absence usually for one year with job security and seniority retained. Industrial insurance plans, including maternity benefits, have been increasing. Maternity benefits usually include weekly cash payments to compensate for some of the loss of income during pregnancy, hospitalization, and delivery. In most instances the weekly cash benefits are for six weeks and the amounts paid have some relation to earnings varying from $20 to $26 per week. Many types of commercial insurance and hospital prepayment plans such as Blue Cross and the Blue Shield are now available, but in most plans there is a period of at least nine months before one is eligible for maternity benefits. Such minimum standards as those recommended by the Children's Bureau and the Women's Bureau in 1942, namely that women should not work for six weeks before or two months after delivery are not recognized by any of the states in their laws governing the employment of women. In addition to group health insurance plans under insurance companies and nonprofit organizations, such as the Blue Cross and the Blue Shield, a great many local and independent group plans have been organized throughout the country. These operate through medical societies, others through community groups, cooperative or consumer's units. More and more of these are including maternity benefits. Maternity leave is also a part of personnel policies in some professions and industry. On maternity leave, women have the right to take a voluntary leave of absence during pregnancy and maintain job security and seniority.

Since there are an increasing number of married women teachers, policies for maternity leave have been worked out in many communities. The Women's Bureau shows that in cities of more than 100,000 population, maternity leave was granted by approximately 90 per cent of public school systems. There was great variety in duration of leave from a few expecting their employees to leave as soon as they become aware of their pregnancy to other situations where teachers would not need to leave before the sixth month of pregnancy.

Since the number of married women on the labor force is likely to continue at a high level, industry and the community in general are studying the situation of the pregnant woman in industry and are trying to make constructive adjustments.

COMMUNITY PLANS AND PROGRAMS

Since the welfare of mother and child is of great concern to the community, it is reasonable to find that both public and private agencies contribute in this field. There are laws covering maternity hospitals and homes, and in most communities individuals support these laws and are interested in raising the standards. The knowledge of what is sometimes called the abortion racket is of great concern to any enlightened community, and since these family situations are often related to the total organization or disorganization in any community and are often directly related to the existence of rackets, communities are interested in eliminating these situations if they exist.

It is very important for the health worker to be familiar with adoption laws in the community. She should know where she can go for information when such a question comes up. (See Chapter 19.) The Children's Bureau has constantly worked to improve conditions for pregnant women and for children in this country. The provisions of the Social Security Act and appropriations made under it to state and local communities have definitely improved maternity care in many areas. Every community should have sources available to women in all economic levels so that the security of knowing that adequate care can be obtained is provided for every pregnant woman and that when her baby is born she can, without fear or financial insecurity, take that child to well-baby clinics and get adequate help and advice. In addition to publicly supported projects and institutions, many privately supported hospitals and clinics have programs and plans for these patients.

STUDY QUESTIONS AND PROJECTS

1. What changing family patterns have contributed different needs for the prenatal and postnatal patient today?
2. Show how the status and role of the modern women in the family and the community may create stresses during this period?
3. Is the "rooming-in plan" used in your community? What are its benefits and what are its disadvantages?
4. If the number of married women in the labor force remains the same as today or increases in the future, what adjustments would you suggest should be made by (a) industry; (b) the community in housekeeping facilities, nurseries, facilities for evening shopping, etc.?
5. Present a patient, showing an adverse emotional reaction to the pregnancy. How might it have been prevented? How was the situation treated?

REFERENCES

Aldrich, C. Anderson, and Aldrich, Mary M.: Babies Are Human Beings, New York, 1941, The Macmillan Company.

Baby's Book: Metropolitan Life Insurance Company, New York.

Carson, Ruth: Having A Baby, Public Affairs Pamphlet No. 178, 1952.

Cooley, Carol H.: Social Aspects of Illness, Philadelphia, 1951, W. B. Saunders Company.

Eastman, Nicholson J.: Expectant Motherhood, Boston, 1947, Little, Brown and Company.

Goodrich, Frederick W., Jr.: Natural Childbirth, New York, 1950, Prentice-Hall.

National Education Association, American Association of School Administrators and Research Division. Maternity-leave Provisions in 157 School Systems in Cities over 30,000 in population. Educational Research Service, Circular No. 6, Washington, D. C., The Association, August 1948.

Prenatal Care, Federal Security Agency, Children's Bureau, Publication No. 4, Washington, D. C., 1949.

Preparing for Parenthood, New York, January 1952, Metropolitan Life Insurance Company.

Upham, Frances: A Dynamic Approach to Illness, New York, 1949, Family Service Association of America.

CHAPTER 17

MENTAL ILLNESS

INTRODUCTION

As with problems of physical health, those working with the mentally ill today prefer to view the problem positively, in terms of mental health indicated by a state of good emotional adjustment in the individual. Conversely variations from this will be indications of mental ill health, although never can a fixed line be drawn separating the mentally healthy from the mentally ill. Many degrees of mental health are seen in those who surround us and inhabit our communities. The National Association for Mental Health has been endeavoring to make this emphasis clear, pointing out that the healthy personality is one who feels secure and comfortable in all situations, is able to get along satisfactorily with family, friends, school, fellow employees, community associates, and who is able to cope with most of the demands of everyday life without becoming upset or nervous. When a person is unable to function effectively, he can be helped first at a mental hygiene clinic, even as the health clinic aids many not up to par physically. But, when the factors of personal disorganization have been operating so that a person is out of touch with the world about him, a potential danger to others, and a loss to himself, he must be hospitalized for treatment. As with physical ailments, the treatment may be effective so that the individual returns to the community, his family, and his employment, or he may need a period of readjustment, or he may need custodial care for a long and extended period of time.

Mentally ill persons must be distinguished from mentally deficient persons. The latter, discussed under problems of children, comprise persons who from birth or early infancy never develop intellectual capacity of what might be called normal caliber. Their treatment is one of habit training and making the most of the intelligence which they have. It is not the problem of restoring an individual to a mentally healthy state. The epileptic is often considered a mentally ill person, although this, too, is a misclassification. Epilepsy is a recognized disease characterized by seizures and convulsions. Because epilepsy has been associated with difficult personality development, classification of epilepsy with either mental illness or mental deficiency has wrongly been made and perpetuated in the facilities available for epileptics.

MEANING OF MENTAL ILLNESS

Great progress has taken place through the years in community understanding of and attitude toward mental illness. In the early days, and in some primitive cultures, the acutely mentally ill person was regarded as possessed by demons or evil spirits, occasionally as endowed with special supernatural powers for good as well as evil. Many of those persecuted as witches during the sixteenth and seventeenth centuries were mentally ill. Subsequent to the witchcraft era, those dealing with the mentally ill were at a loss as to what measures to take, so that in the eighteenth and nineteenth centuries many deranged persons were confined in jails or almshouses, in chains and under the worst possible conditions. These persons were regarded as "lunatics" or "insane," legal terms to facilitate identification and incarceration. Because of the association of the mentally ill with jails, because of much misinformation as to the hereditary nature of the illness, the mentally ill person has been regarded as tainted, as someone to be ashamed of and shunned, as though the illness were sinfully acquired.

Progress has been made during the last 100 years in securing better treatment for the mentally ill, in recognizing and classifying mental illness, in identifying early stages of mental breakdown, and in an ability to face this as a problem which can be handled and cured, not hidden away. Education is still required so that the husband, wife, child, parent no longer feel embarrassed to mention mental illness and so that they and other members of the community at large may be familiar with community resources which may prove helpful. Most persons seem to know of mental hospitals for treatment, that many people go in and return having been helped. More effort and more help from community people are needed in aiding those who have been ill to readjust in the community, which is more difficult for them than in the protected environment of the institution.

A person with a healthy personality, emotionally secure, well-adjusted, can be recognized. The case of acute mental illness in which the individual is completely removed from reality and unable to respond to the demands of everyday life, perhaps even openly hostile and threatening to persons in his environment, can be identified, too. But between these two extremes are many degrees of personalities with almost good adjustment, marked peculiarities, behavior disorders, psychoneurotics. The term "psychotic" covers most of the cases of severe disturbance such that the person is completely divorced from reality, usually needs to be institutionalized. These persons undergo a complete personality change which may take the form of a delusionary system, a feeling of persecution, utter depression. Roughly speaking, the psychoses stem from two causes, the organic, in which damage to the brain or central nervous system is evident, and the functional in which no organic damage can be found. Further research may modify these conclusions. So far as medical knowledge now goes, causes for functional psychoses have to be sought in the early life patterns of the individuals, material that has been repressed, hostility that has lain latent, relationships to family and community, the culture pattern in which reared. Many psychoneurotics need hospitalization and represent serious situations, also without an observable physical cause, although characterized by excess anxiety and many symptoms of unrest. Large numbers of persons are neurotic, worrying and anxious about many things, but still they are able to go about their regular business and routines. Still more persons exhibit varied symptoms of instability, they may be excessively dependent, indecisive, over-meticulous. Many people live happy and useful lives despite evidences of personality difficulties. Some may suffer temporary breakdowns. Perhaps more persons could be happier and more productive if some help were given them in time.

EXTENT OF MENTAL ILLNESS IN THE UNITED STATES

Mental illness is becoming a major social problem. The number of mentally ill who can be identified and diagnosed has been increasing. The increase of the mentally ill hospitalized has been likewise great, taxing the existing facilities to the utmost, costing millions of dollars to the taxpayers each year. Some of the familiar statistics have been frequently quoted:

Out of every twenty-two living persons, one will spend part of his life in a mental hospital. Recent studies indicate that one out of every ten persons in the United States is emotionally or mentally maladjusted and needs treatment for some personality disorder. More than half the patients who visit their family doctor for some physical ailment are really suffering from some type of emotional disorder. Nervous and mental diseases take a larger toll than do cancer, infantile paralysis, and tuberculosis combined.[1]

More recently, Dr. Paul Lemkau has stated:

> The mental illnesses produce greater morbidity than all other classifications of illness with the exception of the arthritides. Mental hospital patients spend almost a hundred times as many days in hospitals as do patients in general hospitals.[2]

Because many mentally ill persons go undetected and, therefore, cannot be counted, only the statistics of the mentally ill in hospitals furnish an impression of the magnitude of the problem.

The U. S. Public Health Service, which compiles these figures, points out that mentally ill persons are institutionalized in a variety of hospitals, those giving prolonged care, and those giving shorter or temporary care including psychopathic hospitals and psychiatric facilities of general hospitals. The so-called temporary care hospitals are for diagnosis and observation, and stress research. Patients needing prolonged care are transferred subsequently to institutions providing this type of treatment. Hospitals vary, too, in the auspices maintaining them. The vast majority of mental hospitals in the United States today are supported by taxes appropriated by state legislatures. Many of these have been severely under fire for the low standards of care meted out to the patient, the poor quality of the personnel, and absence of adequate treatment facilities. Other sources of support are the federal government which maintains a national mental health institute, some county and municipalities, and private doctors or corporations.

During the decade 1940 to 1949, the last year for which data are available, the resident population in mental hospitals increased from 480,637 to 564,160, an increase of 17.4 per cent. When related to the population, this increase was only 5 per cent. The number of admissions, however, increased in number 68.6 per cent during the decade,

---

[1]Thorman, George: Toward Mental Health, Public Affairs Pamphlet, No. 120, 1948, page 22.

[2]Lemkau, Paul V.: Toward Mental Health: Areas that Promise Progress, Mental Hygiene 36:198, April, 1952.

but the ratio of admissions to population increased only 50 per cent.[3] These figures speak eloquently of the problem of mental illness today.

The increase in number of persons admitted to mental hospitals during the past decade is caused in part by increase in veterans admitted to Veterans Hospitals. Neuropsychiatric casualties were heavy in combat divisions during the last war, many of whom have had to be hospitalized. Private hospitals have also expanded, and, on all sides, greater recognition exists of the need for treatment of mental illness when discovered. During this decade, discharge rates have also risen 97 per cent in actual numbers and 62.6 per cent when related to the hospital population.[4] Figures regarding discharges show the greatest number discharged from private and veterans facilities where more treatment is available and where patients are sent for shorter periods of time. Patients needing prolonged care are found in greater numbers in state hospitals. Frequently, too, because of the expense of care, patients who do not respond to treatment in a private hospital or whose prognosis is unfavorable are referred to state hospitals for custodial care.

The costs of maintaining our public institutions for the mentally ill have steadily risen. According to the United States Public Health Service, the total expenditures of all state hospitals reached $405,107,901 in 1949, a per capita expenditure per patient of $720. The costs per patient in the psychopathic and private hospital is higher. The per capita expenditure in 1949 for eight psychopathic hospitals was $5,104.[5]

States vary considerably in the amounts which are appropriated for mental hospitals and range from a low per capita expenditure in 1949 in Tennessee of $319 to a high in the District of Columbia of $1,454. States having high rates of care include Wisconsin, Michigan, and New York. Other low rates are found in the states of Kentucky, Georgia, West Virginia, and Mississippi.

NEEDS AND RESOURCES OF MENTAL HOSPITALS

Why are persons institutionalized in mental hospitals? In general, there are two reasons for this, one stemming from the needs of protecting the community from the disturbed member, and the other from the desire to restore the patient to a fruitful life by treatment not available through the community facilities. In retrospect the former

---

[3] Patients in Mental Institutions, 1949, Federal Security Agency, Public Health Service, 1952.

[4] Ibid., page 13.

[5] Ibid., page 65.

reason undoubtedly was the major influence. When the need was first felt to remove the, then called, "lunatics" from the community, jails and lockups were used, the afflicted individuals being incarcerated there. Treatment was not attempted and was not considered. Cures, if they resulted, were unexplained, perhaps some sort of shock treatment brought on by the savage environment in which the person was forced. That courageous pioneer in the field of mental hospitals, Dorothea Lynde Dix, was one of the first to recognize and demand that the mentally ill be treated as human beings which they were, and not as animals and law breakers which assuredly they were not. The mentally ill owe a great debt to this tireless worker in their behalf, responsible for stimulating many state and private hospitals for the mentally ill.

For many years the process by which a mentally ill person is admitted to the hospital has been a rather painful one as has been pointed out by one writer on this subject; getting treatment for a patient in a mental hospital ought to be as easy as getting treatment for a patient in a general hospital, but it is not.[6] Even now the majority of patients in the mental institutions are there by commitment by the local court, a tribunal, or a body of county commissioners. Examination by one or more doctors is essential. In the majority of states, however, persons may also be voluntarily admitted for either observation or for treatment. Provisions for study of the patient after admission and planning for treatment and final discharge are accepted procedure although varying widely throughout the states in the degree of skill with which they are carried out.

Within the hospital, however, developing knowledge of therapeutic devices to help the mentally ill has been increasingly utilized. According to a recent study:

> At its best the state mental hospital is now coming to be regarded as a "treatment" rather than merely as a custodial institution. Everywhere today mental health authorities are striving to equip these institutions to diagnose, treat, cure, or improve the conditions of the patients so that they may be returned to their own communities.[7]

Undoubtedly this statement represents the desire of state administrators and most superintendents of the institutions. Unfortun-

---

[6]Stern, Edith: Mental Illness, New York, 1942, The Commonwealth Fund, page 24.

[7]Buell, Bradley and Associates: Community Planning for Human Services, New York, 1952, Columbia University Press, page 241.

ately, the state mental hospitals at the present time fall short of this goal. The vast majority of them are overcrowded and understaffed. Many of the staff employed are poorly trained and underpaid, and lacking in enthusiasm for the job. In 1949 the excess of population over the capacity was 18 per cent. This again showed a state by state variation with seven states showing no overcrowding and others showing 35 per cent or more overcrowding such as Illinois, Georgia, and Louisiana.[8]

Presumably more work needs to be done on standards for psychiatric hospitals as to staff needs. In the nursing field alone, the situation is woefully inadequate, on the basis that one graduate nurse should be employed for every 25 patients in a mental hospital. Actually in 1949 there were 4,305 graduate nurses in mental hospitals in the United States and an average daily resident patient population of 471,260, an average of one graduate nurse to 110 patients. Dr. Lemkau has commented on the disproportion between the numbers of psychiatric patients needing nursing care and the nurses who serve them.

> The committee on nursing in psychiatric hospitals of the National Health Assembly, for example, pointed out that half of the nation's hospital beds occupied by the mentally ill were serviced by less than 2 per cent of all the registered nurses; 50 per cent of the beds were serviced by 2 per cent of the nurses![9]

More psychiatrists are needed at once for mental hospitals and it looks as though for some time to come the supply of psychiatrists would be less than the demand. The quality of staff attendants is difficult to assess, but recent stories in popular magazines and books written by authoritative persons have indicated that much needs to be done in this area.

MEANING OF MENTAL ILLNESS TO THE INDIVIDUAL AND FAMILY

The "M's" had been regarded as a very happy family by the neighbors. Mr. M. had a steady position in a machine shop. They were buying their little home, similar to the other inexpensive houses in the surburban area where they lived. Mrs. M. kept the house clean and neat, saw the three children, aged 12, 10, 7, off to school each day. Mrs. M was not a particularly outgoing person, but

---

[8]Patients in Mental Institutions, op. cit., page 68.

[9]Lemkau, Paul V.: Toward Mental Health, Mental Hygiene **36:203**, April, 1952.

she was on friendly terms with all. The children were brought up well by local standards.

But Mrs. M. gradually changed. She seemed morose and sullen. She would neglect to keep up the house or do the marketing. She was indifferent to the children and short with them in their demands. She became very angry with her husband when he questioned her about the housekeeping or the children's activities. At first Mr. M. tried to do the work when he came home, and to share the marketing with his oldest daughter. Mrs. M. became increasingly difficult. She quarreled with her neighbors and she was abusive to the children. Mr. M. tried to take her to the doctor, but she refused to go and accused her husband of wanting to get rid of her. He talked over the situation with his pastor who urged patience.

But her behavior became more and more odd. The children began to be afraid of their mother. One night she began to beat the little boy excessively. Mr. M. interferred and she turned on him savagely. He was obliged to hold her forcibly and had his oldest daughter call the doctor. Mrs. M. was quieted with sedatives, but there was now no question about her admission to the state hospital. She refused to go. Mr. M. secured the necessary papers. His doctor and another doctor, after examining Mrs. M., attested to her condition and she was committed to the hospital indefinitely. Later a diagnosis of schizophrenia was given.

Meanwhile Mr. M. was faced with a number of environmental problems. He lost much work during his wife's illness. He was unable to meet the payment on the house. He had no relatives who could look after the children. The children, too, were in a highly nervous state, particularly the little boy, and the father was at a loss as to how to help him.

This story shows some of the problems which face a family when mental illness strikes. As with physical illness, adjustments are required in the family living arrangements and the attitudes of the father and children. Their ability to cope with the new situation varies widely. Nor does the problem end with the securing of a housekeeper through a social agency and a loan to help meet financial obligations. Neighbors, well-meaning and otherwise, ask about Mrs. M. Not knowing the full details of the situation, some may suggest that Mr. M. did not meet his proper responsibility in sending his wife to the institution. They may suggest that the housekeeper is not giving proper care. Mr. M. wishes to go and visit his wife. She refuses at first to see him and he finds this very upsetting. He feels guilty for having committed her to the hospital. The children do not know when their mother will be back; they do not understand what is happening to her. Some of their friends may taunt them by saying their mother is in the "bug house."

But let us assume that this family can cope with its problems. Mr. M. works hard, the minister and the hospital social worker help him explain things to the children. Then Mrs. M. gets better and wants to return home. The doctors at the hospital recommend a trial visit. Mr. M. hesitates. His home is now running smoothly. He is fearful that the children may again be upset; that his wife will not be able to stand the strain of being at home. The hospital presses him to take his wife. Reluctantly he consents to a trial visit for a weekend. Mrs. M. creates no disturbance when she is sent home on parole. Eventually she comes home to stay, although she may have some relapses and need to return to the hospital for short periods of time.

EPILEPSY

Epilepsy, the Greek word for "seizure," is a disease affecting about one out of every 200[10] of our population. Its effects are grossly misunderstood by the public, because the seizures during which the afflicted person loses consciousness frighten those around him. Inability to prevent the attacks seems to indicate a weakness of the mind. Epileptics are frequently placed in hospitals for the mentally defective or may be considered mentally ill. Actually they may not be either, as most epileptics are normal in every respect except their disease. The cost of the disease amounts to $60,000,000 annually not including lost manpower.[11] But much of this cost and much of the emotional strain on the victim and his family could be reduced with a better understanding of the disease.

To begin with, seizures vary in their intensity, muscular involvement, and frequency of attack. Different types of the disease have been identified. Injuries to the brain, and some disorders of cell metabolism may cause the seizures. Seizures are always symptoms. Fortunately, epilepsy can be diagnosed very carefully with the use of the encephalogram, which affords an electric picture of the brain waves, the best indication of the exact pattern of seizures. It is an expensive but a painless way of getting accurate diagnosis. Persons with epilepsy have also responded well to treatment, and several drugs have been produced in recent years which have reduced the number and severity of epileptic seizures. These drugs are Dilantin, particularly helpful for some cases of petitmal, Mesantoin, Tridione, Paradione and Thiantoin sodium. Experimentation has been done with these drugs and is still

---

[10]Yahraes, Herbert: Epilepsy—The Ghost Is Out of the Closet, Public Affairs Pamphlet, Number 98, 1951, p. 3.

[11]Ibid.

going on. So far results show improvement for many cases when carefully prescribed and that no drug-forming habit ensues. Diet is sometimes effective.[12]

With the great improvement in methods of treating epilepsy, some of the social problems still remain. Persons with epilepsy often feel a deep sense of shame, their families feel embarrassed, because the fainting and convulsive spells are conspicuous. The individual feels helpless because he cannot control his action. Many persons in the vicinity of an epileptic having a seizure can be frightened. Teachers and others need help in understanding the situation and to know what to do. Indeed one teacher was most helpful in explaining the disease to the class, because Alice, one of the class members, was an epileptic. The

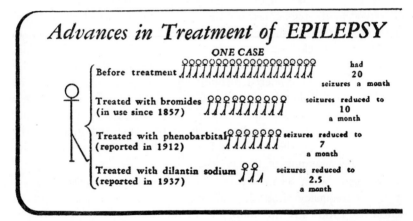

Fig. 6.—(From Facing a Great Task, The Epilepsy League, Boston, Mass.)

teacher told the children about this and asked them to let her know when Alice felt dizzy, so that they could help her. No trouble was encountered, nor did the children make fun of Alice, and her security grew. But many teachers cannot be calm about epileptics and do not want epileptic children in school with others. Epileptics also shy away from social gatherings and situations where they might be noticed. Help given by the drugs has given greater security to many in facing social situations.

------

[12]This material is based on Yahraes, Herbert: Epilepsy—The Ghost Is Out of the Closet, Public Affairs Pamphlet, Number 98, 1951.

More serious is the economic loss to industry of the potential services of epileptics and the drain on the self-esteem of the victim because of inability to obtain employment.   Employers have been loathe to take on an epileptic, feeling he might endanger others or be hurt and thus a liability on them through the provision of the law.   Great efforts have been made by the National Epilepsy League to interpret to employers the capabilities of epileptics and also to train epileptics for jobs in which dangers are reduced or eliminated.   Three types of job situations may be particularly difficult for some epileptics, first where one might be responsible for others, as a bus driver, elevator operator and the like; second, those dangerous to the person if he had a seizure, such as operating a machine, welding, some constructions jobs; and those such as an entertainer, actor, etc., where one is in public view.   Professional and many other careers are open and it has been pointed out that some great persons, Julius Caesar, Lord Byron, and Van Gogh, were epileptics.[18]

The nurse as well as the doctor and the social worker should be aware of the problems of the epileptic.   They can become economic and social assets and should have help in getting the correct medical treatment, the right vocational training, and help with their emotional and social problems of adjusting to the disease.   Complete cure is not known.

MENTAL HYGIENE APPROACH

After he had written *A Mind That Found Itself* describing his experiences in a mental hospital, Clifford Beers helped found a National Committee for Mental Hygiene in 1909.   This organization at first concerned itself with improving the conditions in the mental hospitals, which Mr. Beers had found so inadequate during his hospitalization in the early 1900's.   Later the society broadened its function and they now are engaged in a program of interpretation of mental illness to the general public and with promoting the establishment of mental hygiene clinics for both children and adults.

Since medical knowledge of mental illness has identified many symptoms of future breakdown, early identification of these symptoms so that treatment can be had without recourse to hospitalization seems a natural step.   The theory of the mental hygiene clinic is to provide

---

[18]Lennox, William G., and Cobb, Stanley: The Employment of Epileptics, Boston, American Epilepsy League, Inc.

an agency in the community which will diagnose and treat a troubled person before complete breakdown has occurred. Stress has been placed on such clinics for children when it is easier to modify their personality pattern and usually easier to determine the cause. Educational efforts through schools, parent education societies, and the like have emphasized developing a sound personality in the child, recognition and treatment of behavior difficulties, so that the child may grow into an emotionally secure adult.

The mental hygiene clinics both for children and adults have been established for some time in many communities. The staff in a typical clinic consists of a psychiatrist, psychologist, and one or more social workers who collaborate in the study and treatment of the person applying. The physical condition of the applicant is always considered. The psychiatrist is in the directive role making the diagnosis after the initial study and planning treatment with the help of his staff. The psychologist is responsible for psychometric and other tests which aid in understanding the applicant's problems. The social worker collects a social and environmental history of the applicant and participates in the treatment, particularly in interpreting to other persons in the patient's environment such as relatives, school officials, and employers, and helping remove some environmental pressure. If the worker is a skilled person, she may share with the psychiatrist in working directly with the patient. Much can often be done to modify the environment such as reducing competition in school, providing more outlets for leisure time, and placing a child in a special institution or foster home. In 1946 the National Mental Health Act was passed which has proved a boon to the cause of mental hygiene both in its provisions for research and for grants-in-aid to stimulate the establishment of mental hygiene clinics. The Act provided for (1) erection of a National Institute of Mental Health subsequently established at Bethesda, Maryland, for treatment of mental patients and for research; (2) money grants to states to be matched in part by state or local funds for establishing mental health clinics; and (3) grants-in-aid to public and private agencies for training of psychiatric personnel for mental hospitals and clinics. These scholarships granted to specified institutions include plans for training psychiatrists, psychiatric social workers, and psychiatric nurses. One purpose of the program is to decrease the gap between the needs and supply of trained personnel for the mental health field.

Since the passage of the Act many clinics have been established. There is still much to be desired. Many states at the present time, notably New York and Massachusetts, have gone beyond minimum standards set. But for the rest, most of the country facilities are inadequate. As has been said:

> This (the passage of the National Mental Health Act) is a significant step toward public awareness of the vast unsolved problems of national mental health and toward the assumption of public responsibility for meeting them. Heretofore for every dollar spent to advance knowledge of the cause, diagnosis, and cure of mental disease, the American people have spent $100 to care for the known mentally ill. This new law should mark the beginning of the end of such a lopsided and expensive handling of the mental health problem . . .[14]

The distribution of clinics in the United States is quite uneven although there are some five hundred clinics listed by the National Committee for Mental Hygiene. These are largely concentrated in New England, Middle Atlantic, and East North Central states. A few states have only one or two clinics located in larger cities making clinic care almost impossible for persons in rural areas. Development of clinics, however, is decidedly hampered by lack of trained personnel. Some states, willing and able to participate in plans for establishing clinics under the National Mental Health Act, have not been able to obtain the services of the requisite professional persons. That is, of course, why so many funds have gone into the scholarship program to provide more trained personnel.

One discouraging feature which particularly affects the public health nurse in working in a community is the lack of social services with which she can cooperate. Traveling clinics offer some service, but they are limited. Some are largely diagnostic and only too frequently facilities for following through the recommendation are lacking.

Many of the mental hygiene clinics are held as outpatient clinics at hospitals. Some are held in health clinics or general hospitals. A certain reluctance has been noticed on the part of some to attend clinics at a mental hospital. This represents a carryover of the old misunderstanding of mental illness. Many child guidance clinics are held in the schools. Wherever held, despite some resistance and misunder-

---

[14]Rennie, Thomas A. C., and Woodward, Luther E.: Mental Health in Modern Society, New York, 1948, The Commonwealth Fund and Harvard University Press, Cambridge, Mass., page 161.

standing on the part of the public, there is no question but that the clinic service is expanding and meeting a community need. More use of travelling clinics from central resources to serve rural areas is indicated.

CONCLUSION

All problems of health, mental or physical, require recognition of symptoms, proper diagnosis, treatment, and restoration of the afflicted individual to as satisfactory a situation as possible. This necessitates cooperation of a large number of people and the presence of professional personnel and well-equipped facilities for treatment. Information presented in this chapter indicates that in all these areas, mental illness is well behind physical illness. Symptoms are less readily recognized, diagnoses less precise. Understanding of the problems of mental handicaps is blocked by preconceived notions. Treatment facilities are inadequate in number and in quality. Trained personnel are needed in large numbers to raise existing standards to what research and experience have proved useful. Meanwhile the problem is increasing, as more persons desire hospitalization.

As with physical ailments, too, prevention is better than the best treatment facility. So the mental hygiene movement seeks to enable persons to get the best out of their lives and function with the greatest satisfaction to themselves and to others. In the fulfillment of this objective, early treatment of individuals showing some signs of maladjustment through community clinics and education for effective living are required.

A knowledge of mental hygiene helps the nurse in her work with individuals and groups in hospital, clinic, and community, aids in her personal adjustments, and perhaps acts to prevent personality disorganization from developing in her own life. The nurse who has developed insight into emotional needs and deviations is able to give more satisfying professional service to her patients and their families. She may, because of her understanding of the significance of such conditions and her knowledge of the available community resources in mental hygiene, be able to render valuable help to individuals, hence their families and the community as well.

STUDY QUESTIONS AND PROJECTS

1. What are differences between mental illness and mental deficiency? How do these differences affect the individual in the family? In the community? How early are each discovered?

2. Discuss why you think a stigma seems to be attached to mental illness. What do you, your family, and friends think about this?

3. From the statistics on mentally ill patients, can you tell whether or not mental illness is increasing? What is the trend?

4. What resources for the care of the mentally ill exist in your community? If possible, secure an annual report and notice number of patients in the institution, numbers released during the years. What changes are noted? Are the resources adequate?

5. If possible, visit a mental hospital or a ward in a general hospital where mentally ill patients are cared for. Discuss problems with some one in charge as to treatment, methods used, plans for rehabilitation, visiting hours, program, etc.

6. What facilities exist in your community for diagnosis, and prevention of mental illness? Is there a Mental Hygiene Society? If so, what are its activities? What further plans would you suggest?

7. Why is there such a small incidence of mental illness among children?

8. What are the major health problems of the epileptics? The chief social problems? How can the epileptic be helped with these problems?

9. Discuss the effects on a family when one member becomes mentally ill and needs hospitalization, in cases where there are children, and where there are no children.

10. Discuss employment problems of the mentally ill and epileptics.

11. What are some special nursing problems of the mentally ill and epileptics? Discuss requirements of the psychiatric nurse.

REFERENCES

Deutsch, Albert: The Mentally Ill in America, New York, 1949, McGraw-Hill Book Company, Inc.

Doyle, Kathleen: When Mental Illness Strikes Your Family, New York, 1951, Public Affairs Pamphlet No. 172.

Ginsburg, Ethel L.: Public Health Is People, Cambridge, Massachusetts, 1950, Harvard University Press.

Lemkau, Paul V: Mental Hygiene in Public Health, New York, 1949, McGraw-Hill Book Company, Inc.

Lennox, William G.: The Epileptic Patient and the Nurse, Chicago, 1946, American Epilepsy League (Reprint).

Lowry, James V.: How the National Mental Health Act Works, Mental Hygiene **33**:30-39, January, 1949.

May, Rollo: The Meaning of Anxiety, New York, 1950, Ronald Press, chapter 7.

National Association for Mental Health, Inc.: Psychiatric Clinics and Other Resources in the United States, Directory, 1952, New York.

National Institute of Mental Health, Patients in Mental Institutions, 1949, Washington, D. C., Government Printing Office, 1952.

Rennie, Thomas A. C., and Woodward, Luther E.: Mental Health in Modern Society, New York, 1948, The Commonwealth Fund and Harvard University Press, Cambridge, Mass.

Stern, Edith M.: Mental Illness: A Guide for the Family, New York, 1942, The Commonwealth Fund.

Thorman, George: Toward Mental Health, New York, 1948, Public Affairs Pamphlet, Number 120.

Wright, Frank I., Jr.: Out of Sight, Out of Mind, Philadelphia, 1948, National Mental Health Foundation.

Yahraes, Herbert: Epilepsy—The Ghost Is Out of the Closet, New York, Revised edition, 1951, Public Affairs Pamphlet, No. 98.

II. Problems Due to or Accentuated by Age

CHAPTER 18

POPULATION CHANGES

INTRODUCTION

In the great human drama of population change, the nurse plays a very important part. She is often present at the birth of a baby; she is often there when a patient dies. She is an important member of the team trained to preserve life by the application of science to human bodies, young or old. She along with other health workers is a key person in what is called "population dynamics." In this section problems of the child and the aged will be considered. However, in order to understand the problems of these individuals at the extremes of the age scale, certain factors in the total population picture should be considered.

Communities are composed of people. People can be measured by their numbers and by their movements and they can be classified according to ages and position in the community. The statistical analysis of population can be found in census reports. Since 1790, there has been a decennial census in the United States. With the exception of Sweden, the longest unbroken series of census records in the world are to be found in this country. Demography is that branch of statistics which deals with the life conditions of people or the science dealing with the statistics of health and disease, of the physical, intellectual, physiological, and economic aspects of birth, marriages, and mortality. This approach to the study of people is of great significance to the nurse and to all health workers.

POPULATION INCREASE AND DECREASE

Changes in the distribution of population result from birth rate, death rate, and migration. The terms "crude birth rate" and "crude death rate" refer respectively to the actual number of births and deaths per thousand of the population occurring during a given year. No account of the age and sex distribution of the population or other factors such as race or economic status is considered in the crude rates. When crude birth rate exceeds the crude death rate, the difference is known as the natural increase. An increase of population may raise economic problems in certain countries when a country becomes overpopulated; that is, when its inhabitants exceed the optimum population.

Optimum population may be considered as one of a number and composition which is able to use to the full the natural resources available within the territory and allows the greatest possible development of personal and social relationships in relation to the general cultural system of that particular group. It can be seen then that the concept of optimum population depends upon both natural resources and the total culture of the area. The optimum population will vary greatly in the different countries and in different parts of the same country.

The birth rate in any country will depend upon the reproductive capacity of the women in that area. It will also have relationship to the age composition of the population. Thus, a population with a large number of women of child-bearing age will be capable of higher birth rate than one containing fewer such individuals. Other factors affecting the birth rate would be disease or any condition which interferes with the functioning of the reproductive system, such as sterility, certain diseases, the use of certain drugs, etc. Another important factor affecting the birth rate which must be considered are the folkways or the mores of the group. Customs vary greatly in this area as in all other areas of social interaction. The attitude to contraception considered right by the group, the form of marriage and age at which it is socially acceptable for individuals to marry will also have a bearing on the birth rate.

COMPOSITION AND POPULATION CHANGES IN THE UNITED STATES

The great increase in the population in this country came in the sixty years following the Civil War; namely, between 1850-1910 when the population multiplied almost three-fold. Much of this increase was due to immigration because manpower was needed in the rapid industrial expansion in this country. Immigration came to a peak just before World War I and since that time, because of the quota system established after the war, the number of immigrants coming to this country has been greatly reduced. The seventeenth census which was taken in 1950 gave the population as slightly over 150,000,000 as compared with 130,000,000 in 1940. While the birth rate has fluctuated a great deal in the last 30 years from 28.1 in 1921 to a low of 18.4 in 1932, and 1936, it increased steadily during the war years to a high

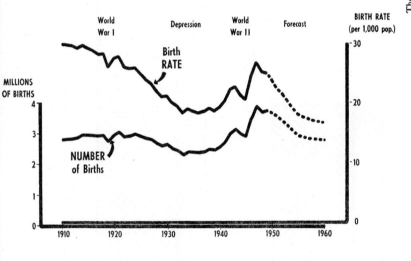

The decade 1940-50 saw great increases in the birth rate and in the number of births

These increases were counter to the long-run trend

Fig 7.—(From A Chart Book—Children and Youth at the Midcentury, Midcentury White House Conference on Children and Youth.)

of 27 in 1947, dropping to 24.4 in 1950. During those same years, the death rate has steadily declined from 12.0 in 1921 to 9.7 in 1950. The life expectation for males in this country has increased from 50.2 years in 1910 to 65.6 years in 1948. For females, the life expectancy increased from 53.6 in 1910 to 71.0 in 1948. For nonwhite males, life expectancy in 1948 was 58.1 and nonwhite females 62.5.

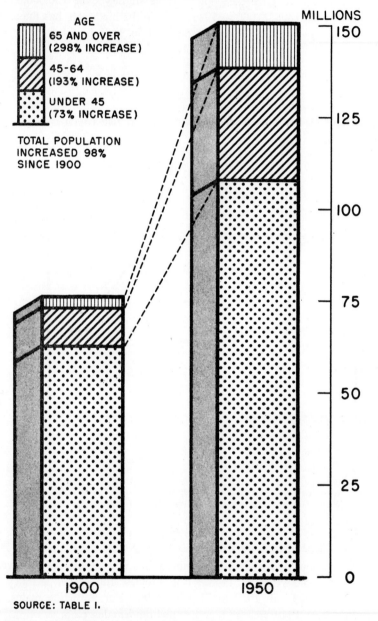

Fig. 8.—(From Fact Book on Aging, Federal Security Agency, Washington D. C.)

Analysis of the census reports is becoming increasingly important to all workers in health and social fields and forms the basis for much social planning. In attempting to provide medical and health facilities, it is important to be aware of certain population trends.

The urban population has increased steadily in this country; urban being defined by the United States Department of the Census as population living in incorporated places of 2,500 or more and according to the 1950 census, the urban percentage in the population has increased to 56.5 The proportion of the population, white and nonwhite, remained about the same in 1950 as in 1940; namely, 89.7 per cent of the population being classified as white and 10.3 per cent as non-white. The general level of the age of the population has been steadily increasing for some time. The median age in 1950 was 30.1 as compared with 29.0 years in 1940 and 16.7 years in 1920. It was interesting to note that the number of persons in the age groups at the upper and lower ends of the scale increased rapidly. For example, the number of persons under 5 years of age increased by 54.9 per cent from 1940 to 1950. The percentage 65 years of age and over increased from 6.9 to 8.2. The most recent census figures show that there has been a great increase in the labor force during the last decade. This is to be expected naturally during the period of great defense activity and the resulting inflation.

Up until quite recently two main movements in shift of population to urban centers predominated: first, the movement to new lands, national resources and jobs in the west; and second, movement to industrial opportunity, the main paths of travel being to the west mainly by the white population and from the rural south to the northern industrial centers by the Negro. Recently, however, there has been an increase in the movement of industries to the south for several reasons— mainly because relatively cheaper labor force is still to be found in the rural south and also the movement toward decentralization in this atomic age with the movement of certain industries away from large industrial centers or centers which might become international air routes.

SOCIAL EFFECTS OF POPULATION CHANGES

The distinct shift from a predominantly rural to an urban people has been very rapid. Urbanization has meant a concentration of population and a centralization of industries and commerce. The reduced numbers of people and the transfer of wealth from rural to urban areas has made the support of local institutions possible only at increased cost per person. The great number of young adults moving to cities has placed a strain on urban institutions for which they were not prepared.

The unparalleled growth of cities in an unplanned way has resulted in the development of slum areas and uncontrolled subdivision growth. All American cities are now faced with problems of city planning to rebuild blighted areas and provide more adequately for the needs of the total population by a better distribution of all city facilities.

The provision of adequate urban housing, particularly for the low income group, is a problem which few communities have satisfactorily solved. Public health facilities have been taxed to maintain standards in blighted areas and among low income groups in cities. While educational and vocational opportunities are greater in urban than rural areas, many young people cannot take advantage of them because of the high cost of living in cities and the need for their contribution to the family income.

Most social problems such as crime, juvenile delinquency, mental illness, problems of child welfare, the aged, have become accentuated by the rapid mobility of our population and by the change from rural to urban living.

The low birth rate during the depression years is also resulting in certain economic and social situations which must be considered. For example, the small number of young people at an employable age has resulted in a shrinkage in the labor force as compared to other groups of the population and this places a very heavy burden on all industry at a time when many workers are needed. This fact is of great importance to the nursing profession because of the great need for nurses of all categories. The shortage of nurses results from increased demands made on her with the great development in the nursing profession and great increase in medical and health activity in addition to an increase in the number of hospitals and health institutions requiring professional and nonprofessional nurses. These increased demands come at a time when the actual number of women available to enter the nursing profession is low. Not only are there fewer single women available at present, but the trend toward younger marriages seems to continue and both of these facts mean that a competition for young women will continue particularly in those professions and industries employing mainly women.

A recent release from the Census Bureau points out "Two out of every three persons in the civilian population fourteen years old and over in March 1950 were reported as married." Sixty years ago when the Census Bureau first published statistics on marital status, only 53 per cent of the population fourteen years old and over were married as compared with 60 per cent in 1940 and 67 per cent in 1950. The most striking decrease in the single population took place in younger age groups, especially among those 20 to 24 years old. In this age range, the proportion of single females declined from 47 per cent in 1940 to 32 per cent in 1950. Although the total female population fourteen years old and over increased by six million in 1940, the number of single females was actually lower in March, 1950, than it had been ten years earlier. Throughout the age range of the female population the figures showed a decline between 1940 and 1950 in the proportion that was single. This decline was most noteworthy for the younger ages.[1] The number of young women in this country entering military service has also increased. It has been pointed out that if the trend toward earlier marriages continues, it may interefere with the number of women receiving specialized training or higher education, since most girls get this before they are married. It is suggested that since the long-term training of women for nursing and teaching, and for other professions depending mainly on women, must be maintained and probably increased in order to meet the needs and therefore the age span for training in these fields should be expanded to include women who have had their families and may be free to study for a career at an older age. It is also recommended that part-time training programs for women might be carried on in certain instances while women are still rearing their families so that they would be trained by the time their children are grown. Another trend is that toward the training of older women for the subprofessional activities, such as practical nurses and hospital aids, in order to take over many of the duties which do not require the highly trained skills of the professional nurse. This is also being done in business where every effort is made to raise the efficiency and output of each worker in order to utilize the shrinkage in the labor force as effectively as possible.

---

[1] U. S. Department of Commerce, Bureau of the Census, Current Population Reports, Washington, D. C.   Series P 20 No. 33, Feb. 12, 1951, page 10.

CONCLUSION

Some problems arising out of recent population trends are obvious; namely, the increase in individuals of the older age groups. This means that as long as there is an acute labor shortage, many industries are planning to continue the employment of older workers, at least part time and in protected areas. An increase in the number of older people in the country, of course, means that provisions have to be made for them when they are no longer able to work, through pensions, insurance schemes, etc. The so-called degenerative diseases will be found more frequently in an older population. Medical and health plans and institutional building must consider the needs of this group and the number who are likely to need such facilities. From a social and economic point of view, it is pointed out that a population composed predominantly of older people may be more conservative and less eager for change than a population predominantly younger.

STUDY QUESTIONS AND PROJECTS

1. What effects will the future trends of our population growth have on the age composition and size of our population?
2. For what age groups has medical science done least to reduce disease and death? How do you account for this?
3. What is the expectation of life at birth in your community? What factors influence this?
4. Find out the age composition of your community. Analyze this in terms of its social significance and community needs.
5. Have the social institutions and agencies in your community changed in the past decade to meet the needs of a changing population? Illustrate.

REFERENCES

Dublin, Louis I.: Changing Patterns of American Life, Statistical Bulletin, Metropolitan Life Insurance Company, May, 1952, New York, N.Y.

Dublin, Louis I.: The Facts of Life from Birth to Death, New York, 1951, The Macmillan Company.

Dublin, Louis I., Lotka, Alfred J., and Spiegelman, M.: Length of Life, Rev. ed., New York, 1949, Ronald Press.

Fairchild, H. P.: People: The Quantity and Quality of Population, New York, 1939, Henry Holt and Company.

Reports of U. S. Bureau of the Census.

Thompson, Warren S.: Population Problems, New York, 1942, McGraw-Hill Book Company, Inc.

CHAPTER 19

PROBLEMS OF THE CHILD

PROBLEMS OF BIRTH

Due to advances in medical knowledge and greater availability of health services, a child being born today has a better chance of survival and a greater expectation of life than ever before. But it is a social problem, as the United States Bureau of Vital Statistics tells us that still some 125,000 babies die during their first year of life. Great strides have been made in reducing infant death rates from 100 per 1,000 live births in 1915 to 31.3 per 1,000 in 1949,[1] due chiefly to effective control of diarrhea, enteritis, pneumonia, and influenza. If further reduction is to be achieved, emphasis must be placed on the child's first week of life, and especially on the first day. Chances of survival are not evenly distributed throughout the United States, however, as infant mortality rates are higher among the nonwhite races, among illegitimate children, and in certain parts of the country where health facilities are less available and the level of living is low. Chances of life expectancy have also increased and each newborn child may expect to live about sixty years.

HAZARDS TO NORMAL PHYSICAL DEVELOPMENT

The child, upon arrival in this world, becomes a part of a family group, who assumes responsibility, shared with the church, the medical profession, the school, and various other community agencies, of helping him develop a healthy body and mind, a well-rounded personality, emotional security. The nurse is presumably oriented to problems of illness and physical handicaps as well as the normal physical development. If a child succeeds in being born healthy and vigorous with no impairments at birth, there yet remain before school is achieved the problems of disease and accidents. Many children's diseases lie in wait

---

[1] U. S. Bureau of Vital Statistics.

for the child, such as typhoid fever, diphtheria, whooping cough, mumps, measles, rheumatic heart, infantile paralysis. Medical science has practically eliminated smallpox, diphtheria, typhoid fever, and whooping cough through a process of immunizing the child to combat these diseases. The chief enemies of the child's physical development now are rheumatic heart and infantile paralysis, both of which may have far-reaching physical defects, and in the latter case some deformity. Some other conditions such as encephalitis and scarlet fever, and other infections may damage the brain and may precipitate deafness, blindness, and a variety of crippling conditions due to lack of muscle control and lack of normal development.

The advance in recognizing and treating children's diseases has progressed to such a degree that accidents have recently become the greatest cause of death among preschool children, according to statistics reported by the Metropolitan Life Insurance Company.[2] During the years one to four, fatal accidents are caused by motor vehicles, a result of our technological culture. Burns and conflagrations are the next most common accidents accounting for deaths of children. This may come as no surprise to a nurse on a children's ward where children with severe burns seem to appear very frequently. Drownings, falls, ingestion of poisonous liquids and solids, and strangulation are other causes of accidental deaths in children. Even if accidents do not result in death, they may produce some physical handicap which the child carries throughout life. Organizations concerned with education for safety have tried to emphasize the hazards of the automobile and in the home, dangerous to adults as well as children. Obviously many children could be saved with more strenuous efforts directed toward accident prevention, especially on the part of parents of young children.

Diseases in childhood and physical injuries to eyes, ears, brain, limbs present many problems not only to the doctor but also to the victim and his family. The progress of a child's recovery may be facilitated or slowed by his parents' understanding of the condition and necessary treatment, of their attitude toward the child, and of the child's adjustment to his own handicaps. Treatment for physical conditions is often fraught with great anxiety to a child, not only because of the pain, but the need to adjust to many frightening and frustrating experiences. (See Chapter 7 for further discussion.) A nurse in working with parents and ill or handicapped children must be aware of some of these problems. Knowledge of health conditions and even of resources may not suffice if the human equation remains unsolved, as the following case illustrates.

Public health measures have almost wiped out some serious communicable diseases

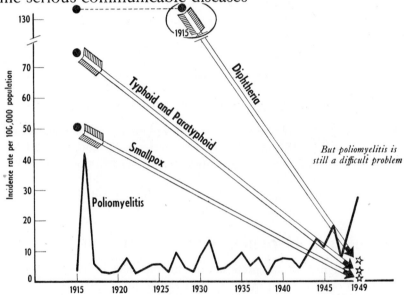

Fig. 9.—(From a Chart Book—Children and Youth at the Midcentury, Midcentury White House Conference on Children and Youth.)

The teacher of a rural school had noticed Billy's limp and body malformation for some time. His parents never came to school so she had done nothing about it. But when she was talking with the public health nurse one day she remarked about it. The nurse became interested, examined Billy at school, and decided to visit the family and request referral to the Crippled Children's Clinic. It was quite evident that Billy came from a poor home as he was dirty and ill clad much of the time, and seemed pale and not well nourished.

The nurse called on the family who lived in a small shack away from the main road. There were seven children in the family. The father held casual labor jobs and had a small garden, a few chickens, and cut wood for his fuel. When the nurse mentioned Billy's crippled condition, and suggested the family should go to court and make application for hospital care as was the practice in this state under the Crippled Children's Services, the father became very angry. He didn't want his children criticized. He became angrier at the mention of court and hospital and declared he would have none of it. "You go to the hospital to die," he said. He wanted his children to live as God made them. He did not want any one interfering in his affairs. He told the nurse to go away.

Billy's father was an ignorant man and he did not realize what he was doing to his child, the nurse told herself. But just because she knew what could be done did not achieve the results. This nurse, however, was not to be defeated. She talked again with the teacher and the social worker in the Welfare Office. The social worker knew the family and stated that a brother of the father of whom he was very fond had gone to a cancer hospital a year previous. He had gone too late and had not returned. This was not a family which sought medical advice or mingled much with their neighbors. The teacher agreed to approach the mother but not to plunge so abruptly into urging them to take the boy to the clinic. The social worker stated she would talk with the father whom she had known and try to see what was troubling him. Sometime later, after the teacher and social worker had listened to the parents' troubles and been able to explain more about the resources, they gave their consent.

Fear of the unknown, superstition, ignorance, and stubborn pride call for different treatment than a straightforward request to go to a clinic. Tedious as it may be, the nurse or the social worker or both have to work through many fears with parents and children and explain many steps in treatment before parents will follow out programs which any nurse knows are good common sense.

COMMUNITY RESOURCES FOR HEALTH CARE

Community health problems of children may be identified as the illness of children, and those physical handicaps of blindness, deafness, crippling conditions of all sorts. A community should likewise be concerned with preventing the occurrence of these conditions wherever possible. To assist the physically ill or handicapped child, a community needs several types of resources, if the child is to be enabled to grow up well adjusted and self-supporting. Primarily, of course, are needed diagnostic and treatment facilities furnished by clinics, hospitals, and practitioners. With certain types of physical handicaps special educational programs are required because of the inability of the handicapped child to participate with the child not so handicapped. This is particularly true of blind and deaf children who need certain skills of communication, reading, writing, and talking to enable them to achieve contact with the world around them. Similarly some of the partially sighted and hard of hearing children need special devices to assist them. A third need is for vocational competence. Every child should learn how to earn a living in a trade or profession which he enjoys and for which he is suited. Physical handicaps may eliminate certain occupations, but much has been done by the physically handicapped and the many devices for helping them so that a variety of vocations are open for them. Community persons particularly on the local level must be alert to discover children in need of special treatment. Early discovery makes possible early accurate diagnosis, and presumably a better chance of correction, more help to the child adjusting to his handicap, more opportunity for specialized education and vocational training. Because periods of hospitalization, operations, prosthetic devices, and hearing aids are expensive, all communities have some provisions for free care, through public or private resources. Local and national service clubs pay for glasses for school children and otherwise meet some expenses for specific cases. State departments of health maintain clinics for well children, provide public health nurses, know local resources and are gold mines of help and information regarding health services. Almost universally they administer funds available from the federal government under the *Maternal and Child Health* provisions of the Social Security Act. These funds, granted to states on condition that specified state funds are put in also, are for establishing clinics and increasing the quantity and quality of personnel involved. This means scholarships for nurses, doctors, and dentists. The focus of this Act is to provide more medical facilities especially in rural areas for care of the young child.

Services for crippled children are found in states, usually but not always administered by state health departments under the provisions of the Crippled Children's Service of the Social Security Act. This program, too, has scholarships available to train professional personnel, but it also seeks to maintain a statewide registry of all crippled children, provide diagnostic clinics, and hospitalization when necessary, convalescent homes, crutches, braces, and aftercare for children referred to them. A broad definition of crippling conditions including harelip, rheumatic fever, and plastic surgery has been included. Since orthopedic care is very expensive, this program has been very helpful. This program as with many provided with public funds is for the medically indigent, those who cannot afford private care.

National organizations supported by voluntary contributions are numerous in the health field. Most do not limit their help to children's cases, and carry on active research in addition to helping individual families cope with their problems. Some of these are the National Infantile Paralysis Foundation, National Society for Crippled Children and Adults, the National Society for Cerebral Palsy, the American Heart Association, and many others.

State and local departments of education frequently maintain schools for the education of crippled, blind, and deaf children. The training in these schools is geared to the child's needs, the child has the special help needed to aid him in talking, reading, writing. He is helped to get along with others and to develop socially and emotionally. Schools for the crippled usually have facilities for treatments, physiotherapy, and the like. For a child not completely handicapped and not needing the more or less protected environment of a residential school, classes in the regular school for the partially sighted, the hard of hearing are found. Small towns usually do not have such facilities. Arguments may frequently be raised concerning the values to the child for keeping him in the regular school, an excellent plan when possible. Such factors as the child's ability to communicate with others, his striving beyond his strength, and the ability of the teacher to help the child all make the decision an individual one regarding the feasibility of the plans. Some private schools and clinics are also available. In all conditions of children, emphasis is being laid on the role of the parent in helping the young child who is handicapped. Clinics for helping the mother work with a deaf and blind child and some nursery schools for both are found. For a child born with a physical handicap, the mother must help the child until he is old enough to go to the schools for instruction. Her attitude toward the child plays a large part in his reaction to his illness. Organizations of parents of handicapped children have been formed in many places to share knowledge and experiences and give help to the individual families with their problems.

EMOTIONAL HAZARDS TO CHILD DEVELOPMENT

Children need a mentally healthy environment in which to grow as much as they need vitamins, and such an environment is one where the child feels loved and secure, is given opportunities to devolop his initiative, and is recognized as an important individual in his own right. As has been seen previously, this can be done in large part by the parents. Perhaps, because of our better knowledge of personality development, symptoms of maladjustment in children can be more readily identified than previously, symptoms which, if disregarded, may develop into patterns of maladjustment, nonconformance, delinquency, and, perhaps, mental illness. A child has many ways of indicating his basic unhappiness; even a young baby may make some of his wants and discontent known by crying or in feeding upsets. Evidences that a child is not in tune with his environment are withdrawal, excessive nail-biting, refusal to eat, vomiting, bed-wetting, and aggressive and destructive behavior. It is the continuity and severity of these symptoms which speak danger; all children presumably indulge in many of these activities on occasion.

What are some of the circumstances which serve as upsetting to a child? They can be summarized as (1) the loss of one or both parents through death, desertion, divorce; (2) temporary loss (from the child's point of view) of a parent due to hospitalization of the parent or child, service in the Armed Forces, necessary visits away from home in which the child is not included; (3) deprivation, real or fancied, of love and affection from the parents, rejection, sibling rivalry, and (4) frightening situations to a child, frequently accompanied with one of the three previous situations which bring unfortunate associations to the child's mind. Frightening experiences can be such as many of the European children suffered in bombing raids, in being removed from home to a camp, in the fear of enemy attack. Less terrific experiences have occurred in accidents, fires, thunder storms, being lost. It should be emphasized again that one single factor does not invariably have a tragic effect on the personality development of every child, but some variation of these causes alone or more likely in connection with other things can undermine the emotional security of a child. There is an interrelatedness of factors. A nurse can understand that a child, who already feels his security is threatened because of frequent absence of the father and quarreling between parents, may be terrified to be left in a hospital even for a simple operation. He might be equally terrified to be left for a visit with a relative where there was no suggestion of any physical pain.

Unfortunately, the causes for the symptoms are not nearly as clear as are the outward evidences. Frequently several contributory causes converge on a poor child, some stemming from lack of satisfaction in his personal relations and some from outer environmental sources. Many psychiatrists are inclined to give major weight in cases of mal-adjustment to the personal relationships of a young child, particularly those stemming from rejection by parents. Extreme deprivation of parental love wreaks havoc. An English authority has said in this respect:

Deprived children, whether in their own homes or out of them, are a source of social infection as real and serious as are carriers of diphtheria and typhoid. And just as preventive measures have reduced these diseases to negligible proportions, so can determined action greatly reduce the number of deprived children in our midst and the growth of adults liable to produce them.[3]

Parents, school teachers, nurses in public health work, school systems, child clinics, and children's wards in the hospital are all in strategic positions to note the early emergence of some of these symptoms. Particularly the teacher and the nurse, who see many children and are aware of normal reaction patterns, should be quick to note some maladjustment and bring it to the attention of the parent.

It was Mary Jo's second grade teacher who suggested to her mother that she seek help from a child specialist or child guidance clinic when Mary Jo began to have increasingly frequent vomiting spells. She had also been Mary Jo's teacher during her first school year, during which the child had had frequent absences, which the mother had excused as due to her weak stomach. Mary Jo had never seemed to adjust to school life and rarely mingled with the other children.

The second year had started off better, but one day Mary Jo was to take part in a little exercise with some other pupils, but felt ill when the time came. Increasingly the teacher noticed that any time the school situation became frightening to Mary Jo, she would feel ill and have to leave school.

Somewhat fearfully, Mary Jo's mother took her child again to the doctor who said there was nothing wrong physically. At length she and Mary Jo went to the Community Child Guidance Clinic where she told the social worker of Mary Jo's trouble at school, of her own worry over letting the child continue in school. She also told of her care in protecting Mary Jo everywhere she went, and it seemed quite possible the child had taken on some of her mother's fears for her.

Fortunately the mother's sincere desire to help the child, and her insight into her own behavior, brought about a better relationship in the family, and helped Mary Jo in making her way at school. The teacher had made a timely referral.

COMMUNITY RESOURCES FOR CHILD GUIDANCE

One of the best community resources for parents whose children are indicating that they are not well adjusted is the child guidance clinic, habit clinic, or mental health clinic as it may be called. Early recognition of difficulties helps but does not always make possible remedial treatment. Nor is the clinic the panacea for all disturbed children, some of whom can be helped by wise parents without resource to a clinic,

---

[3]Bowlby, John: Maternal Care and Mental Health, World Health Organization Monograph, Series, No. 2, 1951, page 157.

and some few of whom may have suffered too severe emotional damage to remain in the community. Clinics seek to diagnose and treat behavior problems of children in several ways. The cooperation of the parent is necessary for best results. Usually the clinic is staffed with a psychiatrist, psychologist, one or more social workers, and perhaps a speech or reading therapist. Each child referred is carefully studied before any diagnosis is made, or plans for treatment initiated. Diagnostic procedures include a thorough physical examination, extensive psychological tests to determine the child's intelligence, school achievement, interests, potentialities, and capabilities. The social worker usually talks with the parents and gathers pertinent information regarding the child's background, origin of his difficulty, tensions in child or family.

Treatment may vary, but usually it is directed toward lessening environmental pressures on both child and parent and helping the persons concerned achieve some insight into their problem, release of anxiety through thereapeutic interviews, or, in the case of a young child, through play. Experiments are being made whereby a group of children work out some of their problems in group play or discussion. These situations must be carefully safeguarded.

Clinics are not universally available. At the present time, there are approximately 500 clinics in the United States available for adults and children, heavily centered in the New England and North Atlantic States. Many states utilize the services of traveling clinics in which a clinic team of psychiatrist, psychologist, and social worker make periodic visits to a community. These 500 clinics operate in about 1200 localities.[4] Between the clinic visits, cooperation with local agencies is essential. Even so, many areas are without coverage. A few states like New York and Massachusetts have some service available to the entire state through the traveling clinics. The National Mental Health Act of 1946 has made federal funds available to states to aid in establishing more mental health clinics for both children and adults and for training of personnel in addition to establishing the National Institute of Mental Health. Psychiatric nurses are among the personnel for whom scholarships are available.

School systems are sometimes equipped to help a child showing inability to adjust to or profit from the school experience. Counselors may be in a central guidance department or assigned to each school. The school system may employ school social workers for this purpose, as

---

[4]Lowry, James V.: Mental Hygiene, Social Work Year Book, 1952, page 323.

well as psychologists, and may provide psychiatric consultation. The approach to the child in any of these set-ups is similar, first a study of the child and his situation, a testing of his abilities, and planning, with the cooperation of the family, to help the child. Good working relationships between all agencies should be established for effective work and elimination of duplication of effort.

CHILDREN'S PROBLEMS NEEDING COMMUNITY ACTION

Back in the time of the Romans, children were considered the responsibility of the state and the state was considered responsible for acting as the parent of all children who had no parents or whose own parents were doing a poor job. This doctrine of state responsibility for the young unable to act for themselves and with no responsible adult to act for them, has been incorporated into Anglo-Saxon law and underlies our child welfare legislation today. It may be hard to realize the legal limits to a child's activity, that he cannot sue or be sued, give permission for an operation, that legal limits specify when he can go to work, get married, leave school, what court he will go to for a misdemeanor. The child, furthermore, has certain protection written into the law; his parents are obliged to support him, see that he gets to school, they may not desert or abandon him, neglect or abuse him. And it is the state's responsibiltiy, frequently delegated to the state welfare department, to see that children whose parents are dead or who have failed their children are protected and properly cared for.

It has further been accepted by the state or local governments that certain provisions should be available for the benefit of all children. While some of these have been largely supported with tax funds, many privately established facilities are used. Public and private agencies work most cooperatively to provide effective service for the child. Some of these provisions include public school, health provision previously mentioned, parks and recreational areas, day care facilities, institutions for those handicapped physically and mentally, financial assistance to families in need, provision for children who have no home of their own. A host of health and welfare services comes to mind. These provisions are available for urban and rural child alike, although studies have repeatedly shown more facilities available in the larger cities. Some of these provisions will be discussed here.

DEPENDENT AND NEGLECTED CHILDREN

Children may lose one or both parents and be living with the remaining parent or a grandparent. Illness may then enter the picture, or the remaining parent cannot keep the home together and work, too, so that plans must be made for the children outside of the home. These children are thought of as being dependent or semidependent.

Many parents neglect their children to a point that neighbors, the school, the nurse may feel something should be done. These cases are referred to a protective agency, or a court which is charged with insuring that children are not abused, beaten, or starved. In cases of suspected neglect the social worker tries to work with the parents. The family ties in our culture are strong and even in situations which may not seem wholesome to us, a child may be getting some degree of security and affection. When the home seems beyond repair, however, parents and children may be summoned to the juvenile court for a hearing. The children may then be removed from the home and the parents placed on probation. Rarely, however, are all parental rights served so that the child automatically becomes eligible for adoption. In most of such cases, the children eventually return home.

All state departments and also some privately supported agencies provide shelter and care for both neglected and dependent children deprived of their own homes. This care may be in an institution or in a foster home where the foster parents are paid to care for the children. Sometimes it is difficult to realize that the children in the case have a hard time adjusting to these arrangements where loving house mothers or foster mothers are wanting to care for them and the physical aspects of the home are better than that to which the child is accustomed. But a child may feel he is not wanted, resents his family's inability or refusal to care for him, and may be so stirred up inside that he cannot accept the care which is awaiting him. Children have to be taken into partnership in arranging any plans of this nature. They need the assurance that their family still loves them, they need to have visits, they need to feel proud of the home folks. A child cannot have all his security knocked from under him without trouble. Similarly foster parents have to be helped to understand the problems through which the children are going, that the children do not necessarily reject them, but the system, the failure of their own homes, the resentment of a child who is not wanted against children who have a secure place in their own homes. It takes time to help children to adjust.

There are large numbers of such children being cared for in the United States mainly by public funds allocated for this purpose. Private agencies are located usually in large cities. Many church-supported institutions are found throughout the country as well as some supported by fraternal organizations. In general, the privately supported organizations help families who are not entirely dependent on sources outside themselves, but are not able to swing the entire problem of child rearing.

Some agencies in a few cities have trained homemakers to come into a home where there are several children but the mother is dead, or out of the home, ill or in a mental institution for long periods of time. This arrangement keeps the children living in the same familiar surroundings with their father, going to the same school, playing with the same friends. Problems do exist sometimes in difference in disciplinary procedures, difficulty in getting the right homemaker for each home needing one and the expense of the plan. The more successful homemakers are those who, in addition to a natural way with children and a sympathy for them, have had some training in buying on a limited budget and in understanding of children's problems. These women can also get other jobs if the agency does not have regular work for them, so there may be community expense involved in keeping a supply of expert homemakers available. They fill a real need in the situations where used.

THE ILLEGITIMATE CHILD AND ADOPTION

Some phases of children's problems are particularly apparent to nurses, and these are illegitimacy and adoption. The unmarried mother needs prenatal and good delivery care as much as does the mother of a legitimate child. She does not always get this, not because it is not available but because of her reluctance to admit her condition or because society still condemns the unmarried mother. Many girls seek no prenatal care or if they do it is not until the seventh or eighth month of pregnancy. Those who seek maternity home care probably receive earlier medical care than some who remain in the community and then seek hospital delivery at the last moment. Complicating the mother's situation is need for making some plans for the baby. With the birth of the illegitimate child, the mother is forced to make a decision for which she may not be ready and only too frequently she is in such a highly emotional state, she cannot make a wise decision or one which satisfies her or is the best for the child.   In many communities several agencies exist to help the mother with her problems.   The hospitals' social worker is frequently called in.   Many mothers can see only releasing the child for adoption.   In fact they may even seek to enlist the help of their doctor and nurse.   But no professional person should make the mistake of trying to help her personally rather than referring her to the appropriate agency because of the many complicating social and legal problems.   For example, states have laws governing who may place a child in a home for adoption; how a child may be legally relinquished by parents.   The number of illegitimate children has been increasing.   Accurate statistics are not available because many states forbid the recording of the fact of illegitimacy on the birth certificate, but an estimate of 130,000[5] shows that the problem is sizeable. The child if not adopted has certain strikes against him unless he is legitimated later.   He has limited support from his father unless his mother takes some court action; he has limited chance of inheritance. In some states he is tagged with a birth certificate which reveals the circumstances of his birth.   Advances are being made to substitute a birth card, however.

The "black market" in babies of which a great deal is heard lately flourishes because the poor unmarried mother does not know what to do and the so-called baby broker promises her help and what is apparently more promises her anonymity.   Furthermore the demand for babies to adopt is greatly in excess of the supply.   She is relieved of her baby and no questions asked.   Later regrets are too late.   Large fees may change hands between the couple who desires a baby and those who would sell babies for profit.

Nurses are more likely to become a part of the gray market, an unauthorized market but with no money changing hands, if they try to help place a child for an unmarried mother.   When one knows a good family seeking a child and a poor upset woman wondering what she can do with her baby, often with the hospital pressing to discharge patients, it seems only a kindness to help out.   But this is too frequently a mistaken kindness as many instances have shown.   But the nurse should know where the mother can turn for help in getting her child adopted or where a family may adopt a child as questions on adoption are frequently asked nurses.

---

[5]U. S. Bureau of Vital Statistics, 1949.

The tragedy of some adoption placements is illustrated in the following:

Nora L. entered the hospital in labor. Her child was born in a few hours. Nora had been living in a rooming house and worked in one of the retail stores. Her landlady had questioned her about pregnancy, but she had denied it. In the hospital Nora was fearful lest her family know about the situation. She wanted to keep the baby but did not see how she could do so. The hospital in a small town had no social worker. Nora talked over the situation with the doctor. She had no place to go, was not prepared with clothing for the child, and decided she had to give the child up for adoption.

The doctor knew a family who would be glad to take the child. They came to the hospital and signed papers with Nora in which she released her child to them. They even contributed toward her hospital expense. They were delighted with the baby and everything seemed fine. But despite the baby's early attractive appearance, he did not develop normally. Before the year was out, during which time the final adoption papers were not filed, it was apparent that the child would become a mongoloid idiot. The couple wished to give the child up. This, then, presented quite a problem to the state child welfare worker to whom the child was taken. According to the law, despite the papers which were signed in the hospital, Nora was still liable for the support of the child. The would-be parents gave up the child, and in the meantime, Nora had moved to another city and was most upset when finally contacted.

Here was tragedy for all except probably during the first months when the couple were happy with the baby.

Adoption involves the legal transfer of a child from his natural parent or parents to other parents who, after the proper court procedure have the rights, responsibilities, and privileges of the natural parents. Sound adoption procedure requires protection for natural parents, child, and adopting parents through specification of relinquishment requirements, study and investigation of adopting home, careful study of the child. Usually, too, a trial period is required before the adoption can be consummated. It is usual for parents, even an unwed mother to be most reluctant to release all rights to a child, so that the decision comes with difficulty, perhaps accompanied by considerable guilt at denying the normal role of the parent. Some persons wishing to adopt a child may not have the interest of the child foremost in their minds. Perhaps the child is desired to bolster a failing marriage or to satisfy some inner drive of one of the prospective parents. In short, so many factors on all sides may vary that adoption deserves the utmost of skilled services to all the persons involved.

The number of children adopted has been increasing through the years. The United States Children's Bureau has estimated a total of

80,000 adoptions filed in court in 1951.[6] Complete records from twenty-five states showed that 42 per cent of all adoptions in those states were by relatives and step-parents. Thirty-one per cent of the children for whom petitions were filed had been placed independently and the remaining 27 per cent were placed by a recognized social agency. The median age at adoption is 3.3 years but 40 per cent of the children were under two years of age.[7]

THE MENTALLY DEFICIENT CHILD

Another unhappy situation which many families have to face is the problem of the mentally retarded or feebleminded child. While children of some mental retardation can make an adjustment in school and the community, the child with marked mental deficiency always needs special care and protection usually in an institution. It has been recognized for some time (actually accurate ways of classification are only about fifty years old) that there are degrees of retardation which are amenable to measurement in terms of the Intelligence Quotient, I.Q. Persons whose native intelligence never gets above that of a child of three, the idiot class, usually need institutional care. Some habits of personal care and a few other activities may be taught, but learning is limited, and the idiot adult can rarely become self-supporting. Such a child remaining in a home after his disability is noticed presents many complications when there are other children in the family. The mother may give too much time to this child, may neglect the others. The other children may feel sensitive about the child. It is usually a difficult decision for a family to make as to what will be best for the child as well as the rest of the family. Because many institutions will not take a young child, some states offer training to mothers to help them in caring for the feebleminded child at home. Some nursery schools for retarded children have been established.

Children whose mentality increases to about the age of a six-year-old, can remain in the community for a longer period of time but may eventually need to go to an institution. In any case they will need some special instruction for they cannot learn at the same rate as other children. This may be given in a regular school in special classes, or it may be given in one of the residential schools for the mentally defec-

---

[6]Perlman, I. Richard, and Wiener, Jack: Adoption of Children, 1951, Children's Bureau Statistical Series, No. 14, 1953, page 1.

[7]Ibid. pages 3-4.

tive. Usually the residential schools have teachers specially trained and make full use of crafts and vocational skills which the child can learn. Some can undertake successfully duties about the institution. In the long run these children when grown to adulthood will always need protection and supervision. Some may be able to hold a job, one of an unskilled nature, if they do not have to assume much responsibility. But they can rarely be self-supporting. Many, of course, will need custodial care in an institution, although there they may be trained to do work about the farm or in the institution. Many women are able to do remarkable feats of crocheting and embroidery, or weave rugs firmly and attractively under the supervision of an occupational therapist. But existence in the community unless carefully protected by some family member is usually not possible.

The mentally retarded classified as morons, or those whose intelligence does not rise over twelve years, present a great problem to society. Usually these children can remain in the community for their early years of school if not until they complete all the schooling they can absorb. Many are affectionate, pleasant, agreeable persons, causing no disturbance in the community. But there are decided limits to their intellectual accomplishments and particularly to their judgment. A great deal of trouble is encountered with mentally retarded girls whose willingness to please and lack of judgment get many of them in trouble and perhaps illegitimately pregnant. Many can be trained for jobs and several studies have shown the competence of both girls and boys, trained in a training school or a special class and able to get along in the community. Certain social hazards must be watched, however.

With the seriously retarded child, institutional care is the only solution and difficulties exist in many communities finding one who will take preschool children. One city hospital commented that many beds in the children's wards were filled with mentally defective children who should really be placed elsewhere. These children were getting good physical care, but no facilities were available to teach them any of the habits and play procedures. All mental institutions for the mentally deficient are filled and have waiting lists. Society faces a real problem of adequate care to these young and older mentally deficient members of the community. Because of the impossibiltiy of getting enough institutional care for all applicants, concentration of community effort has been on keeping as many as possible in the community, training parents to teach them, making school facilities available, planning vocational programs, and also placing "graduates" from the institutions as much as possible. Attempts at sterilization of the feeble-minded girls, allowable under specified conditions in most states, have not served to eliminate the feebleminded even of the familial type. Medical science is still trying to help those with brain injuries or glandular deficiencies.

A general estimate of 2 per cent of the population which may be mentally retarded has frequently been made. This would mean a considerable number to be cared for. Obviously they do not all require institutional treatment. Institutions for the feebleminded are crowded and many have long waiting lists. In 1949, the most recent year for which data are available, show 150,826 patients on the books of institutions for the mentally defective. Most of these, 126,746, are classified as mentally defective; but 22,710 are epileptics.[8] The remainder are unclassified. Of the mental defectives 118,180 are in public institutions. Like other problems the care of the mentally ill has been and is a responsibility primarily of state governments. Most institutions have arrangements whereby parents may pay for the care of their children. Admissions have been exceeding discharges so that it is easy to see why the institutions become crowded.

ORGANIZATIONS CONCERNED WITH CHILDREN'S PROBLEMS

Perhaps the best known organization when one thinks of children's problems is the United States Children's Bureau of the Department of Health, Education and Welfare. This Bureau supervises the service programs of the Social Security Act in the various states, has consultants available in regional offices throughout the country, carries on research, and has much literature for distribution on all phases of children's problems. The Children's Bureau and the National Commission on Children and Youth were responsible for calling together the Midcentury White House Conference on Children and Youth, frequently quoted here. This conference, attended by more than 5,000 child welfare experts in many fields, had representation from all states and territories. Its recommendations are being applied locally by states and communities. Practically all states have state-wide committees following up progress of children's welfare in their own states. The focus is on the individual locality, assessing gains and charting the future course to make local

---

[8]Patients in Mental Institutions, 1949. op. cit. page 69.

community facilities more adequate.   Fact-finding reports are available and research on a wide scale has been done.[9]

Actually this Conference was the fifth in a series, the first of which was called by President Theodore Roosevelt in 1909 at the White House, hence its name.   Subsequent conferences have been held elsewhere in Washington every ten years but have stressed continuously children's needs and ways of meeting these.   Considerable research has preceded or followed each conference, but efforts are now being directed to get more of this applied.   These conferences have focussed on the child's development and how parents and responsible citizens can help them develop to the best of their capacities.

State health, welfare, and education departments are likewise familiar with state needs for children and can be relied upon for help and information in any locality within the state.   Many privately supported organizations are likewise concerned with trying to help children get a better deal from life.   Many of these are mentioned in a subsequent chapter and in the Appendix.

This chapter has sought to present some of the outstanding problems which may occur in early childhood, to show something of the extent and resources for meeting them.   The human side of the picture as to what it means to child and parents to be one of these problems has also been indicated.   We know much about what may be done but unfortunately we are not always able to provide experiences and resources commensurate with the best of our knowledge.

STUDY QUESTIONS AND PROJECTS

1. What measures do you think can be taken to reduce infant mortality further?
2. Make a study of children in the children's ward of a hospital over a period of time and classify them as to whether hospitalization was caused by disease or accidents. Discuss your findings.
3. In what different ways have you observed families acting toward their sick or handicapped child? How has this affected the child? What attitudes seem to you most helpful? What seem to you most harmful?
4. What are some emotional problems of children physically handicapped or chronically ill, such as the deaf, blind, crippled, child with rheumatic heart, etc? How can they be helped?
5. Suppose a child who had been beaten by his parents was brought to your hospital or you came across the case of a neglected child, to whom would you

[9]For reports on this conference, write to Health Publications Institute, Inc. 216 North Dawson St., Rawleigh, N. C.

report it? What would then be done about the case? In your community what agency handles such situations?

6. If possible, visit a children's institution or a child-placing agency and discuss their policies in taking children under care, planning with them and the family, supervision, etc.

7. What state department supervises dependent and neglected children in your state? What duties does the department perform?

8. How can mentally deficient children be identified and distinguished from retarded or emotionally blocked children?

9. What facilities are there in your community for helping children with emotional problems; mentally retarded children?

10. If someone asked you where they could get a child for adoption, to whom would you refer them? What are the laws governing adoption in your state?

11. As you view the problems of children throughout the United States as revealed by various studies, in what sections of the country are there most facilities for children? Where are these lacking?

12. What advice could you give to parents regarding problems of child training?

13. How will the changing population affect facilities for children?

14. Discuss factors and conditions in society today which are responsible for an increase in the scientific interest in child welfare.

REFERENCES

American Academy of Pediatrics: Child Health Services and Pediatric Education, New York, 1949, The Commonwealth Fund, Chapters 1, 2, 5, and 6.

Buck, Pearl: The Child Who Never Grew, New York, 1950, John Day. (The story of a mentally deficient child.)

Burmeister, Eva: Forty-five in the Family, New York, 1949, Columbia University Press. (Story of a children's institution.)

Carlton, Ruth: So You Want to Adopt a Baby, Public Affairs, Pamphlet, No. 173 New York, 1951.

Child Welfare League of America: Day Care of Little Children in a Big City, New York, 1946, Child Welfare League.

Davies, Stanley P.: Social Control of the Mentally Deficient, New York, 1930, Thomas Y. Crowell Company.

Keister, Mary Elizabeth: Day Care Centers and Nursery Schools Have the Same Goals, The Child **15**: 159-162, 1951.

Lockridge, Frances: Adopting a Child, New York, 1948, Greenberg, Publisher, Inc.

Midcentury White House Conference on Children and Youth, A Chart Book, Washington, D. C., 1950.

Midcentury White House Conference on Children and Youth, Proceedings: Washington, D. C., 1951, Raleigh, North Carolina, Official Conference, Health Institute Publications, Inc.

Morlock, Maud: Babies on the Market, Survey Midmonthly **81**:68-69, 1945.

Morlock, Maud: Wanted: A Square Deal for Babies Born Out of Wedlock, The Child **10:** 167-169, 1946.

Rose, Anna P.: Room for One More, Boston, 1950, Houghton Mifflin Co. (The story of a foster home.)

Smith, Barbara: Helping Neglectful Parents Become More Responsible, The Child **14:** 36-38, 1949.

Stern, Edith, and Castendyck, Elsa: The Handicapped Child, New York, 1950, The Commonwealth Fund.

Wallin, J. E. Wallace: Children with Mental and Physical Handicaps, New York, 1949, Prentice-Hall, Inc., Chapters 3, 4, 5, **7,** 14, and 15.

CHAPTER 20

PROBLEMS OF LATER CHILDHOOD

INTRODUCTION

No logical age limit separates later from early childhood. Some problems which were discussed in the last chapter continue as the child grows out of childhood. But after the child has been in school a few years and as he grows into an adolescent, his interests and personality change. The child's personality patterns have already been marked, but they are still modifiable. He is growing up and has more friends outside the home, first his gang, his organization, those with whom he likes to identify and then those of the opposite sex. Many bodily changes develop. The boy often becomes more aggressive, noisy. Some of the girls become silly, become interested in the boys before the latter are interested in them. All children are trying to emancipate themselves from home and yet feel dependent on their home desperately. This age may be frought with problems, sometimes health, although the deaths of children ten to fifteen are much less than in earlier age groups. Their problems are more of an emotional nature. As Dr. Spock has said:

> Emotional disturbances are unfortunate enough at any stage of life. In adolescence there is greater likelihood that they will be "acted out" in antisocial behavior. This not only pushes the child outside the pale at an age when acceptance by the group is particularly vital, but often embroils him in the all too undiscriminating processes of the police, the courts and corrective institutions. We know today that delinquent behavior is only a reflection of what the child has received from parents and society. We know that the experience of being branded and of serving time in an institution that is not ideally organized and

> staffed frequently hardens the heart of the offender. Yet in most parts of the country we show little recognition of our responsibility.[1]

[1]Spock, Benjamin: What We Know About the Development of Healthy Personality in Children, Children and Youth at the Midcentury, Official Conference Proceedings, prepared by the Midcentury White House Conference on Children and Youth and published and copyrighted, 1951, by Health Publications Institute, Inc., Raleigh, N. C., page 67.

Of course all activity does not become delinquent activity. But this is an age when much antisocial activity is displayed.

MEANING OF ADOLESCENCE

Adolescence is a broad term and may be roughly defined as the "teens." It is a period which forms the transition between childhood when the individual is dependent, and adulthood when the person attains independence and emotional maturity. Many changes occur in the boy or girl during adolescence, physically, psychologically, socially, and emotionally. These changes are interrelated and a remarkable correlation exists between the individual's development in these areas. Physically, as the nurse knows, many bodily changes occur during the years from twelve to twenty. The boy or girl grows taller and heavier. Growth may occur very rapidly and thus cause the adolescent to be very conscious of his hands and feet, it being difficult to develop a corresponding mastery of his movements. Sex characteristics also develop during this period, and in fact the culmination of the adolescent period is the achievement of maturity of body structure and the functioning of the glands serving the reproductive system. In a girl breasts develop and menstruation occurs. Pubic hair grows in both sexes. The boy undergoes changes in voice, develops further his sex organs. The girls mature earlier than boys. With such rapid changes in body growth externally and internally, it is a small wonder that these years present psychological problems.

A number of contradictory behavior patterns occur during these years. Every child anticipates emancipating himself from his family and becoming a free agent. This feeling is strongest during adolescence and a teenager usually feels extremely confident of his ability to fend for himself, to make his own decisions, and assume responsibility for himself. He resents restrictions placed upon him by his family. Yet this emancipation process is hampered by his feeling of dependence on his family which he is also very reluctant to terminate. Thus the teenagers must adapt themselves to this struggle to be free and yet to maintain the approval and the pleasant relationships with their parents.

Another area of adaptation is in the social relationships both with the same and opposite sex. Social pressures to conform with group standards are never stronger than during adolescence. A teenager wants to be one of the group in which he finds himself, often called his "peer group." He feels an inner compulsion to conform to the group standards.

He derives security and status from membership in this group. As Dr. Irene Josselyn has said of these relationships:

> The peer group dominates the adolescent's thinking and his behavior. Deliberately to violate peer group patterns is extremely difficult for him. . . . The peer group is composed of individuals at approximately the same emotional level of development. It is not primarily determined by chronological age or intellectual ability, although both play a part. . . . Excessively insecure individuals may seek membership in an incompatible peer group, but they imitate the members in order to gain status.[2]

The adolescent also has to work out his relationship to persons of the opposite sex. Paramount problems of the adolescent girl concern dating, "petting," marriage. Because of the adolescent's casual or confused knowledge of sexual relationships, guilty feelings often arise if pleasure is derived from physical contacts. It is most important during these years that members of the two sexes get to know each other well through games, discussions, hikes, picnics, as well as dances and auto rides. It is in this area that education and opportunities for discussion help to promote the sound adjustment to these many problems of growing up.

Another area in which the adolescent must plan is for his future. Heretofore, plans were nearly always made for him. Completion of grammar school graduation is quite the usual pattern in many places and required in a few states. But plans for after high school now become a reality. College, trade training, getting a job at the completion of high school, and now service in the Armed Forces, are openings for him in regard to which he must make some decisions, for these are part of his progress toward independence.

PROBLEMS OF ADOLESCENCE

Frequent articles in the popular literature in the past two years have emphasized with a rather terrifying aspect the asocial and dangerous activities of many teenagers today. These may vary from the reckless driving of "hot rod" cars, to the use and even sale of drugs such as marihuana and heroin, and to the brutal slaying of persons in

---

[2]Josselyn, Irene: The Adolescent and His World, New York, Family Service Association of America, 1952, page 39.

a cold-blooded way. Many of these activities are particularly products of this age group. Certainly the invention of the automobile, mentioned previously because of its many ramifying effects on present day culture, has served to stimulate adolescent youth. Many youths own cars, or drive their father's, drive recklessly, and are a menace to their passengers as well as to the traffic on the highway or the city streets. Sometimes the drivers have also been drinking even though most states have laws against selling liquor to minors. This recklessness is a part of youth and a need apparently at this age to express themselves, to show off that they are growing up. Misplaced values as to what is an indication of sophistication may account for this.

Other activities displayed include tendency to hang around pool halls, drug stores, to try out smoking "reefers" or other elicit acts. The youth, often supremely confident, feel that they can succeed in indulging in these pastimes without becoming affected. Reports of increase in juvenile users of habit-forming drugs have been current in recent years. A spirit of callousness and indifference has also seemed to permeate many of the young who rob, assault, and even kill with little apparent motive and with equally little remorse. These crimes may be small in number but of concern to society and those charged with helping the youth. Frustrations in the adolescent age are many, and it is a common reaction to fight against it by unacceptable or indifferent behavior but the community must be protected against them.

Every generation has viewed with some alarm the problems of the rising generations. At the present time perhaps more understanding of some of the causes for antisocial behavior exists and many opportunities and facilities are availble for helping the adolescent with his problems. In this area, the usual sources of help from parents, school, and church can be counted upon. In this age, too, because of the influence of the group, membership in groups has been especially helpful. Opportunities for the young people to get things out in the open and discussed, and provision of useful educational courses have been assets. A really disturbed adolescent, as a younger or older person, undoubtedly needs individual, skilled, and concentrated therapy. The experts seem to agree that the period of emotional growth is painful as well as pleasurable but a necessary phase to be gone through before maturity can be attained. The problem is to grow up and to achieve adulthood in as normal and healthy a way as possible.

JUVENILE DELINQUENCY IN CHILDREN

The juvenile of today who breaks laws and ordinances of his community is often regarded as a victim of warped personality development. Not that he does not know what he is doing but that his delinquent acts, be they truancy or stealing, or yet peddling of dope, are symptomatic of an inner frustration and hostility and inability to make adequate socially acceptable adjustments. Undoubtedly other factors are superimposed, such as a bad environment or membership in a group of undesirable social acceptability. Officially the delinquent is defined by law in terms of offenses committed and the juvenile is designated by age, usually between the ages of 7 and 17. Theoretically before the lower age limit the child is considered incapable of distinguishing right from wrong. Obviously, unless the offender is caught in the act, one does not know of his delinquency. It is indeed difficult to get accurate measures of the extent of delinquency because only those offenders who are brought to court are tabulated. Some who are apprehended in the act may be released after a good "talking-to." Or a child from a "good" family will be released without a record. Statistics of juvenile delinquents, which soared to new heights during World War II and then receded, have shown a pronounced increase since 1950. In 1951, the United States Children's Bureau estimated 350,000 children were brought into the juvenile courts in the United States.[3]

Statistics also reveal that more boys are picked up than girls in the proportion of four to one, and their offenses are likely to be theft, truancy, running away, burglary. Girls are more likely to be sex offenders, or "ungovernable," which really is not an offense at all but a finding in court after complaints from parents that they cannot control the girl. Most of the male offenders were between the ages of 16 and 17; the girls between 15 or 16.[4] The causes for juvenile delinquency are many and are often indicated by earlier symptoms before the specific act of delinquency which brings a child before the court. All attempts to reduce each case of delinquency to a unit cause have been failures. Delinquency results from a combination of many factors acting on the personality of a child impelling him to commit the act. These are usually found in the family life of the child, in the home and conditions and neighborhood in which he lives, in his school, in a variety of other

---

[3] A Few Facts About Juvenile Delinquency, The Child 17:64, December 1952.
[4] Juvenile Court Statistics, 1946-1949, U. S. Children's Bureau, Statistical Series, No. 8, 1951, pages 12-13.

causes stemming from his biological and physical make-up, his mental incapacity.   Many authorities now lay the greatest stress on deprivation suffered by the offenders in early life denying them the basic satisfaction in family relationships.   Broken family homes, symptomatic of lack of parental functioning, crowded and unsanitary conditions, lack of play space, an ill adapted school curriculum or a program in which the child is not individualized are all factors.   Preventive measures which have been undertaken have not served to reduce the number of delinquents or make better citizens of those now in the toils.   It is difficult to assign a cause for juvenile delinquency.   Nor are two delinquents similar.   Take the following case for example:

Dick W. and Jack N. were caught "red-handed" about 12 o'clock one night by the policeman on the beat, as they were trying to break open a cash register, locked for the night.   They were in a small drug store and had gathered in their pockets and in a bag they brought with them, candy and cigarettes, flash lights.   The boys were cornered in the small entrance way.   The policeman took them to the Detention Home since this was a large city.   Meanwhile their parents were notified.   Dick's parents wanted to come right down and take him home, but Jack's parents could not be located at first.   A younger brother and sister were at home alone, but his father was on a periodic visit to jail for drunkeness and his mother worked nights as a scrub woman in an office building.   When she was told about Jack, she said he was just like his "old man".

When the juvenile court hearing was held, the W's and Mrs. N. were there. The probation officer had given the judge a summary of the boys' background, what the families had told them, the record in school, and what the boys had said.   The boys had had a physical examination.   Dick was a big, dull, overgrown boy, living in a home where lack of parental love was obvious, although both parents felt responsibility for Dick.   His mother, the dominent one in the family, scolded him bitterly for his conduct.   It was not Jack's first offense, as he had been trying to better his personal lot by small thefts before and had broken into a store near his home the previous summer.   But the proprietor who knew the family did not prefer charges. Jack's home was dirty and unattractive, Jack was accustomed to beatings from his father when the latter was around. His mother was worn out with the struggle of keeping the family together.

The judge placed Dick on probation and released him to his family.   He referred Jack to a children's agency, to see if they could find a state foster home or small institution where he could be helped to become an acceptable member of society again.   The judge felt at this point the state training school was not a good place, although it might be necessary later.

The procedure followed here is similar to the treatment of most juvenile offenders when caught.   Recognition that younger offenders needed different systems of punishment and rehabilitation because at this stage they were not "hardened" led in 1899 to the establishment of the first juvenile court in Chicago. A milestone in judicial history, the court's philosophy was to study the offender and work out a plan of treatment which would be most beneficial to the individual. The court was not a tribunal where the guilt or innocence would be established and suitable punishment for the offense. After fifty years of juvenile courts in which the philosophy has been tried in many different adaptations, the results have not been entirely successful. Again many reasons account for this. It is difficult to have a court hearing even in a small room and not have some of the judicial procedure influence it. Many judges and probation officers are not trained in children's problems. Many cities do not have need for a full-time judge and other duties take the bulk of his time. But the juvenile offenders do have in many places a separate hearing and their cases are studied in some detail in an effort to get at causes.

Treatment for the offender consists of probation, which may carry also a suspended sentence to one of the correctional schools, referral to specified community agencies, such as the House of the Good Shepherd for girls, use of a child-placing agency or institution in other instances, or commitment to a correctional school. The decision is the judge's. A few states, California, Wisconsin, Minnesota, Massachusetts, and Texas, have substituted a central authority, in California the Youth Authority, in Massachusetts, the Youth Service Board, to which the judge commits the juvenile offender, where a study of the child is made and a variety of plans adopted. This takes the decision as to specific treatment out of the judge's hands and places it with a commission.

The correctional schools in many states leave much to be desired. Lack of qualified personnel, use of punitive, even sadistic methods of punishment, no attempt at rehabilitation of the person committed are frequent. The principle of individualization has been forgotten in large part and the program attempts mass application and frequently fails. Some training schools have made progress in methods of treatment. Community wide attacks on the problem call for better parent education, more understanding teachers, more flexible school systems, varied and abundant recreation facilities, better housing, and fundamental socio-economic attacks which mean better wages and standards of living. Any of these take time, and take acceptance on the part of the community of their value.

CHILD LABOR

As the child grows, he naturally wants to do things, around the yard or in the house. Most parents give a child responsibilities for certain household chores. Soon a child wants to earn money and he should be encouraged to do so, but not at the expense of his physical ability. Fortunately much of the exploitative child labor has passed. Now it is chiefly in agricultural operations that children are found laboring long hours and at difficult tasks. All states have laws protecting children from working in manufacturing establishments and at hazardous occupations, and in places which are regarded as morally harmful. But exempt from these laws are children in agricultural pursuits and the street trades. During World War II, jobs were so plentiful because of the realization of some of these laws that many children were leaving school and taking up paid employment, mostly in blind alley jobs. The situation is slightly changed now. Most states also insist on issuing work permits for children under sixteen who are still in school. This issuing of work permits has been a positive factor in eliminating much child labor.

The areas of greatest hazard are the cotton fields, berry and vegetable picking. Children as young as six years of age accompany their parents in cotton picking time. Some take naps in the field as needed. The money which is earned may go toward the child's clothes and it is reported that many take pride in the amount earned. In the picking of vegetables also young children help the parents and frequently are not on the payroll. Much of the work is arduous and requires the child being out in the sun and using muscles he is not accustomed to using.

Many of the children who are working in agriculture also follow the crops with their families. This means their schooling is inadequate and interrupted, theirs is not a stable home life, and the conditions of living are very poor indeed. The children of the migratory workers are more disadvantaged than any other children in the United States today.

Children working in or on products being shipped in interstate commerce are protected by the Fair Labor Standards Act which prohibits children under sixteen being so employed. State laws are not always as strict. Even with good laws on the books, enforcement is sometimes lax, or an employee pays a fine which is less costly to him than employing older workers at higher wages. There is no doubt that great strides have been made in eliminating harmful labor of children. But there are still some areas for work.

In terms of numbers, more older children work than do children under 14 years of age. In 1949, about 7,500,000 young people 14 through 19 years of age worked full or part-time, about 58 per cent of all children of those ages. Most of those 14 through 17 were likewise attending school. Of the 18- and 19-year olds, about 2,225,000 were employed, approximately 60 per cent of all boys and 45 per cent of all girls of that age.[5] Some of this work is character-forming, without doubt, and some of these young people may be establishing a foundation for future earning. On the contrary, many are in blind alley jobs and perhaps not in situations best suited to the young person's development and work program. It concerns educators, too, that many children leave school for jobs where they are frequently at a competitive disadvantage.

VOCATIONAL GUIDANCE

Since adolescence is a period when a young person's thoughts naturally turn to careers and the future, guidance facilities of high quality are needed in communities. Many times school systems have counsellors to assist the student in selecting a career. Federal funds are available for development of these programs. As with so many other provisions benefiting youth, those in rural areas or attending small schools are at a disadvantage compared with young people attending large city schools. Most youth are not well versed in opportunities for the future nor in job requirements. Many of them have little or no knowledge of their own capabilities, and some have hazy and unrealistic notions of their vocational interests. So-called "glamour" occupations outshine other more practical considerations. All of these factors make guidance facilities almost mandatory if youth is to be used to the best of his potentialities in the labor market.

Many schools have good opportunities for vocational education, again probably more in the cities, although vocational courses are being offered in rural schools. Courses in various trades are also available for adults interested in additional training. While most of the vocational courses at the secondary school level do not profess to turn out a completely trained mechanic or machine operator, such courses afford youth

---

[5]Fact Finding Report, Midcentury White House Conference on Children and Youth, Additional Digest Material, 1950, pages 18-19.

an opportunity to test their interests and to acquire an acquaintanceship with certain useable skills.

The Midcentury White House Conference report emphasizes common misconceptions which programs of guidance and training do not endorse. These are:

1. A college education is necessary for success.
2. White collar work is more desirable than trade or technical work.
3. Vocational guidance results in the selection of one's life work.
4. Aptitude testing answers all vocational problems.[6]

SUMMARY

The period of the teens is frequently a difficult one for youth. He is going through many physical and emotional changes in his growth to maturity, and needs patient understanding and help. This is the age of the greatest number of juvenile delinquents, and great activity in gangs and groups of young people. This is also a period when youth wants to work and turns his thoughts to a future job. And finally it is a period when the young person is trying to work through his heterosexual adjustment. Youth bears the responsibilities for the world of tomorrow and the best possible insurance for all concerned is to see that they are as well prepared as possible for the task.

STUDY QUESTIONS AND PROJECTS

1. Discuss the influence of physical changes on the personality of the adolescent.
2. Adolescense has been described as a restless age. Do you agree or disagree with this contention? Explain.
3. What environmental factors in your community contribute to juvenile delinquency?
4. What do the statistics of juvenile delinquency in your community reveal? Is delinquency increasing? Do the delinquents come from certain areas of the city? What ages are the delinquents? What are the chief offenses?
5. What agencies in your community work with juvenile delinquents after delinquency has occurred? What are the qualifications of the personnel? How effective do they seem?
6. What kind of program for prevention of juvenile delinquency does your community have? Aims, facilities, coordination, effectiveness? What organizations are engaged in these activities?
7. How do you explain why some boys in the same neighborhood, sometimes even in the same family, commit delinquent acts and others do not?

---

[6]Ibid. p. 24.

8. The term "pre-delinquent" is widely used. What symptoms or actions would you regard as indicating future delinquency?
9. What facilities are available in your community to meet the leisure time needs of teenage youth? Of what different types are they? Do you regard them as adequate? What changes would you make?
10. What is the age at which a child may go to work in your community? How does this compare with the age at which he can leave school? Are there restrictions on type of work?
11. What agency in your community is responsible for enforcing child labor laws? Have there been many violations in the last few years?
12. What has been the experience of the school department in your community as to children leaving school after finishing grade school and before they finish high school? Why do the children leave? Do more or fewer seem to leave now?

REFERENCES

Ackerman, Luton: Children's Behavior Problems, Chicago, 1942, University of Chicago Press.

Bell, Howard M.: Matching Youth and Jobs: A Study of Occupational Adjustment, Washington, D. C., 1940, American Council on Education.

Deutsch, Albert: Our Rejected Children, Boston, 1950, Little, Brown & Company.

Gardner, George E.: Mental Health of Normal Adolescents, Mental Hygiene **31:** 529-540, 1947.

Hollingshead, A. B.: Elmtown's Youth, The Impact of Social Classes on Adolescents, New York, 1949, John Wiley and Sons, Inc.

Josselyn, Irene M.: The Adolescent and His World, New York, 1952, Family Service Association of America.

Landis, Paul R.: Adolescence and Youth, New York, 2nd edition, 1952, McGraw-Hill Book Company, Inc.

Langdon, G., and Stout, I. W.: These Well-Adjusted Children, New York, 1951, John Day Company, Inc.

Manning, Lucy, Ten Years Progress in State Protection of Child Workers, The Child **13:**152-155, April, 1949.

Merrill, Maud A., Problems of Child Delinquency, Boston, 1947, Houghton Mifflin Company.

Midcentury White House Conference on Children and Youth: Proceedings, Raleigh, North Carolina, 1951, Health Publications Institute, Part 6.

National Probation and Parole Association Yearbooks. Issued Annually.

Sellin, Thorsten, ed.: Juvenile Delinquency, Annals of the American Academy of Political and Social Science, January, 1949.

Taylor, Florence: Child Labor Fact Book, 1900-1950, New York, 1950, National Child Labor Committee.

Teeters, Negley K. and Reinemann, John O.: The Challenge of Delinquency, New York, 1950, Prentice-Hall, Inc.

U. S. Children's Bureau, The Child, Juvenile Delinquency Issue; Washington, D. C., December, 1952.

CHAPTER 21

THE AGED

INTRODUCTION

The group comprising the aged has increased numerically as the span of life has been expanded mainly through curative and preventive medicine. The threshold of old age traditionally has been placed at 65 years in our culture, although it is being pointed out to an increasing extent that the chronological age is no indication of the aging process. Good nutrition and good general hygiene have contributed much to good health, both physical and mental, in adult life. During the last fifty years the population in this country has doubled, but the number of individuals past 65 years of age has quadrupled. There has been an uneven increase in different parts of the country; for example, the total population of the west has grown almost fivefold while the number of persons 65 and over has increased tenfold. The attractions of the west, particularly California for retired persons especially elderly widows has accounted for this.

In 1950 there were 90 men over sixty-five years of age and over for every hundred women. A recent study[1] points out that the typical man over 65 is married; the typical woman of this same age, a widow. One reason for this is that women tend to marry men older than themselves and relatively more women than men lose a spouse by death. Remarriage is more frequent among men than among women. At 70 years of age, more than one-half of all the women are widows while at this same age, almost three of every four men are still married. This same Fact Book points out that relatively few older people proportionately live alone or in institutions. Most live in families. In 1950, seven out of ten individuals 65 years of age and over maintained their own households. Many of these individuals had a spouse or other relative living with them. Only about one-fourth of those past 65 were not living in a family household.

[1]Fact Book on Aging, Committee on Aging and Geriatrics, Federal Security Agency, 1952.

ECONOMIC CONSIDERATIONS OF THE AGED

From an economic point of view, the aged might be classified as follows:

1. Those who continue working and remain self-supporting until very old;
2. Those who are retired and living on their savings or on investments;
3. Those living in a home with children or other relatives, partially or totally supported by them;
4. Those provided for by the retirement plan as in the case of some teachers, ministers, and other white collar workers and members of labor unions;
5. Those dependent on public or private funds for their support. These include those getting old age assistance from the state and those in religious or private homes for the aged.

While old age and economic dependency is only one aspect of this problem, it is the one most often emphasized. Because of the frequency with which old age and economic dependency has occurred, society has always been faced with this problem. In some past cultures, the aged were exposed to some isolated regions and allowed to die. In others, they have a privileged position. The public almshouse has since the middle ages been the place for dependent old people in our western civilization. The development of the Old Age Pension system has been an attempt to solve the economic aspect of this problem. (See Chapter 22.)

In this country the old age pension movement began in Massachusetts in 1907. By 1933, twenty states had established commissions to study old age dependency and many states have passed laws providing for pensions for the needy. The Social Security Act demonstrates the change in public opinion in this country to community responsibility for aged individuals.[2] Census figures show that in 1950, one-half of the families with a head 65 or over had a cash income below $2,000; three in every ten families with an aged head has less than $1,000. In 1950, the Bureau of Labor Statistics estimated that an aged couple living in a city would need from $1,602 to $1,981 to maintain an adequate level of living.

---

[2]This material obtained from Fact Book on Aging, Committee on Aging and Geriatrics, Federal Security Agency, 1952.

WHERE AGED GET THEIR INCOME
PERCENT OF PERSONS 65 AND OVER, DECEMBER 1951

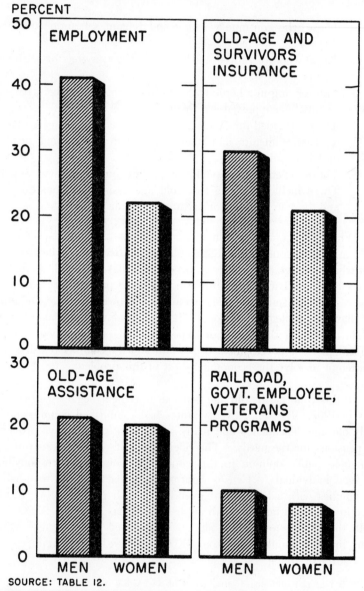

SOURCE: TABLE 12.

Fig. 10.—(From Fact Book on Aging, Federal Security Agency, 1952, Washington, D. C.)

It is interesting to note the changes in the employment pictures of the aged. More than one-half of the men between 65 and 70 were still in the labor force by March, 1952. This ratio dropped to between four and ten between the ages of 70 and 74, and two in ten over 75 years. Since a great many aged women are widows and many of these never worked outside the home, the proportion of working women over 65 is very much less than that of men. Many aged workers are self-employed, such as farmers, small business men or professionals.

About seven out of eight of the 60,000,000 persons in paid civilian employment were covered by public programs of old age benefits in 1951. This expansion of social security benefits has developed mainly in the last twenty-five years.

SOCIAL AND EMOTIONAL ASPECTS

Retirement at 65 or 70 years may compel an individual to unaccustomed inactivity regardless of the economic considerations. Gradual slowing down in all activities including work, if at all possible, is much better for the individual than the abrupt stopping of productive work. Many individuals need to be conditioned to retirement. It is interesting to note that a few industries are expanding their counseling and guidance programs to include help for the older workers with a view to preparing them, perhaps for a change in their occupations, or to retirement. The feeling that one is no longer important or necessary presents a real problem to many an individual who has been the head of the family and the main economic contributor. This situation, of course, is felt more keenly if because of retirement the resources for the wage earner and his dependents are reduced and he becomes dependent upon married children or other relatives. Remunerative work is very important for all older individuals who are able and willing to work. When insecurities and dejection develop among older people, physical illness and mental disorganization are quite likely to advance more rapidly.

Again in this field, culture lags are evident. The resources in few communities have kept pace with the need of the aging population. Job opportunities, recreational activities, group participation and community responsibilities must be analyzed with a view of meeting the needs of the aging group. Many communities have made a good beginning in the development of programs for adult education in which many older people participate and find great satisfaction in finding out about things which they were not able to master in their formal education. Idleness among any large segment of the population is to be avoided at all costs. Since this group is increasing and likely to continue to increase, occupational opportunities and the incentive to work and keep busy must be developed by individuals, their families, and the community. Older individuals frequently have much to give to the community. Years of experience should not be entirely wasted. Every individual should be given the opportunity of continuing his usefulness to himself and the community.

MEDICAL AND HEALTH NEEDS OF THE AGED

Health needs of all individuals are being studied today. The improved personal hygiene, including nutrition and improved living conditions have much to do in keeping the individual in good health during adult and later life. At the same time, proper medical care for all acute infections, continued medical supervision during convalescence, periodic health examinations are contributing to keep older people in good physical condition. Figures do show, however, that older people are ill more frequently and that more of them have chronic illnesses than is true in other age groups. Such major physical defects as blindness and deafness and orthopedic conditions are found very frequently in the older age group. Chronic diseases are the leading causes of death in this group, heart disease accounting for almost one-half of the deaths among individuals 65 years and over. The reader is referred to the chapter on Chronic Illness for a detailed discussion of these conditions.

Because of poor physical condition and because they may no longer be able to work at all or full-time, older persons are less able to pay for medical care, which results in physical conditions becoming worse. Studies show that in 1951 only about one in four persons 65 years of age or over had some insurance, such as Blue Cross, for hospital care. The corresponding ratio in the general population was a little over one in two. Since enrollment in many of these insurance and hospital benefit plans is through the place of employment and since more older people are women than men, and since many of these women are not employed, one can understand what the situation is.

Medical science is expanding its facilities for the study of diseases most common in middle and later life, such as cardiac, cancer, and kidney diseases; and a new science called Geriatrics has developed. Changes in hospitals are resulting in more provisions for patients suffering from these conditions and the rehabilitation of the aged patient is just as important as the rehabilitation of younger adult persons. Rehabilitation of the aged in such conditions, for example, as hemiplegia has brought quite amazing results. It is estimated that there are over a million and a quarter patients in the United States suffering from hemiplegia resulting from apoplexy. In the past, many older patients afflicted in this way were allowed to "vegetate." Studies made and programs initiated in rehabilitation centers show that many hemiplegic patients can learn to care for themselves, to walk and even to return to some form of gainful employment.

The aged person who becomes mentally ill presents a problem. Certain mental conditions can undoubtedly be prevented by adequate care in the acute stage, such as syphilitic infections and their treatment. Certain other emotional conditions may not develop if the individual continues to feel that he is useful and a productive member of society. Many aged individuals with mental illness must be institutionalized and communities must make provision for adequate care and supervision of such groups.

COMMUNITY PLANS AND PROGRAMS

Traditionally, the aged have been cared for by their families whenever possible or in old age homes. Homes for the aged have ranged from the workhouse type, giving mainly custodial care, to privately supported homes where individuals might live in comfortable and pleasant surroundings for the rest of their lives. Economic status was a main determining factor in the kind of environment one could buy. Great increase in retirement plans and the expansion of old age benefits under Social Security will, in the future, enable many more individuals to live in their own homes and be independent, if, at the same time, the health of the older age group can be improved so that health problems are not a major factor in the total picture. Some institutional care will undoubtedly always be desired. Homes for the aged who are physically and mentally quite competent will be necessary. Every effort should be made to give as much freedom as possible so that older people can have their own possessions and can visit in the community and keep their contacts. The protective environment of a good home as far as room and board and medical supervision is concerned is very necessary.

Another type of aged person needing institutional care is the individual with physical or mental defects. Nursing homes may be the solution for this group. These nursing homes must be carefully super-

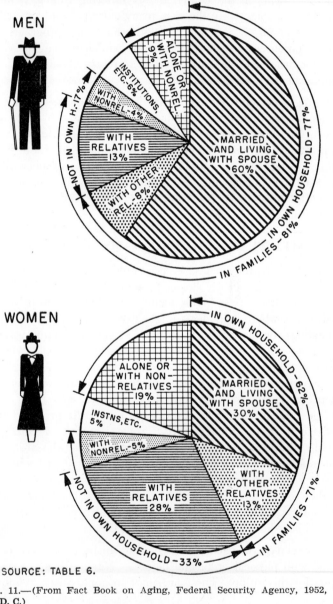

MOST AGED LIVE IN FAMILIES
HOUSEHOLD RELATIONSHIPS OF
MEN AND WOMEN 65 AND OVER, 1950

SOURCE: TABLE 6.

Fig. 11.—(From Fact Book on Aging, Federal Security Agency, 1952, Washington, D. C.)

vised and controlled in the community and should meet standards set up by public health, medical, and hospital authorities. Hospitals, clinics, and general facilities must be developed to meet the need of this group. Because there is usually a slowing down of all processes, these individuals must be considered in the hospital or clinic routine. They should never have the feeling that they are being "pushed around." When a nurse admits an older patient, she should be particularly aware of any deficiencies in sight or hearing or communication or in his ability to move around and do things for himself. His general mental orientation should be considered and the nurse and all other workers in the hospital and clinic should consider and analyze each patient so that steps can be taken to protect him and prevent such accidents as falling out of bed or injury in other ways about the institution.

Many communities are working out boarding arrangements for the aged. Adequate institutional care is not available in many communities and perhaps institutional care is not always the best solution. Accompanying a boarding arrangement, some communities have worked out a day center program for the occupation of older persons. One of these centers was originated in 1943 by the Department of Welfare in New York City and is known as the Hodson Center. The purposes of such a Center are:

1. To promote the social and emotional adjustment of the older person to make it possible for him to find companionship and create a satisfactory environment, giving him a sense of security;

2. To promote the rehabilitation of personal efficiency by making it possible for the older person to make the maximum use of his condition;

3. To promote community usefulness by creating an adequacy and accomplishment through an activity program. It was hoped that this would lead to participation in community projects.

In 1935 by the passage of the Social Security Act a federal system of old age insurance was set up for the first time. It was thus made possible for individual states to set up their own unemployment insurance systems and provided better aid to states for financial assistance to the aged, blind, and dependent children. Under the Social Security Administration, two plans benefit the aged. One is Old Age and Survivors Insurance and the other is Public Assistance for the Needy Aged. Old

Age and Survivors Insurance provides retirement and survival protection for 45,000,000 workers and their dependents: retirement benefits for workers 65 years or over when they stop work in employment and to their aged wives, aged dependent husbands, young children or wives at any age caring for their young children. Benefits are based upon the worker's wages or self-employment earnings. Public Assistance for Needy Aged is also provided under the Social Security Act by providing Federal grants to states. Each state establishes the eligibility requirements, the standard of living with no support, and decides who is eligible and how much the payments should be. (See Chapter 22 for a fuller discussion of Social Security.)

CONCLUSION

Communities are tending to face the problem of the aged with greater reality than ever before. Loss of productive work and the feeling of frustration which may develop from unaccustomed idleness may result in unwholesome attitudes and often personality disorganization. The crowding of aged persons into institutions because no other provision has been made for them should not be encouraged. All health workers must study their community and utilize all available resources in meeting the problems of the individual aged and his family. The importance of keeping the individual active physically and mentally in providing recreational and group community activities is very essential. Many of these individuals have much to give and they should be encouraged to contribute to society.

The community problem of aging as with other problems is being considered from the multidiscipline approach. That is, no one group of specialists attempt to try to solve this or any other community problem alone, but working together as a team, great progress is being made. A recent conference on aging[3] indicated major issues involved as follows: The hygiene of the aging; mental health for older people; disease and disability; organization of health services for the aging; rehabilitation; institutional care; housing and living arrangements; health and employment; professional personnel and community planning for the aging. It can be seen that these areas cut across many specialized fields and in order to explore these areas and to utilize advances in specialized fields for the aging population, many different types of professional and

[3]Problems of Aging: Transmissions of the Fourteenth Congress, September, 1951, St. Louis, Missouri.

nonprofessional workers will be involved. The nurse as well as other health and social workers in the community play a very important part in all these plans and programs.

STUDY QUESTIONS AND PROJECTS

1. What changes have contributed to making care for the aged a community rather than a family responsibility?
2. For what classes of the aged will institutional care always be necessary?
3. Discuss some of the most important community problems in old age.
4. Visit some voluntary and governmental institutions and agencies for the aged in your community. Do these existing institutions for the aged meet the medical, economical, emotional, recreational, rehabilitative, and other needs of the aged? What adjustments do you suggest?

REFERENCES

Bardwell, Francis: Adventures in Old Age, New York, 1933, Houghton-Mifflin Company.

Bernie, L. E., and O'Malley, Martha: Improving Health Care in Private and Public Nursing Homes, Geriatrics, July and August 1952, pages 252-258.

Clow, H. E.: Psychiatric Factors in the Rehabilitation of the Aging, Mental Hygiene **34**:492, 1950.

Dublin, Louis I.: Problems of An Aging Population, Setting the Stage, American Journal of Public Health, February, 1947, pages 150-155.

Goldman, Franz: An Adequate Program of Medical Care of Elderly People, Public Health Reports, February, 1952, page 132.

Johnson, Ralph J., and Pond, M. Allen: Health Standards of Housing for the Aging Population, Journal of Gerontology, April, 1952, pages 254-258.

Keys, Ancel: Nutrition for the Later Years of Life, Public Health Reports, Vol. 67 No. 5, May, 1952, pages 484-489.

Kinnaman, Joseph H.: Problems of an Aging Population, Sheltered Care of the Aged, American Journal of Public Health, February 1947, pages 163-169.

Klumpp, Theodore G.: Problem of An Aging Population, American Journal of Public Health, February, 1947, pages 156-162.

Lawton, George: New Goals for Old Age, Columbia University Press, 1943.

Man and His Years: Health Publication Institute, Raleigh, N.C., 1951, Federal Security Agency, No. 6, Health Maintenance & Rehabilitation, Washington, D. C.

Mulaney, S. Gertrude, and Waterman, Theda L.: A Community Plans for the Aged, Public Health Nursing, October, 1950, pages 568-573.

Newton, Kathleen: Geriatric Nursing, St. Louis, 1950, The C. V. Mosby Company.

Nursing Homes in Two States, American Journal of Nursing, November, 1951, pages 638-640, 658-660.

Pibbits, Clark: Socio-Economic and Public Health Aspects of the Aging Process, American Journal of Public Health, August, 1951, pages 944-947.

Randall, Ollie A.: The Aging—The Aged, Public Health Nursing, January, 1948, pages 61-65.

Robson, R. B.: What the General Practitioner and the Industrial Physician Should Know Regarding Problems of Retirement, Canadian Medical Association Journal **63**:457, 1950.

Rogers, Agnes: My Mother Lives With Us, Harpers Magazine, Nov., 1952, pages 34-39.

Steinberg, Martin R.: The General Hospital in Community Planning for the Aged, Geriatrics, July and August, 1950, pages 231-232.

Weil, Julius: The Aged Ill, Hospitals **19**:48-42, 1945.

III. Social Problems Mainly Economic

CHAPTER 22

ECONOMIC PROBLEMS AND DEPENDENCY

THE MEANING OF DEPENDENCY

The close relationship between health and economics has been shown previously. Good medical care is expensive and many persons delay getting adequate care because of this factor. Among families in low income groups, also, much illness and many health problems exist. In fact in any study of persons receiving financial assistance from public or private sources, illness has always loomed large as a cause for needing financial aid, or as one of the many factors preventing the family from functioning independently.

The picture of the "American Way of Life" is based on a self-supporting family with the wage earner meeting his family's basic needs, being supplemented by public services provided by schools, public safety measures, parks, libraries, and other governmental services, and preparing for his old age and "rainy days" by savings. The social insurance provisions of the Social Security Act have added security to this picture. Needs of families vary according to the standard of living which they adopt. The American acceptance of public responsibility for persons in economic need, adapted from the English law years ago, has meant that some financial help is available for those unable to provide a basic minimum living for themselves and families. Implicit in these plans is the ideal that families should be rehabilitated to take care of themselves, but that it is not dishonorable to apply for and receive public assistance. The reliance for financial aid, on sources outside the family, public or private, is what is known as dependency today.

In this country during the depression of the thirties, when unemployment was widespread, the presence of dependency as a social problem was demonstrated. State and federal governments were forced to give much time and money to alleviate the conditions even on an inadequate basis. Efforts have been undertaken since then to prevent a recurrence of such a widespread depression. In the overpopulated countries of Asia and the middle east, a continuous problem of poverty and starvation plagues the governments. Causes may be deep-rooted in the economic system, land tenure, cultural beliefs and habits, but the problem is claiming international attention.

Dependency tends to produce personal problems as well, particularly if extended over a long period of time. Work skills diminish, feelings of inadequacy develop in the wage earner because of his inability to get a job, reproaches may be directed at him by the wife, loss of status with family and friends develops. Environmental factors also press on the individual; poorer and poorer quarters, inability to get proper health care, few opportunities for leisure time. The cumulative effect of these inner and outer pressures conspire to undermine the self-confidence of an individual so that he becomes insecure and incompetent as a worker and a frustrated member of the family group.

The greatest threats to earning capacity are unemployment, illness, or physical handicap, old age, mental or other incapacity, any of which prevents the wage earner from earning. Other factors affecting the amount of income in a family are lack of training for a job, mental deficiency, poor or no schooling, maladjusted personality. So interrelated are social problems that it is rare that lack of income alone will make a family dependent. Widespread economic depression, however, affected otherwise able and self-sustaining persons in this country so that they were obliged to seek relief during the 1930's. Many of those temporarily out of employment were able to rehabilitate themselves during periods of high employment during and since the war. Likewise those whose productivity was slowing down were able to make a contribution when the demand for labor was at a premium, subsequently to be laid off when the pressure for labor slackened.

INCOME VARIANCE IN THE UNITED STATES

The amount of money which each family has during a year varies widely. More persons live on small earnings and few persons enjoy large yearly incomes. Other wide discrepancies are noticed. The average income in urban areas is greater than in rural areas. Families with large numbers of children have less yearly earnings than do families with fewer children. These facts are shown in Table III.

TABLE III

AVERAGE INCOME OF FAMILIES IN THE UNITED STATES—1948

TYPE OF FAMILY	AVERAGE YEARLY INCOME
U. S. Average	$3,187
White	3,310
Nonwhite	1,768
Urban	3,551
Rural, nonfarm	2,954
Farm	2,036
Husband-wife families	3,272
Families headed by women	2,064
Families with 1 or 2 children	3,315
Families with 3 or 4 children	3,072
Families with 6 or more children	2,488

Source: Children and Youth at the Midcentury—A Chart Book, 1950, Charts 20 and 21.

As Table III shows, yearly income is particularly low for farm families, for members of minority groups, for families without a father, for families in which there are large numbers of children.

But actual earnings do not tell the whole story. The cost of living has been steadily climbing since 1940. Food prices have more than doubled, rents have increased after removal of controls imposed during the period of World War II. Clothing and household goods have also increased in price. The American dollar is now worth about one-half that amount in terms of purchasing power. All costs for services, for schools, for hospitals, for salaries, and administration of government are higher so that community costs have risen. Since community services are supported largely through taxes, these have risen, too.

The American standard of living still remains the highest in the world. Some articles in our culture, as automobiles, radios, or television sets, are within the grasp of many families with small incomes. Families in the by and large adapt their scale of living to their earning. In low income families, obviously, a greater percentage of the income must go for food and shelter than goes for these items among more wealthy families. Clothing is another essential item. Home economists have worked with the facts enough to distinguish several levels of living, of which the lowest is the minimum necessary to maintain decency and health standards used in determining needs of families applying for financial help. But many families whose income affords them a standard of living even slightly above this basic minimum are unable to meet costs of illness when it strikes. Thus many of the programs designed to treat illness, and handicaps are available to many persons on a free basis or at greatly reduced prices and not limited to persons on the very lowest income level.

HOW DEPENDENCY AFFECTS A FAMILY

Perhaps the effect of family needs and the meaning of dependency can be visualized through some illustrations. This simple case also indicates some of the services which communities have provided for helping the families.

After a routine x-ray from the mobile unit of the county health department Tuberculosis Unit, Mr. W. was referred to a hospital for a more complete examination. His condition was precisely diagnosed as tuberculosis and the doctor recommended that he go to the state sanatorium for treatment for an indefinite stay. Mr. W. was a bus driver, married and with four children between the ages of 12 and 3 years. He was extremely upset at the diagnosis, but more by the recommendation that he should leave his family, to whom he was very much attached. Nor did he see how they could manage financially to get along without him. He decided to put off the hospitalization, take life easier. Both he and his wife tried to save more money against the future. In a few months, however, Mr. W. broke down and then he decided he could no longer evade the issue and went to the sanatorium.

Mrs. W. found it very difficult to manage on the small savings. She had depended on her husband a great deal with the disciplining of the children and had difficulty with them, too. She worried continually about becoming financially dependent on the community. Neither she nor her husband had relatives who could help them substantially enough to make much difference. The family moved to a smaller, less expensive place. Mrs. W. made inquiries regarding employment but she was not skilled sufficiently to earn more than she would have to pay out to have some one care for the children while she worked. With the help of the medical social worker at the hospital Mrs. W. was referred to the public welfare office, where she made application for financial assistance from the program for dependent children until such time as Mr. W. returned to the home.

She discussed her situation with a social worker. Together they estimated the needs of herself and the four children according to the budgets allowed by the state. Then they substracted any income which Mrs. W. might have, to discover what was the budget deficit. The worker visited the home. The fact of Mr. W.'s absence was verified. Then Mrs. W. was declared eligible to receive the grant.

The bare outlines of this story show the coming of dependency to a normally self-secure family, associated, as is true in so many cases, with illness. The study does not show the feelings of the parents and the children which might affect their capacity as persons for their roles in the family. Other families might have had more skill and education, more of a backlog of savings, might not have had so many children, might have had more relatives to help. Mrs. W. could have adopted other solutions. She might have gone home to her parents; she might have placed the children in an institution or foster homes under the auspices of private charibtable agencies. But the course she chose, the Aid to Dependent Children (ADC) program, preserved the home and helped the family during the hospitalization of the father.

Although this situation showed a family who encountered dependency and unemployment complicated by illness, there is always a residue of families who have known poverty all their lives. Some of these persons have never been endowed with enough mental ability or physical strength to earn an adequate or even minimum subsistence, may have become victims of large numbers of social problems, may have been sharecroppers always living on the fringe of hunger and dependency.

Plans of various natures have been devised to help them. Sometimes these have included plans for rehabilitation of the individual or family. Financial aid for the ablebodied adult man has been less frequently given except on a temporary basis.

METHODS OF MEETING PROBLEMS CAUSED BY DEPENDENCY

That the community has a responsibility to care for certain of its members who are dependent financially was established back in the time of Queen Elizabeth in the historic "poor laws" passed in 1603. Heretofore only churches, convents, religious organizations, fraternal orders, as well as individuals charitably inclined played the helping role for the poor and needy. Efforts of poor relief officials for many years were to discharge this responsibility as niggardly as possible, to make relief given very unpleasant and unpalatable, to stigmatize those who were recipients of this grudging charity. Theirs was a philosophy of individual responsibility, a person was considered at fault if he had not succeeded in being adequate. Not until many years later, was there any recognition that economic conditions had some effect on the ability of the individual to look after himself and family. Nor was there any early vision of the possibility of rehabilitating the so-called paupers. The system almost prevented a person, once on the relief rolls, getting off.

The United States, taking shape as a nation not long after this major step in assumption of public responsibility, followed the English precept for some time. Relief responsibility was a burden on local government units. Local "Poor Boards" were unnecessarily frugal in the grants of relief, because of a prevalent feeling that an open frontier existed and everyone desiring work could find some. More sympathy for widows and orphans existed. By the nineteenth century private charitable organizations were also working in local communities. Some of these were for specific groups of people, as early orphanages, benevolent societies providing for their own members, churches taking care of the poorer members of their congregations, organizations for immigrants or other specified groups. During the nineteenth century, states took a hand in providing some facilities for the sick and disabled, mainly setting up institutions for mentally ill, mental defectives, delinquents, the crippled, blind, etc. The state also undertook to supervise the institutions it set up and coordinate their work. Late in this century states established systems for the care of dependent children in foster homes or institutions.

Supplying funds for public assistance in the United States has been primarily a responsibility of local governments up until the depression of the 1930's. States accepted responsibility for supervision of welfare institutions, offered consultation services, tried to coordinate effort and contributed state funds to certain categories of needy persons, mainly those residents who had not lived in a local community long enough to be eligible for aid. States had contributed funds to towns for relief but not on a widespread basis. But as unemployment increased in the period of the depression states gave considerable financial help to the towns. But local and state funds soon proved insufficient for the rising tide of needy persons applying for help. Congress authorized in 1932 the Reconstruction Finance Corporation to lend to the states $300,000,000 of federal funds for relief purposes. This soon became exhausted, so great were the demands upon it.

In May, 1933, with the passage of the Federal Emergency Relief Act, the federal government accepted responsibility for relief, a marked change in previous precedent of making this a local and state responsibility. Grants of money were made to states on a matching basis, although some outright allotments were made to needy states. The government followed this with other programs designed to ease the plight of the needy unemployed, best known of which is probably the Works Progress Administration. Projects requiring various skills were to be set up in local communities and be manned by persons on relief. The aim of this program was to preserve work skills of the unemployed head of a family or family member, and to preserve his pride in working rather than to provide a financial dole from the government. Although widely criticized, the program helped millions of families. Other programs, especially for youth, into which federal funds were placed, were the Civilian Conservation Corps and the National Youth Administration.

Some plans of granting financial aid to states had been undertaken even prior to the depression. Subsequent to the second White House Conference on Children, the Sheppard-Towner Act had allowed federal funds to states to strengthen the maternal and child health work of the states. Also after World War I funds had been given by the federal government to support the first Vocational Rehabilitation program for civilians. Thus, some of the provisions of the Social Security Act had been foreshadowed.

THE AMERICAN SOCIAL SECURITY ACT

By 1935 there was more or less widespread acceptance of the need for cooperation between federal, state, and local governments to meet the relief needs of the people. The Social Security Act was passed in August 1935 culminating many discussions and studies. It provided for three distinct types of programs; social insurances, financial assistance to specified needy persons, and health and social services. The insurance programs were two, Old Age and Survivor's Insurance and Unemployment Compensation, designed to bulwark the threat to the family of death of the wage earner, or prolonged unemployment, and to provide security for the worker himself as he grows older. The assistance sections provided for federal matching of state and local funds to provide at least a monthly stipulated sum of money to certain categories of needy people, those over 65, those blind or nearly blind, dependent children in a broken home. The third section of the Act provided for grants-in-aid to states for the establishment of specified services, mainly to improve the facilities available for children in rural areas. These were four, Maternal and Child Health, Crippled Children's Services, Child Welfare Services, and Vocational Rehabilitation. Funds could be used for setting up clinics, salary of personnel, scholarships for training of needed personnel, administration, hospital care, prosthetic devices; but no money was to be given to families using the services. These funds were mainly to be matched with state funds, although some grants were given in addition to the poorer states without matching. These programs are discussed elsewhere in this book.

The Social Security Act has been amended in 1939, 1946, 1950 and 1952. The Act now does not include Vocational Rehabilitation provisions which were incorporated in the Barden-LaFollette Act. Otherwise the changes have been to increase coverage of the insurance programs, increase amounts which the federal government would make available to states, to raise the amount of maximum toward which the federal government would contribute on the assistance programs, to increase the amount of benefits on the insurance program, increase somewhat the amount of the federal contribution on the assistance program, and to provide a new category of needy persons, the Permanently and Totally Disabled.

This Act does not guarantee complete financial security for life. This would be financially impossible and of doubtful merit. But social insurance should provide for those persons covered by it some protection against certain threats to earning power. Public assistance, meanwhile, has been established as rightfully being available for those who are indigent, not as something carrying a stigma. Hopefully, families receiving public assistnce can be rehabilitated so that they will no longer need assistance. The service programs have proved most helpful in extending services and enabling social workers, doctors, nurses, nutritionists, to acquire special training for work to staff the new programs.[1]

THE SOCIAL INSURANCES

Perhaps the best known of the two insurance programs is that of Old Age and Survivors Insurance (OASI). This provides for contributions by employees and employers into a fund from which at age 65, the insured person retiring, or at his death, his survivor and minor children will get certain benefits. Various restrictions govern the lengths of time contributions must have been paid and the benefits available. Industries in which this program operate are called "covered" industries.

---

[1]For a good discussion of the Social Security System, see Burns, Evaline: The American Social Security System, New York, 1949, Houghton Mifflin Company.

Coverage included about 35 million workers prior to the 1950 amendments. Subsequently, almost ten million more were included, formerly not eligible, among these, the self-employed, some agricultural workers, domestic workers, employees of nonprofit organizations, government workers. Contributions to the OASI funds are figured on earnings up to $3,600 per year only. The minimum and the maximum benefits for the worker at retirement vary according to length of employment, earnings and family status.

Unemployment compensation is operated through the various state employment offices. Here the employers pay a payroll tax to the federal government. Actually taxes for this insurance are paid to states and applied toward the federal government requirements, if the state's plan meets federal approval. All workers are not covered with these provisions, not even as many as under the OASI provisions. Not covered are agricultural labor, domestic services, casual labor, those working for various governmental units, charitable corporations, and several others. Benefits vary from state to state but usually are in terms of a percentage of the wages earned and for not more than twenty-six weeks. The worker must register at the state employment office and show that he has lost his job through no fault of his own. Efforts are made to find a job for the workers, although he is not compelled to take any job which is available regardless of his suitability and qualifications for it. Provisions of this plan have tided many a worker and his family over rough times.

PUBLIC ASSISTANCE PROVISIONS

Every county in the United States has at least one public welfare office where applications for assistance may be made by any needy citizen. County welfare offices are, on the whole, responsible for administering these programs under state supervision. Federal funds are given through the state offices on a grant-in-aid basis. Usually state and local funds as well as federal funds finance these programs. The assistance provisions are only for persons in need; in addition to need, the applicant must fit one of the categories, be 65 or over, have a specified limited amount of vision, be a dependent child, under 16 or 18 if in school, in a home with one parent or a specified relative, or be permanently and totally disabled. The federal government insists that the needy person after investigation must be helped on a minimum scale of assistance if federal funds are available. There are no restrictions on the states or locality putting in more than the federal gov-

ernment. Changes in the amount toward which the federal government will contribute have been increased several times. Currently it
is $55 for the Old Age Assistance (OAA), the Aid to the Blind, and
the Permanent and Totally Disabled program. For the dependent
children (ADC), it is $30 for the caretaker, $30 for the first child, and
$21 for each successive child.

The government requires that public assistance provisions be state-
wide in operation, that the merit system apply to all employees, that
quarterly reports be submitted.

Within these federal requirements the states have many problems.
How much shall their minimum budgets provide? Shall extra allow-
ances for the sick be included? How much property may an oldster
have and still receive OAA Grants? Shall relatives be required to
support aged kinsmen if they can do so? Shall pressure be brought
on them to do so? Must a recalcitrant and deserting or divorced
father be brought to court to support his children before his dependent
children are eligible for assistance? The federal government leaves
such problems to the states. It interferes if the objectives of the program are not being met; for example, if investigation of need was
not being made for those over sixty-five, it can, and occasionally has
withdrawn funds where requirements have not been complied with.

Amounts given in any of these categories vary from state to state.
Generally, the west coast states and the eastern states of Connecticut,
Massachusetts, New York, and Pennsylvania give higher grants. This
means the states must put more money into the program than is
matched by the government. For the month of April, 1953, for example, the average OAA grant in the United States was $48.85. The
lowest state average grants were $27.37 in Alabama and $28.24 in
Mississippi. The highest grants were $78.81 in Colorado, $67.62 in
Massachusetts, and $65.89 in Oklahoma. Similarly for the ADC pro-
gram, the United States average grant per family was found to be in
this same month $82,44. The lowest grant was in Mississippi with
$27.67, followed by Alabama with an average of $39.61. Idaho and
California similarly gave an average of $121 per family. Southern states
are relatively poorer than the rest of the United States. Standards of
living are also somewhat lower as are some costs.[2]

At the present time increases in amounts spent for OASI have decreased the number of persons receiving Old Age Assistance and a

---

[2]Current Operating Statistics, Social Security Bulletin **16**:26-28, June, 1953.

greater decrease should be noticeable in the future. Less change has occurred in the ADC program although the number of survivors' beneficiaries has been rising. The number of recipients of some of these programs is given in Table IV.

TABLE IV

RECIPIENTS AND TOTAL AMOUNTS EXPENDED FOR SOCIAL SECURITY
PROGRAMS FISCAL YEAR 1952

PROGRAM	NO. OF RECIPIENTS	TOTAL AMT. EXPENDED (IN THOUSANDS OF DOLLARS)	AV. MO. AMT. PER PERSON
Old Age and Survivors Insurance	4,593,801	$1,940,000[a]	$41.98[b]
Old Age Assistance	2,659,661	1,487,605	45.19
Aid to Dependent Children	2,041,447	547,253	75.88[c]
Aid to the Blind	97,651	58,184	49.99
Aid to the Permanently and Totally Disabled	145,345	75,067	46.06

Source: Annual Report of the Federal Security Agency, 1952, Social Security Administration, pp. 74-76.
[a]Estimated
[b]Old age benefits only; survivors not included
[c]Family average

From the preceding discussion of the categorical system, it can be seen that there may be some needy persons, who do not have children, who are under 65, who are not blind and totally disabled. These persons as yet share no federal program but are eligible for funds, called "general relief," provided by local and state governmental units. These funds are usually dispensed through the same welfare office and by the same social workers as the other grants for needy applicants. In some communities, however, greater restrictions are placed on these funds than in the other programs.

OTHER FINANCIAL ASSISTANCE AVAILABLE

Public funds are available for two other groups of persons, namely, veterans and their families, and dependent children whose families are unable or incapable of caring for them and who must be supported outside of the home. The Veterans Administration furnishes a variety of services and pensions for veterans and their families or survivors, medical care, compensation for injuries, hospital service. Some states have additional benefits for the veteran. All states provide some kind of care for children, who because of dependency or neglect must be cared for outside of the family group, the family being unable or unwilling to care for their child. Most states have a child welfare division charged with responsibility for studying all such children referred to them and for finding foster homes or institutional care for them.

Although throughout the United States, the principle is well accepted that the public agencies assume major responsibility for basic maintenance, resources are also found for more temporary care in private social agencies. In large cities and many small ones, family service societies, formerly called family welfare or associated charities, are found supported by private endowments and community chests, Red Feather services. These agencies offer a skilled counseling service to families experiencing personal problems as between husband-wife, or parent and child. Financial assistance is frequently given as part of the plan of helping the family, but it is not given on a long-range plan. For specific families in need of more than the public may allow, as in some severe illnesses or a family burned out, the charitable instincts of churches, civic clubs, and philanthropic individuals always rise to the front. Many sectarian agencies provide services for members of their faith.

The American Red Cross, the American Legion, and some other veterans organizations help the serviceman under certain circumstances and stand ready to aid him in filing his claim or to refer him to the correct service officer. Fraternal orders, such as the Masons, will help their members when in need and have their own plans for study. Many unions have their own welfare funds as well as pensions for their members, for aid during strikes, unemployment, sickness and retirement, or for survivors.

Industrial accidents are a great threat to the wage earner in manufacturing and construction industry. Injury on the job may cause loss of time and perhaps permanent physical handicaps. Workmen's Compensation Laws on the books of all states have reduced these accidents greatly and provided financial assistance for the injured worker as compensation for the accident if it was the fault of management. These insurance plans are borne by management. The big industrial insurance companies have made it profitable for management to install safety devices and procedures.

Illness of the wage earner takes a large toll in wages lost and in income expended for care and treatment. Various private insurance companies have plans to insure the worker against such loss of work, some providing hospitalization, doctor's fees, and even stipulated amounts per week during illness. Many of these are group plans which usually make the cost lower, for example, the Blue Cross plan for hospitalization. Suggestions have also been made, some of which have been incorporated into law, for some form of compulsory sickness insurance supported in part at least by public funds. Some of these plans have been branded "socialized medicine" and have not found favor here yet. Representatives of the medical profession and public health workers have been studying to provide some plan of prepaid medical care affording some protection to the wage earner against heavy expenses of illness.

SUMMARY

Economic dependency is a drain on any community, and represents a loss of manpower and a wastage of human resources. Some of this dependency can be prevented. Governmental units have accepted a responsibility for meeting the needs of the dependent group in every community. Not all of these endeavors have sought to analyze underlying causes of dependency, although recognition is given to the objective of complete rehabilitation of the needy family. The public insurance provisions have as their goal prevention of need for public assistance and indeed have served their purpose and presumably will be increasingly more effective. The public assistance provisions are the most comprehensive of all efforts to ameliorate the conditions of basic financial help for maintenance. They are the right of all needy persons eligible for them. Other efforts provide substantial help to the individuals involved although they are not widely available.

The effects on the community of widespread dependency are perhaps better known than the effects on the individual. Rarely is the individual faced with one problem which can be isolated as economic need. Usually the need is the result of a series of interwoven causes. As has been said as a result of a widespread study of economic need and dependency in St. Paul:

> Methods for distinguishing between dependency caused by personal disabilities and dependency due to economic imbalance have yet to find their way to acceptance in community practice. There are few procedures for gaining accurate knowledge about the constellations of personal disabilities . . . or . . . of employment hazards which may be producing much

of the community's need for assistance. In short there has been as yet very little systematic thought or practical experiment directed toward determining what a community ought to know in order to plan a concerted attack upon its total problem.[3]

STUDY QUESTIONS AND PROJECTS

1. If possible, visit the local Public Welfare Office and discuss the policies of relief giving, case loads, trends, and problems in your community.

2. What has been the relation in the United States between the programs of the social insurance and the public assistance programs? Do you think practice carries out the theories on which they are based?

3. Study family budgets used by agencies in your community. Are these revised with changes in the cost of living? Is there a difference between budgets used by public and private agencies?

4. Discuss conditions causing economic need: in the environment, in the person, in the family.

5. In cases which you have known or which may be known to the Visiting Nurse Society or to the Public Welfare Office, study relationship between ill health and poverty.

6. What is meant by "unemployable"? How can this group be made smaller? Can it disappear completely?

7. What are likely to be the social and emotional effects of prolonged unemployment on the individual? On the family?

8. Discuss all the steps that the modern worker can take to prevent economic insecurity.

9. Outline a long-range program which a community could undertake to insure greater security of employment and decreased economic need.

10. Discuss the feelings of persons receiving public financial assistance. Is this a stigma? Are children discriminated against because of their family's relief status? If so, how? Do families receiving relief seem to be making the most of themselves?

11. Discuss arguments in the current controversy over making public the names of persons receiving relief so that they can be identified. What do you think about such a measure? Would it act as a deterrent to others?

12. Consult some studies of persons in the lower economic group receiving relief. What has been their education, family composition, and other social factors accounting for their condition?

13. Examine statistics presented in the Social Security Bulletin on number of recipients of assistance programs. How do you account for variations between states?

---

[3]Buell, Bradley, and Associates: Community Services for Meeting Human Needs, New York, 1951, Columbia University Press, pages 34 and 35.

14. List all the resources you know in your community which will help a needy family financially or otherwise. Is the help given continuously, at special times, as Christmas, or in special instances.

REFERENCES

Buell, Bradley, and Associates: Community Planning for Human Services, New York, 1952, Columbia University Press, chapters II-VI.

Burns, Evelina M. Economic Future of the Family, Survey Graphic **37**:370-372, August, 1948.

Burns, Evelina M.: The American Social Security Systems, Boston, 1949, Houghton Mifflin Company.

Buritt, Bailey B.: Welfare Measures and Their Effect Upon the Family, American Journal of Public Health **39**: 214-215, February, 1949.

Close, Kathryn: Whither Public Welfare, Survey **88**:34-36, January, 1952.

Federal Social Security Act Amendments of 1950, Monthly Labor Review **71**:457-460, October, 1950.

Freeman, Lucy: Children Who Never Had A Chance, Public Affairs Pamphlet, No. 183, New York, 1952.

Fink, Arthur: The Field of Social Work, New York, revised edition, 1949, Henry Holt & Company, chapters 2 and 3.

Kasius, Cora, ed.: Relief Practice in a Family Agency, New York, 1942, Family Welfare Association of America (now Family Service Association of America).

Koos, Earl L.: Families in Trouble, New York, 1946, Commonwealth Fund.

Merriam, Lewis: Relief and Social Security, Washington, 1946, Brookings Institute.

Miles, Arthur P.: An Introduction to Public Welfare, Boston, 1949, D. C. Heath and Company, Part III.

Smith, Marjorie J.: Rural Case Work Service, New York, 1943, Family Welfare Association of America (now Family Service Association of America).

Stroup, Herbert: Social Work, An Introduction To the Field, New York, 1948, American Book Company, chapters 2, 11, and 12.

IV. Crime

CHAPTER 23

CRIME AND THE OFFENDER

INTRODUCTION

The offender as defined in law includes in this category any one who violates a law or an ordinance of any unit of government, city, county, state, or federal.   Actually there are modifications of this definition in practice.   Offenses are classified into those which are regarded as more serious, such as murder, assault with a deadly weapon, arson, and those which may be considerably less serious, as violation of traffic rules.   It has often been pointed out that many persons who break laws and ordinances have never been caught, so that from the point of view of society they have never been numbered among the offenders. In common usage, however, one thinks of the offender as an apprehended lawbreaker, and the "crimes" reported are usually those of serious offenses.

Yet another concept has entered into the practice of justice, that of the wilfulness of the offender. If one acknowledges the doctrine of free will, the person who breaks a law knows that it is morally wrong but chooses to take this action rather than another more socially acceptable. It logically follows from this that there are some circumstances when the lawbreaker was not able to distinguish right from wrong and therefore incapable of making a free choice.   Such has been held to be true of children under six or seven, and persons insane.   The fixing of the lower age limit has been somewhat arbitrary, for it is difficult to understand just when a child may reach an age of discretion and be able to make his choices with an understanding of the right from the wrong.

Differentiation is found in the handling of offenders.   As has been pointed out previously, all states have different court procedures for children under specified years of age, usually 16 or 17. These youngsters are not considered adults and are treated quite differently. Variation in the upper age range in the several states reflect the doubt in the minds of the lawmakers as to just when the boy or girl becomes responsible under adult laws. Some further distinctions are made regarding treatment of young offenders, many states having a reformatory for youths over the juvenile court age but much younger than the adult lawbreakers who may be sent to the state penitentiary.

EXTENT OF CRIME

The Federal Bureau of Investigation points out in its annual report for 1951 and for the first six months of 1952 that crime is on the increase in the United States. In 1951 the police reports submitted to the Bureau showed an increase of 5.1 per cent over the preceding year, and the first six months of 1952 showed an increase over the first six months of the preceding year of 6.4 per cent.[1] Furthermore both of these bulletins indicated that auto thefts had increased the most; other types of larceny were the next largest. Although there are still a large number of wanton killings and felonious assaults, both of these types of crime showed slight decreases in 1951, but in the first half of 1952 an increase in all types of crime except rape was shown.

The FBI figures include reports from chiefs of police and represent arrests. The figures also should be viewed with caution as the FBI is unable to guarantee their completeness. In actual numbers, a total of 1,882,160 offenses were known to the police in 1951; 960,000 of these were committed in the first half of the year. In the first half of 1952, however 1,022,200 offenses had been reported, a substantial increase. As the report goes on to state, "This estimate of major crime is considered conservative because such other important crimes as arson, embezzlement, carrying concealed weapons, and others are not included."[2]

Crime data need some analysis to indicate the type of persons involved and also of the problem presented to the community where the crimes occur. Cities contain the greatest number of criminals and on the basis of population have a higher rate of crime than do rural areas. Interestingly enough there is a gradual reduction in rates from large cities to small villages. Some differences in type of offenses which

---

[1]Federal Bureau of Investigation: Uniform Crime Reports, Annual Bulletin 1951, p. 67, and Semiannual Bulletin 1952, p. 1.
[2]Federal Bureau of Investigation: Uniform Crime Reports, 1952, p. 4.

brought the offender to the police occur also between urban and rural crimes. As has been shown in other studies, rural crime rates are similar to and frequently exceed the urban rates in crimes against the person, while crimes against property are generally lower.[3]

Type of offense has been classified in eight categories and consistently over a period of years the greatest number of offenses has been shown in the following:

> Larceny—theft
> Burglary—breaking and entering
> Auto theft
> Aggravated assault
> Robbery
> Rape
> Murder and nonnegligent manslaughter
> Negligent manslaughter

Some differences also exist throughout the country in that New England is low in murders, robberies, and aggravated assaults, and the East South Central and South Atlantic States have the highest rates of aggravated assaults.

Always a greater preponderance of males are involved in breaking the law, almost ten times as many men are arrested as women. Slightly less than one-half of the total persons arrested in the first six months of 1952 were less than 30 years of age, 29 per cent of whom were under 25, and 15 per cent under 21. This points up criminality as being preponderantly occurring in early adulthood. Male arrests occurred most frequently at age 18.

More white persons are always arrested than Negroes, yet the ratio of white persons arrested to the population is lower than that for Negroes. This is due to many factors, poorer economic conditions under which many of the nonwhite race live, cultural attitudes toward law enforcement, and manner of handling offenses by the police.

Only a small per cent of persons known to the police as having committed offenses are later institutionalized. In 1950, the Federal Bureau of Prisons reported 167,173 prisoners in state and federal prisons and reformatories for adult offenders, an increase of 1.2 per cent over 1949, but a decrease of one per cent when related to the estimated

---

[3]All of these data are taken from the Uniform Crime Reports..

civilan population.[4] These same figures showed that twenty-six times as many men as women were incarcerated.

Other prison statistics show that the prisoners are young men, mainly between the ages of twenty-five and thirty-five, in the prime of life or when their activities should be devoted to constructive ends. Marked diminution in the age groups over forty are found in prisons. In numbers there are more white than nonwhite persons in prison, but in proportion to the population, the nonwhites have a higher prison rate than do the whites. Native born persons appear in prison populations in somewhat greater frequency than they do in the population at large. Prisoners are also more likely to have had less education than those outside, 43 per cent of prisoners had less than seven years' schooling compared with 24 per cent of the country as a whole.[5]

THE INDIVIDUAL CRIMINAL

Searches for causes of crime have been many and have been mainly unrewarding. Many factors, not one, contribute to making an individual into a crimnial, some social in origin, most are personal or resulting from conflicts and warped personality patterns within the individual. Social factors such as poor housing, poverty, discriminatory practices particularly against minority groups, lack of group moral standards of honesty, all have some effect. But each individual must make an adjustment to his environment and all do not adopt criminal ways. Disorganization of the personality stemming from mental conflicts, deprivations of early childhood, inability to find acceptable outlets for hostility and aggression, antisocial reaction to frustration can be seen when the individual criminal is studied carefully. Factors indicating stability in some area as in holding a job, good family relationships, have proved helpful in deciding upon parole.

With so many divergent factors influencing the offender and the complicated nature of his personality, the problem a prison faces of turning these individuals into responsible citizens is tremendous. Results of studies of causation have reaffirmed need for taking all possible steps in prevention of personality breakdown, especially among juvenile delinquents, many of whom go on to adult prisons. Reduction

[4]National Prisoner Statistics, Federal Bureau of Prisons, Washington, D. C., Nov. 27, 1951.

[5]Sheldon, Henry D.: "Correctional Statistics" in Tappan, Paul: Contemporary Correction, New York, 1951, McGraw-Hill Book Company, Inc., page 27.

or elimination of factors of social disorganization fostering a criminal career is also indicated.

Our thesis has been throughout this work that for all the statistics showing the social problem there are men and women who are involved whose personal disorganization has led them to anti-social methods of satisfaction. The following case story illustrates one such prisoner. In its abbreviated form the reader does not see the feelings and reactions of this boy, but one does see something of his family and environmental situation. This shows his story until he gets to prison. The effect of prison and his subsequent release is discussed later.

Leo Reynolds was a good-looking young man of twenty-six years. Physically he possessed a powerful build. He was the product of a home broken by the father's death when Leo was eleven years of age. However, his parents were emotionally at odds long before that. He recalled little of love or support from his parents. At the age of thirteen he was committed to a juvenile institution as a sneak thief for which commitment he blamed his mother. At the age of sixteen he was released from the training school defiant, desperate, and ready for trouble. Eventually he found a lot of it.

For the next four years Leo ran wild. He hitchhiked over most of the country, became a seaman for short periods of time and secured occasional work of an unskilled nature. He wandered restlessly with little sense of purpose, time, or accomplishments. He had occasional brushes with the law and for one of these offenses he served thirty days on a chain gang. In 1936 he committed armed robberies in North Carolina, Maryland, and in Pennsylvania. He was captured in one of these southern states but succeeded in getting away. His record there bore the notation "Escaped-Wanted." He was finally arrested in Pennsylvania and given the ten-to-twenty-year sentence which he was now serving. Detainers were placed against him by the other two states from each of which he could reasonably expect an equal amount of prison time. At the age of 20 then Leo had entered the state penitentiary with the possibility of thirty or more years of prison life ahead of him.[6]

METHODS OF HANDLING CRIMINALS

All societies have worked out systems for handling misdemeanants whether they break tribal customs or the written statutes of present-day government. The pattern is frequently similar. First, the offender is apprehended by someone who is delegated the power to do so. Most societies feel that some hearing is then due the offender. His accusers must place their complaints and evidence, and the accused has opportunity to present his defense. In our society with adult offenders

---

[6]Fink, Arthur: Field of Social Work. New York, Henry Holt & Co., 1949, Revised edition, pages 416-417. (Quoted by permission of publishers.)

we call this a trial and lawyers are assigned to each side of the case. Furthermore, the accused has a right to appeal to a higher court than the criminal court which hears cases of serious offenses. Usually, too, the accused is entitled to a jury of his peers. It is then up to the judge to decide what shall be done with the offender.

Although the above may sound simple, many confusing elements have insinuated themselves into this process. First of all, the theory of dealing with the offender contains fundamental difficulties in operation. Reduced to simplest terms, offenders must be punished for the protection of the remaining members of society, but in the punishing, the innocent, if accused, must be protected from injustice. This leads to many practices which some think enable the guilty to escape his just desserts whereas originally they were designed to prevent a miscarriage of justice. Once the criminal has been found guilty, what is the objective of treatment? Traditionally punishment has been meted out as retribution to the wrong doer for doing wrong and to others as a deterrent. The wrong doer was a free agent, capable of distinguishing between right and wrong at the time he perpetrated the offense. Most thinking members of society realize that persons have not been deterred from breaking laws by the spectacle of prisons or even hard labor and electric chairs. Differences in length of sentences imposed and the various classification systems utilized in the modern penitentiary are full proof that in dealing with the criminal, society, through its established institutions, recognizes individual circumstances in each case. Theoretically prison programs provide some individually planned rehabilitative measures for the inmates. Obviously, most of the inmates of the state penitentiaries will be returning to their own community and should be helped to make an adjustment upon their return. Yet many prisons today use repressive and autocratic control or methods of handling the prisoners which prevent the achievement of established goals. The recent series of riots in several state penitentiaries are indicative of the gaps between theory and practice.

Society's first arm of defense against the law breaker is its police force. They have the power of arrest, and are the first persons to be called in by the local observer of law-breaking in action. The police in most places merely have the power of arrest and booking the offender, although they also question him. Detectives are an arm of the police in every large city. Many police systems have policewomen to work with women offenders.

Much has been written concerning the quality of the police force today. Many times the members are untrained; their personal integrity may be questioned as some are open to bribes. On the other hand, police training courses have been established in many states, and genuine efforts have been put forth to get men of high standards and good intelligence on police forces. Communities frequently are unwilling to appropriate enough money to insure an adequately trained police force in sufficient numbers to do a good job.

The Federal Bureau of Investigation reports an increase in number of police reported in 1952 over 1951, 175 per 100,000 inhabitants in 1952. When related to the size of the community, a steady increase in average number of police per 1,000 persons is shown from communities of under 10,000 to communities of over 250,000.[7] This tells little except the number of police department employees. Differing administrative procedures are observed from place to place, particularly in handling traffic. A trend to use part-time policemen and policewomen in many cases to take care of traffic around schools has found acceptance.

The local jail is often times the first place which the offender visits. It is an understatement to say that many of these, more than 3,000 local institutions, leave much to be desired. An assortment of people are held in jail for a short or longer period of time. Frequently a premium is placed on the ability of the offender to post bail. The jails, too, have taken less strides forward than the penitentiaries, on the whole, and communities seem unconcerned about them. Over a period of years inspecting jails in the United States, the Federal Bureau of Prisons rated 83 per cent below 50 on a scale of 100 points.[8] Some of those rating higher are examples of what can be done, but the pity of it is that so few localities take any pride in their jails. Courts in which the offenders have their hearing or trial vary according to the nature of the offense committed. Petty offenders, drunks, etc., are brought before "police" or "magistrate" courts. Judges of these courts are not always lawyers, and many times full records are not kept. The person appearing before these courts is given a brief hearing, may be dismissed, may be fined, or may be referred to a higher court. Serious offenses are referred to the criminal court where legal procedure is carefully defined, and judges have legal training. A prosecuting attorney elected by the people is responsible for presenting society's side of the case. If the defendant cannot hire a lawyer, there may be provision

---

[7]Uniform Crime Reports, 1952, op. cit., pages 21-23.
[8]Van Water, Miriam: Adult Offenders, Social Work Year Book, 1951, p. 37.

for a public defender. Frequently Legal Aid societies help the indigent individual. Counsel must be provided for various types of serious offenses.

Courts vary from state to state in the qualifications of officials and the manner in which officials receive their office, whether by election or appointment. Higher courts usually have more competent judicial staffs than lower courts. Associations of lawyers have done much to raise the standards of legal practice and the judiciary in many places. In the last analysis it depends on the community to demand a court system efficiently and honestly operated, with sufficient safeguards to prevent corruption and miscarriage of justice. Other court officials, besides the judge, with whom the prison is closely in contact are the prosecuting attorney and the probation officers. Prosecuting attorneys are elected officials, and it is their duty to see that the laws are upheld by bringing in the law breakers. Evidence must be presented when the case is tried. Jury trials are frequent. If the criminal has been tried and found guilty, courses open to the judge include fining the prisoner and releasing him, placing the prisoner on probation with a suspended sentence, or sentencing the prisoner to a correctional institution. The use of probation occurs mainly after minor and first offenses. Institutionalization for usually a definite period is used on the whole more largely than probation, although here again there is great difference between states. All states have provisions by which the inmate of any penitentiary may apply for parole after serving a portion of his sentence and having a good behavior record.

TREATMENT OF THE CRIMINAL

Since 1848 when John Augustus, a Boston shoemaker, asked to have some drunks, who were arrested, released under his surety, some form of probation has existed. At its best, probation offers the wrongdoer the best chance of reshaping his life in conformity with the law. He is allowed to remain in his natural surroundings without being withdrawn and incarcerated. He receives from his probation officer, who should be well trained, or from some community agency, help with his personal problems so that he will be enabled to function to his fullest. At its worst, however, the probation officers may be untrained and may not care what happens to the probationer. Supervision is sometimes routine and rigid, and if the prisoner does fulfill the obligations, he does it on his own initiative. Faults for the inadequacies of the system have been found in low standards for qualifications of officers, and low pay. Civil service examinations and more exacting job specifications have helped many states to set up an adequate probation service. About 35 per cent of persons tried have sentences suspended and are placed on probation.

In the penitentiary where the remaining 65 per cent go, many abuses are found. In these prisons, the prisoner is supposed to repent of his crimes, give payment by his incarceration for his sins, and yet at the same time, be rehabilitated, an almost impossible task. Although lip service is given to the problem of rehabilitation, the need for protecting the community, and the desire that the prisoner be punished make for confusion in prison administraton.

The program usually includes some classification of prisoners as they are admitted to the institution, some work program (many prisoners make articles for other state institutions), some educational opportunities in classes and library privileges, and some recreational outlets as movies, band, and sports. Precautions to protect the prisoners' health are also taken. Chaplains are assigned to prisons, and all have religious services regularly. Some prisons maintain farms where the more trusted workers with more freedom work under guard. Prisoners in some states have been used for road work, but the chain gang is now a part of history.

After some portion of a sentence has been served, a prisoner may make application for parole. States usually have a parole board appointed by the governor, composed of public spirited citizens who review applications and grant the paroles. Many of these have been charged with being influenced politically and some even accused of selling paroles. In the area of parole, much study has been given to see which prisoners have succeeded best, what are the characteristics in the person or in his history which enable some to succeed and others to fail? This work has led to systems of parole prediction, still in the testing stage. When validated these will substitute a scientific procedure for the subjective judgment of persons. About 40,000 persons are released annually from the prisons in the United States on parole.[9]

Conditions in the world outside are difficult many, many times for the parolee and the discharged prisoner. First of all, what is the attitude of the family to the prisoner? Are they ashamed of him? Are they overprotective, taking up his cause, thinking he has been unjustly incarcerated? Can he earn a living? Who will employ him? Should he try to hide the fact of his prison record or should he tell of

⁹Ibid. p. 41.

it? Will he be received in his circle of friends, in his church? All these are problems which the person emerging from prison must face; families are usually more tolerant than the employee. A number of societies have been established by humanitarians to help the prisoner get a job. Let us see how some of these problems worked with Leo Reynolds.

When it neared time for his parole, Leo asked to see the social worker from the Prison Society, who helped prisoners in their adjustment to the outside world. At the time he asked, he had been eight years in prison. He had taken advantage of the courses offered and had diplomas for his work with gasoline and diesel engines, and had even taught in the auto mechanics school. At the present time he was working in the prison laboratory learning to be a medical and x-ray technician. He planned to live at home, although he expressed some resentment toward his mother for the infrequency of her visits. His chief concern was in trying to have his sentences at North Carolina and Maryland commuted.

One of the jobs of the social worker was to stimulate Leo to help himself, so Leo wrote the petitions to the other states and also asked the State Employment Office for openings. He needed a sponsor as that was a requirement for persons leaving prison. Leo asked the Prison Society to be his sponsor and the case worker with whom he had talked to continue working with him. One of the states which had a detainer for him released him from it. The other required him to come to the state for trial, gave him a suspended sentence for good behavior. He completed his registration with the State Employment Office and was ready to come out.

The first few months were difficult and discouraging at the least. A number of requirements for registration and reporting were part of the parole procedure. He felt very sensitive about the attitude of people in the community and his own family. He did succeed in getting a job as a mechanic and earned fair money. Finally he met a girl with whom he fell in love and this influence, with the help of his relationship with his sponsor and his success at his job, helped him to gain assurance and maturity. He finally married his girl and shifted his sponsor to his minister. He had served his apprenticeship and was able to manage for himself.[10]

Leo's experience sounds perhaps easier than it really was. Prisons do not specialize in preparing inmates for life after release. The community is always suspicious of those who have "served time." Much stamina and encouragement are needed on the part of the parolee to maintain the standards which are expected of him. Not all are able to progress as satisfactorily as Leo did. Returned parolees vary from 15 to 40 per cent of those released on parole. But systems are so different that it is impossible to draw any conclusions from these figures. Certainly the parole officers and the social agencies such as

---

[10]Fink, op. cit. pp. 417-430.

the Prison Society, the John Howard Society, and others have been of great assistance in interpreting to the community the ex-prisoner's problems and helping the prisoner and his family more directly.

STANDARDS FOR CORRECTIONAL WORK

The reader may be impressed with several remarks referring to varying standards and reference to poor practices. It is unfortunately true that low standards exist. While the best in prison construction and treatment is known, the worst or near worst is too frequently practiced. The National Probation and Parole Association has made surveys and done extensive research, seeking to promote progressive legislation. Other private societies interested in bettering prison conditions are the Osborne Association and the American Prison Association. It is lamented that there is not more professional training for corrections officers and that more trained officials are not available. Perhaps developments in the science of human relationships will develop more and better leaderships in this field.

The needs for the future are many. They can perhaps best be summarized in the words of Austin MacCormick, long interested in the field of delinquency and treatment of the offender.

> Our ultimate success in the correctional field and the speed of our progress will be dependent in large part on public understanding and support of our aims and methods, on the passage of laws which provide for the utmost flexibility in dealing with offenders, on the provision of adequate physical facilities of widely diversified types, and on the establishment of programs of care, training, and treatment of every type that is essential to achievement of our aim of rehabilitation. More than on anything else, however, the degree of our future success or failure will depend on the factor of personnel.
>
> The future of correctional work in America depends on the provision for all our institutions, agencies, and services of personnel adequate in numbers and adequate in quality. Personnel on every level from top to bottom of the correctional system or service must meet high standards of native ability, training, experience, personality, and character. They must be assured good working conditions, adequate pay, reasonable working hours, annual and sick leave and retirement provisions. Above all, they must be given security of tenure and complete freedom from political control or interference.[11]

[11]Quoted by permission from Contemporary Correction by Paul Tappan, copyright, 1952, The McGraw Hill Book Company, Inc., page 422.

WHITE COLLAR CRIME

Although no criminal class can be identified, and crimes are committed for a variety of reasons, certain types of conduct are indulged in by a segment of society which has been called "white collar" crime. This type of criminal is a well-educated, astute person, knowing the limits of legality and illegality so precisely that under the limits of legitimate business, personal profits are made through exploitation of technical knowledge, in the manipulation of stocks, in the use of confidential information, in misuse of funds. Persons performing these transactions, sometimes called "rackets," usually are respectable members of society and enjoy frequently privileged social status in the community. It is apparently an ethical sense which is lacking. As described by some writers.

> It (white-collar crime) operates above the law in the sense that it can be carried on without legal interference except in a period of hysterical crime probes. Influence is its chief stock in trade. It is ably supported by the sharpshooting lawyers and by bribery or public indifference, and here, primarily, it is similar to professional and organized crime.[12]

Some types of white-collar crime are discovered by state auditors, by persons whose duty it is to examine books of banks and corporations. Many embezzlers have been so caught, and thousands of dollars are embezzled yearly by bank clerks and cashiers. Other instances are discovered by the appointment of investigating committees to look into suspected misuse of funds or privileges. During World War II, a Senate investigating committee unearthed many cases of war profiteering, sending to the services defective goods, materials not properly tested. Some of these persons were caught and punished. In a technical sense they had not broken a law, but they had delivered goods not according to the contract of specifications.

During recent years the Kefauver and other commissions have brought to light many cases of corruption and large scale organized gambling rings. Also under investigation have been the so-called influence peddlers, the five percenters, who made a living in Washington getting favorable consideration for the contracts of certain persons .

---

[12]Phelps, Harold A., and Henderson, David: Contemporary Social Problems, ed. 4, New York, 1952, Prentice-Hall Inc., page 445.

willing to pay for this service. Public officials were also revealed as being open to bribes or tacitly ignoring the illegal operations. Corruption has spread to government officials, too. The public has been shocked at the apathy of some of the elected officials in dealing with these individuals and failure to discover the transgressors at an earlier time. Many income tax evaders have been discovered and brought into court to explain discrepancies in their incomes and taxes. With the rise in the amount of tax, the number of evaders seems to have risen. Culprits in these cases are frequently respected citizens, well and favorably known in their communities. That these people would seek to evade the law is evidence of some lack of social control, a weakness in moral standards which permit so much graft and corruption.

CONCLUSIONS

Lawbreakers, whether in the so-called criminal class or white collar offenders, represent a menace to society's growth. Persons engaging in criminal activities are examples of personality disorganization preventing them from functioning in a socially acceptable manner. When widespread breaking and evading of the established legal code occurs, social disorganization appears in some community forces which may spread if not checked.

Efforts to meet this problem have proceeded largely along the lines of providing institutions, prisons, and reformatories, where the offenders may be placed. This affords protection to the public. Benefits to the offender are more questionable because of the manner in which the prisoner is handled while incarcerated. Yet attempts have been and are being made to work out individual plans for the prisoners commensurate with their personalities and, to a certain extent, with the seriousness of the offense. Criminal justice also varies in its administration and seems to lean over backwards to give the accused a fair trial. Less seems to be done in this area on the preventive angle. Efforts at prevention and understanding of juvenile delinquency, currently stepped up by the U. S. Children's Bureau, are directed toward preventing these young people from continuing their delinquent activities.

The nurse may not encounter any social problems in this area. Yet she may be caring for a member of the family of a man soon to be released from prison and realize the difficulties facing him. The nurse will realize, too, that any steps preventing personal disorganization will have at least an indirect effect on this problem. More study of the background of the criminal and the social situations from which he came is needed for an effective program.

STUDY QUESTIONS AND PROJECTS

1. Discuss the role of the police in crime prevention and apprehension. How does your community compare to the points you mention? Explain.

2. Discuss causes of "white collar" crime. How do these causes differ from those of other types of criminals?

3. What court and prison facilities exist in your community? If possible, visit and talk with some of the officials as to their problems and policies.

4. What are the values of probation as compared with a prison sentence for a criminal? Is probation used much in your community? How many probation officers? What is their training?

5. Study the statistics of crimes from the FBI Uniform Crime Reports. What types of crimes are most frequent? What is the trend in ages of criminals? Is there any relation between age and type of crime? Between sex and type of crime? If possible to get local statistics for your city or county, how do they ocmpare with the national figures?

6. Describe what you would consider a good program for prisons and penitentiaries. What classifications would be necessary?

7. What are the social and emotional effects on the individual of becoming a convicted criminal? On his family?

8. What are some of the social and emotional problems faced by the offender when released from prison? How can he be helped?

9. What agencies or services in your community are available for helping families of prisoners and prisoners after their release?

10. It is assumed by many that modern society has a responsibility for a program of crime prevention. If you agree with this, outline some parts of such a program as you deem absolutely necessary. If you feel it is not society's responsibility, where would you place the responsibility? What measures for prevention would you suggest?

REFERENCES

Bates, Sanford: Prisons and Beyond, New York, 1936, The Macmillan Company.

Federal Bureau of Investigation: Uniform Crime Reports, issued annually.

Fink, Arthur E.: The Field of Social Work, New York, revised edition, 1949, Henry Holt, chapter 9.

Glueck, Sheldon, and Eleanor: After Conduct of Discharged Offenders, New York, 1945, Macmillan Company.

Lindner, Robert M.: Stone Walls and Men, New York, 1946, The Odyssey Press.

National Probation and Parole Association Yearbooks.

Phelps, Harold A. and Henderson, David: Contemporary Social Problems, ed. 4, New York, 1952, Prentice-Hall, chapters 18, 19.

Porterfield, A. L.: Crime, Suicide, and Social Well-being in Your State and City, Fort Worth Texas, 1948, Leo Potishman Foundation.

Sutherland, E. H.: White Collar Crimes, New York, 1949, Dryden Press.

Tappan, Paul, Contemporary Correction, New York, 1952, McGraw-Hill Book Company, Inc.

Wilson, D. P.: My Six Convicts, New York, 1951, Rinehart and Company.

C. COMMUNITY PLANNING AND INTEGRATION OF COMMUNITY SERVICES

CHAPTER 24

SUMMARY AND REVIEW OF EXISTING PROGRAMS AND PLANS

INTRODUCTION

Throughout the discussions in this book, the nurse has been constantly reminded that a patient may have many problems in addition to illness and that resources for helping him can probably be found in hospital social workers, visiting nurse societies, public welfare offices, family and children's agencies and the like. It is proposed here to focus on the community and the nature of the social welfare resources there. Everyone is part of a community group, at some time if not all one's life. Community agencies and people have their share in shaping our lives in many ways; yet we are not equally aware of what these are.

As the nurse works with individuals and families in the hospital or in the home, it is important for her to know her community and the people living in it. Every nurse, in whatever special field she may be practicing, is influenced in her work by the health organization and the health consciousness as well as by the health conditions in her community. Since basic health and social problems are interrelated, the nurse should understand that the cooperation of community resources for health is an indispensable factor in the modern community's program for social and physical well-being. The nurse should be aware of the interest in health on the part of people, of their knowledge about basic health and welfare principles. She must consider their beliefs, prejudices, and superstitutions as well as their diseases. In working with individuals and their families and in helping them to solve their sickness problems, she must be able to bring into effective relationship all the resources of her community that can aid the individual family in meeting its sickness problem.

The community, as used here, refers to a geographic unit, usually some political subdivision as a city, a town, a county. One can think of a community in smaller terms, such as a neighborhood, or in large terms as a group of states or regions. The smaller the concept the closer can the individuals get together and the more common are the problems they face. The larger the geographic area, the farther removed do the problems seem. Yet modern society today with its many mechanical inventions and the rapid social change going on at all times, cannot long survive in small isolated units, integration of the various communities is necessary and a mutual dependency exists. In fact this very mutual dependence is the reason in back of our regional plannings. But the nurse, as with the rest of us, should begin with the city or town in which she lives.

BASIC COMMUNITY RESOURCES

Among the large number of elements which combine to make up a community, it is difficult to know where to begin. The following outline is taken from one of the most useful books describing community sources, written by Miss Joanna Colcord.[1] The main headings discussed are quoted here for the outline of community understanding which they afford.

1. *Community Setting.*—Geographical characteristics, population, industries, trade and commerce; history.
2. *Local Government.*—Form of government, elections, administrative duties and powers; personnel for the government and its appointment; taxation and finance.
3. *Provisions for Dealing With Crime.*—Lawbreakers; arresting procedure, prosecution court system, punishment; probation; conditions which contribute to delinquency and crime.
4. *Provisions for Public Safety.*—Maintenance of public order, traffic supervision; fire prevention and control; accident prevention, and first aid, coordination and safety measures.
5. *Workers, Wages, and Conditions of Employment.*—Occupations; working women and children, seasonal and migrant workers; wages; unemployment; employment offices, placement; workers' organizations; personnel admin-

---

[1]Colcord Joanna C.: Your Community, New York, 1947, Russell Sage Foundation.

istration; governmental safeguards; social insurance such as workmen's compensation and unemployment; old age and survivors insurance.

6. *Housing, Planning, and Zoning.*—Public housing; governmental aid to private housing; public control of housing; urban dwellings, rentals, repairs; rural dwellings; planning and zoning.

7. *Health Conditions and Resources.*—Health indices, births and deaths, morbidity; community as a health environment; water supply, sewerage and refuse disposal, smoke nuisance, health facilities, medical personnel, hospitals, and clinics, nursing service; public health authority; voluntary health organizations; informing the public about health.

8. *Organized Care of the Sick.*—General public medical care; voluntary medical care; special medical care programs, mothers and children, school children, communicable disease, chronically ill persons.

9. *Provisions for Special Groups.*—Homes for the aged; care of homeless and transients; special services to travelers and migrants; services for physically handicapped persons; the partially seeing and the blind, the hard of hearing and the deaf, the disabled, crippled children; services for mentally handicapped persons, the mentally ill; the mentally deficient.

10. *Educational Resources.*—The public school system; teachers, curriculum, pupils, school and community; private schools; institutions of higher learning; adult education; libraries; museums.

11. *Opportunities for Recreation.*—Unorganized recreation; public provision for education; privately supported agencies for recreation; commercial recreation; planning the recreation program.

12. *Religious Agencies.*—Churches and their activities; social-religious agencies; interchurch and interfaith cooperation.

13. *Public Assistance.*—Administrative arrangements; eligibility; numbers assisted, standards of assistance; work relief.

14. *Special Provisions for Family Welfare.*—Marital status and number of families; formation of new families; dissolution of marriages; family court; family finances; family income; home ownership; facilities for family saving and credit; consumer protectional cooperatives; family service.

15. *Special Provisions for Child Care.*—Legal protection of children; the juvenile court; protective organizations; provisions for day nursery care: institutional care, camp care; institutions for delinquent children and young people.

16. *Racial Minorities and the Foreign-Born.*—Immigration; deportation; naturalization; assimilation; discrimination on grounds of race or nationality.

17. *Agencies for Community Planning and Co-Ordination.*— Social Service Exchange; councils and federation of agencies; Community Chest; conferences of social work; fact-finding organizations; public information about health, education, safety, and welfare.

LOCAL HEALTH AND WELFARE SERVICES

Every community, rural or urban, will have a certain number of basic health and welfare services which are of most concern to the nurse. Some of these will be supported with public funds and some with private and voluntary contributions. Both types of agency support are necessary and, as it is made clear in the next chapter on planning, good community procedure means that the two integrate and supplement their activities. Competition between public and private agencies has no place in the welfare picture.

Any scheme of classification of health and welfare agencies has faults, but some list of social agencies, so many of which have been mentioned, is needed to indicate services which may be found in any community. The following list is adapted from that of Johns and DeMarche.[2]

Family Services.—Provided chiefly by private support; seek to help troubled families and individuals with problems of a personal nature and those affecting the existence of the family as a unit.

Child Care Services.—Supported by both private and public funds. Includes foster care in homes or institutions; specialized services as for physically and mentally handicapped children.

Health and Medical Services.—Supported by both public and private funds. Hospitals and clinics, health insurance; visiting nurses; work shops for the handicapped; social hygiene societies; societies for specific work as the tuberculosis, the crippled. Mental hygiene services.

Public Welfare and Public Assistance Services.—These are publicly supported programs for providing basic maintenance and services to the needy population.

---

[2]Johns, Ray, and DeMarche, David: Community Organization and Agency Responsibility, New York, 1951, Association Press, pages 37-58.

Courts, Probation, and Parole.—Essentially publicly supported, may utilize other agencies in their work; provide service for apprehending and hearing cases of law violations; plans for helping the person on probation; supervision of correctional institutions, and of release of offenders from these institutions.

Leisure-Time Services.—Both public and privately supported. Great variety of services, parks, playgrounds, community centers, groups, such as scout clubs, adult education, craft and hobby shops.

Other Welfare Services.—This includes a miscellany of services to veterans, special services for transients, foreign born, legal aid, disasters, etc.

Public funds come from local, state, and federal sources. Public welfare services have been considerably strengthened in the twentieth century, and more particularly in the past thirty years, by contributions to local communities from state and federal sources. The Social Security Act provides substantial grants to states for furthering health and welfare services through the Public Assistance programs of direct financial aid, and the service programs in which the nurse has a large stake, that is, Maternal and Child Health Services, the Crippled Children's Program, and Child Welfare services. The Vocational Rehabilitation Office is similarly set up and operates through state offices. The National Mental Health Act of 1946 likewise supplements existing services by improving and extending them through clinics, research, and training of personnel.

All of these programs operate through a single state department which assures of matching the required funds, submits a plan of activity, and maintains the required records. This state agency also sets local policy, activates the program throughout the state and submits necessary reports to the federal government. State Departments of Welfare and Health are the usual agencies to administer these funds and services. In the programs where financial assistance is given to needy persons, the federal government insists that the program be state-wide in operation, that no needy citizen of the state should be deprived of essential assistance. Service provisions need not be state-wide and are designed particularly to build up facilities in rural areas where surveys have shown less resources than are found in cities.

Several sources of federal funds are available for the local community on direct application and do not have to go through a state

agency.   Two of these are the school lunch funds and the funds for
hospital construction under the Hospital Survey and Construction Act
of 1946.   Local school boards can apply to the Department of Agricul-

AGED PERSONS AND CHILDREN AND MOTHERS RECEIVING PAYMENTS UNDER THE SOCIAL SECURITY ACT [1]

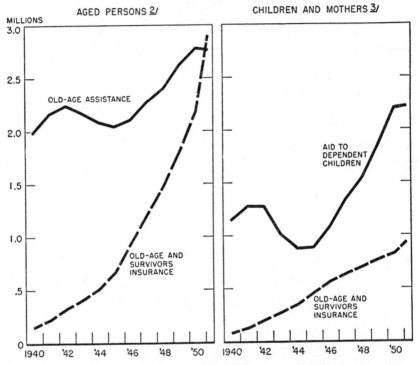

¹ Average monthly number, by years.   For old-age and survivors insurance, 1940 data represent
beneficiaries at end of December.

² For old-age and survivors insurance, represents all beneficiaries aged 65 and over receiving old-age,
wife's or husband's, widow's or widower's, or parent's benefits.

³ For old-age and survivors insurance, represents sum of child and widowed mother beneficiaries;
after August 1950, includes about 25,000 wives under age 65 with child beneficiaries in their care. For
aid to dependent children, represents children plus 1 adult per family when an adult or adults are
included in assistance group.

Fig. 12.—From Federal Security Agency, Social Security Administration, 1951.)

ture School Lunch Program and find the details for establishing this
hot lunch program, a benefit for all but particularly for the undernour-
ished child in a family of inadequate income.   Local communities needing additions to their hospitals, whether the hospital be publicly or

privately supported, can submit the plans and may receive approval for the funds.   As with the state federal programs these are all based on financial contributions from the federal government and local funds. Standards of operation and reporting are established.

Without any doubt, any survey of resources has shown that rural areas are more disadvantaged than are urban areas in terms of health and welfare facilities and trained personnel.   More publicly supported gencies serve the rural areas than private.   Among these are The Farmers Home Administration, the Farm Security Administration, the 4-H Club, and the Agricultural Extension Programs.   The County Agent and the Home Agent are well known in any farm or rural area.[3] They have done much to improve farming methods and to make farming more prosperous.

The trend to city and urban life revealed by statistics has caused some consternation to many because of need for basic agriculture as a source of supply.   No nation can live without food.   The chief perspective of the Point IV program is to raise the agricultural yield in backward areas.   Thus, objectives of some programs at the moment are to bring more resources within the reach of rural dwellers.   Several states, notably Kansas, have developed plans for making hospital service available within a reasonable radius of all.   Expanded use of mobile clinics for dentistry, x-ray, immunization, etc. will probably be seen.   The rural areas are by no means forgotten.   Studies have also pointed out that rural areas and small towns are less plagued with personality breakdown, and fewer cases of mental illness come from these areas than from the city.   Communication by transportation or by radio and television has served to reduce differences in knowledge, concepts, and entertainment possibilities between the city and the farms.

A community, it has been said, will proceed as fast as its members wish to go.   Thus, a lack of facilities for health in towns and cities may be due to apathy on the part of the citizens, a failure to demand that they be furnished as good as they could have.   To this end, health councils on a local and state level have been urged.   These councils composed of interested citizens and representing a large number of those concerned with local conditions have been formed in many places, and proved effective in making the community aware of what it has, what

---

[3]For further information see Landis, Benson Y.:   Rural Welfare Services, New York, 1947, Columbia University Press.

it could have. This development is being pushed and the public health nurse will undoubtedly encounter many such efforts.

Other attempts to educate the public to its health needs are found through state departments, particularly through health education in the schools. School children are made aware of good nutritional habits, habits of dental and bodily care. Parent-teacher organizations discuss these problems. Home economists are usually available to indicate and help with meal planning on limited budgets. This planning with children should reap its greatest reward later when they become community members, cognizant of various ways of keeping healthy, and will be a demonstration that it can be done.

STATE AND NATIONAL PROGRAMS

State governments usually assume responsibility to see that minimum standards in many areas are met and to exercise supervisory responsibility over many community establishments. State governments may set standards for performance as well as specify facilities and equipment. Perhaps their horizons are limited to those conditions inimical to a healthy community, the mass approach, such as sanitation, restaurant inspection, factory inspection, institutionalization of persons dangerous to the community for one reason or another. But they can, under competent persons, extend their influence greatly. State departments also offer consultive services and are glad to help when asked. All state departments are resources of information for what goes on in a state. Sometimes legislation is needed which must be supported to insure adequate provisions, licensing of personnel for example, and practical nurses have been included here. All states have laws, but they do not always meet local needs and may need revising from time to time.

Federal agencies which most concern the local health and welfare agencies are included in the Department of Health, Education and Welfare, formerly the Federal Security Agency. This Department includes

Social Security Administration
    Bureau of Old Age and Survivors Insurance
    Bureau of Public Assistance
    Children's Bureau
    Bureau of Federal Credit Unions
Office of Education
Public Health Service
Office of Vocational Rehabilitation
Food and Drug Administration

Other departments are the Department of Agriculture, the Department of Labor, Veterans Administration. In fact, so numerous are these government departments that a plan has been worked out at the governmental level to integrate the work of these agencies where functions may overlap.

In addition to federal agencies, there are branches of many health agencies in a community. While these agencies vary in function, many have funds available for help to someone in the locality. Some of these are the Society for Crippled Children and Adults, the National Infantile Paralysis Foundation, the National Epilepsy League, the National Tuberculosis Society. Camps are maintained for children or adults by some. Funds for treatment, prosthetic devices are sometimes furnished. All sponsor some educational programs and have much material in pamphlets, posters, filmstrips, and films which are available for local consumption. At the national level these agencies carry on research.

At the Midcentury White House Conference on Children and Youth, representatives of nearly 500 national voluntary agencies were present, all of which had programs touching children and youth. This is a stupendous number. While the Midcentury White House Conference drew them together, as far as children are concerned, there have been other attempts to provide for sharing of opinion in the National Social Welfare Assembly. The National Social Welfare Assembly is composed of national organizations in the health and welfare field concerned with integrating services, planning research, facilitating operation of public and private welfare programs, and acting as a clearing house for information. It is divided into subcouncils, one, the National Health Council, to which all the health agencies belong, others concerned with recreation and leisure time, family, and children's social agencies, social work education. Created in 1945, this agency has gone far in discussing administrative problems at the top level.

Some of these national agencies, both private and governmental, have worked out standards of what a good community should have to provide adequately for its citizens. The nurse is probably familiar with those of the nursing profession such as one public health nurse for every 5,000 population and others fixing the number of nurses in hospitals varied according to type of work done. The nurse will know, too, that in many communities these standards are not met. Rural areas in particular lack nursing services and doctors. In some parts of the country, the standard is topped, so that health workers in such cities have pushed on to a higher standard providing for even better medical care such as one public health nurse for each 3,000 of the population. By any standard the country is critically short of nurses at the present time and the same is true of doctors and other health officers.

Some of the same situations obtain in the school system. The schools are overcrowded and short of teachers particularly in the elementary grades where the enrollment is swollen with all the babies from the years of increasing birth rates. The need will continue for several years more. Recreational resources in communities are often insufficient. The National Recreation Association has compiled a detailed method of scoring one's community for a variety of recreational resources, many of which are needed in many communities. Trained recreational personnel are likewise in great demand. In this area increasing attention has been given to the older age group. Inasmuch as we are living longer, yet economic usefulness ends, the retired person needs hobbies and leisure time activities to keep mentally healthy and interested.

COORDINATING AGENCIES AT THE LOCAL LEVEL

Many communities even fairly small in size have achieved joint effort at planning. In cities this is often done by a Council of Social Agencies or a Social Planning Council, whose membership is composed of persons on boards and staffs of the agencies in the city. Representation is widely sought from public and private agencies and from civic clubs. The council functions largely through standing committees which take up problems in the several areas of welfare planning, study assembled facts, and make recommendations to the Council's Board of Directors. New services are initiated in this manner, duplications reduced, more central services of research and publicity may be provided and better integration between agencies promoted. Some smaller cities do not have such an organization but many do cooperate in joint fund raising efforts. If these funds are raised through the Community Chest they are for the support of the private agencies in the town. Some planning must inevitably go into these fund raising efforts, as budgets have to be decided upon and there is always a relationship between the needs of private and public agencies. Thus, some communities often carry on a planning function in cooperation with public agencies, with a wide representation from the citizen groups. City planning commissions, usually concerned with matters of housing, community beautification, transportation systems, and city growth are aware of social needs, too, and cooperate with existing agencies.

Thus in any community a centralized agency such as a Council of Social Agencies represents a resource of great importance in regard to what exists in each community and what is needed. To make any of these councils work, much interest is required from a wide segment of the community. Too frequently a community organizer is faced with opposition or met with apathy and indifference. Structure alone is not a successful instrument unless a core of concerned citizens exists to implement it.

As one community organizer has expressed it:

> If our social agencies in America could get together social work would not be where it is now. It would be much further advanced. If our health agencies could work more closely together instead of in competition, efforts to promote the public health would be far more effective. If in each of our communities all the civic organizations could get together and work unitedly, our communities would be far happier places in which to live. If the nations of the world could get together in an effective United Nations organization the peoples of the world would not be as they are now—wracked by war and the fear of war.[4]

OTHER COMMUNITY FORCES

This emphasis on structure should not obscure the social forces present in any community. Most communities are exceedingly dynamic. This postwar period has forced many changes on them. Business may be expanding, houses are being constructed; additional schools are being built; transportation facilities are taxed. Conflicts between groups for power, prestige, advantage may be in operation. Cultural influences always make themselves apparent. Moreover, communities are now more interdependent than ever before; they cannot depend on themselves for existence, nor can states for that matter. The discussion of the control of the Missouri River which overflowed disastrously several times in recent years is a case in point. If a dam is built in one state, the river may wreck worse havoc in another. How can it be diverted not to eliminate prosperous farm areas needed for agriculture? At once the planning transcends state boundaries. On a larger scale this is getting to be true of nations. But any resident who examines her community thoughtfully will be aware of many social forces at work

---

[4]King, Clarence: Organizing for Community Action, New York, 1948, Harper & Brothers, pages 128-129.

in the town. People must determine the course of the community's activity. In the last analysis they vote or fail to vote, which keeps an administration in power. They perform the jobs, they serve the community in many ways. They must be educated to know what the problems are, how to meet them well with the resources at their command or to develop more resources.

It is absolutely necessary if communities are to do the best for their people who are in need, that a reassessment of what is needed takes place. The recent national election shows that individuals will turn out and express their conviction on occasion, but so often they are phlegmatic about it. Mr. Bradley Buell and his associates, who have studied many communities and community forces at work, and have recently made an exhaustive study of the social services rendered to families in St. Paul, feel that the health and welfare services currently organized do not offer the people of our communities "a purposeful, comprehensive, well-integrated program." They do not facilitate what the writers assume to be desirable in American life, "a belief in a progressively better way of life which would minimize continuously and realistically the ancient hazards of poverty, disease, social abnormality, and of unrewarding leisure."[5]

One reason for these conditions are failures in what the authors term "strategic ferment" necessary for progress. In this area they see need in the American communities for greater unity of purpose, better scientific and professional disciplines in all phases of social welfare, and coherent national leadership. Confusion and misunderstanding in these areas, with some definite conflicting competition between factions, and inadequate professional leadership have impeded forward development as far as it might go.[6]

The authors do point out what they term "realistic approaches for the future." Here they review some of the agencies mentioned here and suggest possibilities as they see them for improvement. We shall quote what is said about community health, not as the ultimate on the subject, but because it broaches questions which are being discussed in all communities, and to which solutions must be found.

> In urban communities a single public health department has long been considered the pivotal agency in the administration of the program for the community-wide prevention and control of disease. Authorities believe that in most instances

---

[5] Buell, Bradley, and Associates: Community Planning for Human Services, New York, 1952, Columbia University Press, page 411.

[6] Ibid. pages 412-426.

a county-wide setup is preferable, and that in sparsely settled areas its jurisdiction should be extended to cover a population of at least 50,000 persons. There are precise standards as to the budget required for public health nurses and other personnel in the administration of this unit.

Principles governing the relationship of the public health nursing services to the public health program for the control of communicable disease, and the hazards of maternity and infancy, also are well established. Preferably the administration of these services should be by not more than two separate units —the public health department itself, and a voluntary visiting nursing association, combining both public health and bedside nursing care of the sick. Serious experimentation is now being undertaken with the combination of these services into a single unit.

National and local leadership in many fields of service subscribe to the principle that private agencies should experiment with procedures and services that eventually can be turned over to, and strengthen, the program of the public unit. This has long been a cardinal plank in the platform of voluntary agencies concerned with the communicable diseases and with maternal and infant and child health. Authorities generally agree that this principle should be applied to the program being developed by an increasing number of voluntary agencies concerned with special aspects of chronic illness and disability.

The pivotal agency in the community-supported program for the diagnosis and treatment of illness is the general hospital, with both inpatient and outpatient service. With the possible exception of the largest cities, hospitals specializing in particular diseases or conditions are now considered unnecessary. Generally accepted also is the principle that special clinic service should be consolidated in the administration of generalized hospital outpatient departments. Increasingly accepted is the principle that both public and private general hospitals should not only be equipped to serve all types of diseases and conditions but all income groups as well on a full-pay, part-pay, or free basis. The trend is to link together, within prescribed geographical areas through contractual or administrative arrangements, the resources of large general hospitals with smaller hospital units and health centers.[7]

This quotation and the many facts in this chapter emphasize the need for planning. In effective planning are inherent cooperation and

---

[7]Ibid, pages 433-434.

integration of the many services and agencies designed to develop individuals, families, and communities, personally and socially organized. The next chapter discusses some of these.

STUDY QUESTIONS AND PROJECTS

1. What is the population of your city or county? What are the characteristics of this population, race, sex, age, education, nativity, etc.? How may this knowledge be useful in shaping a community program for social welfare? (This material should be available from the 1950 census.)

2. Get a map of your city, and locate any problem areas, that is, where there is high incidence of disease, high death rates, crime rate, etc.

3. Study the location of social and health agencies. Are they well located to meet the need?

4. Does your community have a Council of Social Agencies? If so, visit it or get a report. What agencies and departments are members of the council?

5. What are some of the social problems which the Council is working on? If there is no Council, what do you see as social problems of a community nature that a Council of Social Agencies could undertake?

6. Does your community have a Community Chest? What agencies belong to this? How much money is raised? How is this allocated? Study the reports for recent years and see what has been the success of this program.

7. If there is no central agency such as a council of social agencies, list all the health and welfare agencies you can find. Do these seem to be adequate? How can you test to see if they do meet the needs?

8. How many hospitals are there in your community? How are they controlled? How many patients do they provide for? Are the hospital beds in your town sufficient for the people's needs?

9. Does your community have slum areas? Where are they located? What attempts have been made to provide adequate housing?

10. From a study of the local newspapers, make a list of the state and national agencies mentioned, particularly those supported by voluntary funds, such as have been mentioned in this book.

11. Outline steps you would take to have a program of education for the people in your community that they might become aware of the existing facilities for social welfare and the unmet needs.

12. Make a subjective judgment about your community, that is, do you feel it is a good one in which to live, a poor one? Analyze why you think so and list the factors which influence you. Do they have to do with your personal satisfaction; quality and quantity of amusements provided, resources available, vocational opportunities, or what?

REFERENCES

Buell, Bradley, and Associates: Community Planning for Human Services, New York, 1952, Columbia University Press, chapter 22.

Colcord, Joanna C.: Your Community—Its Provision for Health Education, Safety and Welfare, New York, Revised Edition, 1947, Russell Sage Foundation.

Community Chests and Councils of America, Inc.: Expenditures for Community Health and Welfare, New York, 1949.

Community Chests and Councils of America, Inc.: Teamwork in our Town Through a Community Welfare Council, New York, 1950.

Community Chests and Councils, Inc.: What Councils of Social Agencies Do, 1939.

Fink, Arthur E.: The Field of Social Work, New York, revised edition, 1949, Henry Holt & Company, Inc., chapter 11.

Gunn, Selskar M. and Platt, Philip S.: Voluntary Health Agencies; an Interpretive Study, New York, 1945, Ronald Press.

Hillman, Arthur: Community Organization and Planning, New York, 1950, The Macmillan Company.

Johns, Ray, and DeMarche, David: Community Organization and Agency Responsibility, New York, 1951, Association Press, chapters 1, 2, 3, and 6.

King, Clarence: Organizing for Community Action, New York, 1948, Harper and Brothers.

Landis, Benson Y: Rural Welfare Services, New York, 1949, Columbia University Press.

Lippincott, Earle: Our Home Town, New York, 1949, Association Press.

Ogden, Jean and Jess: Small Communities in Action, New York, 1946, Harper and Brothers.

Sanderson, E. Dwight, and Polson, Robert A: Rural Community Organization, New York, 1939, Wiley Book Company.

CHAPTER 25

PRINCIPLES AND TRENDS IN COMMUNITY PLANNING

INTRODUCTION

Today the nurse needs to know much more than how to make the patient physically and emotionally comfortable while he is in the hospital. She needs to know a great deal about her community, how it functions, and the position and activities of her patients in the community. Health workers are realizing today that it is rather futile to send patients from the hospital to environments which will not be conducive to carrying out the medical and health treatments prescribed or will not enable the patient and his family to lead reasonably healthy lives. Certain studies recently made show that illness is very closely associated with the disruption of community life patterns.[1] The professional nurse today understands how an individual's attitudes and modes of behavior are affected by the community in which he lives, and she will not underestimate these influences in planning with the patient. In addition, the professional nurse must have an understanding of how the community is organized in matters of health and disease and what health and welfare agencies exist and how she can work with them and through them in the total care of her patients. Every community has certain responsibilities in the field of social welfare. In small primitive communities, mutual aid and neighborliness often were fairly adequate to meet most of the problems that developed in life. Increasing urbanization and improvements in transportation have increased mobility. Economic insecurity has increased since the industrial revolution. Therefore organized and planned ways of meeting these problems effectively have evolved as community rather than an individual responsibility. There has always existed some form of relief for the poor supported by public funds or by religious organizations, but until the end of the nineteenth century it was largely unorganized and unsupervised.

[1]Halliday, James L.: Psycho-Social Medicine, A Study of the Sick Society, New York, 1948, W. W. Norton & Company, Inc.

COMMUNITY ORGANIZATION

The development of community organization in the field of social welfare has been an outgrowth of the social work movement and its endeavors to integrate social agencies and institutions. An effort has been made to build up a well-balanced community-wide program based on the needs of the particular community. Today social agencies represent the responsibility of the community for the provision for its members, when they fail to provide for their own basic individual requirements. This failure may be due to personal or environmental causes, to those related to physical and mental health, as well as to those commonly looked upon as belonging in the field of social welfare.

The effort to coordinate the work of different social agencies in this country began in 1908, with the establishment of the Associated Charities of Pittsburgh. This trend, which was observed in only a few cities before World War I, received great impetus both during and immediately after that war. Many central councils of social agencies, include representatives from the public tax-supported social agencies as well as those connected with private agencies.

The Central Council of Social Agencies described by Queen[2] plans and works to coordinate community problems as follows:

(1) By bringing about the improvement of methods, policies, and ideals in the work of individual social agencies.

(2) By developing a better interplay between the work of different agencies, resulting in greater economy and efficiency of effort on the part of all of them.

(3) By demonstrating to their respective communities the need for the establishment of new social agencies, either public or private, or the extension of the work of old ones.

(4) By developing joint action for the advancement of reforms in public administrative departments or for the passage of new social legislation.

(5) By developing a program of social development which may look many years into the future, but which will make clear just what new activities in the social field should next be undertaken by the community. That is, councils should always have formulated plans for progressive and logical development in the social field.

(6) By holding conferences and printing material on subjects of general interest to the social agencies; as, for instance,

---

[2]Queen, Stuart A.: Social Work in the Light of History, Philadelphia, 1922, J. B. Lippincott Company, pages 41-42.

on right methods of publicity for different kinds of agency. This may include joint schemes for educating the community as to the methods and ends of social work.

(7) By inaugurating and carrying on joint activities for the benefit of all the agencies. Thus the central councils have in a number of places become responsible for the social service exchange. In Chicago, Milwaukee, and Minneapolis they have established bureaus for the enrollment and assignment of volunteer service. In Chicago and Milwaukee the council is considering the question of joint purchase of supplies.

The Community Chest is usually a part of the federation of social agencies. Some attempts in joint finance had been made before 1914. These attempts had been efforts to collect and distribute money to recognized social agencies. However, community cooperation, which reached a high peak during World War I, also stimulated this movement.

In 1918 the small number of local chests and councils decided to band together for better community effort and planning and formed the Community Chests and Councils, Inc. The purpose of this national organization was to serve as a clearing house for ideas and information, bring united and varied experiences to the help of other localities, to keep local communities informed and alert to social trends. This national organization has grown until nearly 500 chests and councils are members. Help is given through:

(1) Advisory and consultation service through field visits and correspondence.

(2) Regional conferences.

(3) Institutes for staff training.

(4) Publicity for local use, posters, and radio bulletins.

(5) Publications on social planning, business administration, etc.

(6) Statistical information.

(7) Special studies and community surveys.

The result of this joint effort is evident today in better community planning and coordination of social and health agencies.

The Social Service Exchange was one of the first methods used to bring about cooperation between social agencies in the urban community. A visit to the local office of this association will add greatly to the nurse's understanding of its administration and functioning. The

Social Service Exchange is a clearing house for social agencies. It gives identifying information to those agencies which are registered with it. The purpose in general may be summed up by saying that the use of this exchange should avoid duplication of work when an individual or family is known to several agencies. In "clearing" a family with the exchange the agency gives identifying information about the client and his family. The exchange then sends back to the inquiring agency a list of other agencies and the dates with which this family, or any member of it, has had contact. The exchange then notifies these agencies previously interested that the inquiring agency has now registered a particular member with the exchange.

The value of such a system to the individual and his family is more efficient service and a better understanding between social agencies interested in his problems. To the social or health worker, it gives a key to the agencies that she may use as sources in helping the family. It saves her time and avoids much duplication of effort and planning. To the community, it should mean greater cooperation and unity of effort among the various agencies as well as a saving of community money. It implies a certain give and take, not only between individual workers, but also between agencies.

PLANNING FOR HEALTH

It has been an accepted policy for many years that the state should protect its citizens against epidemics, from both within and without; therefore, quarantine service was established at ports and various communicable disease and inspection programs became the function of city, state, and federal governments. Certain types of illnesses, particularly if of long duration, namely, mental illness, tuberculosis, were also more and more becoming the matter of public concern and fell within the realm of legitimate activities of the state. Quarantine service which first of all only embraced the prevention of disease, generally developed to public health services, concerned with pure drinking water, regulations of standards for marketing and preparation of food, the supervision and processing of milk for the market and many others. Thus changing social, industrial, and economic conditions have brought about many changes in what the state, through city, state or federal government, should or should not do to protect its citizens against disease and infection.

In the last twenty-five years, many surveys concerned with health and disease have been made in this country. The best known is the survey made by the Committee on the Cost of Medical Care and the National Health Survey. The National Health Survey based its conclusions on information obtained from a house-to-house canvass of more than 700,000 homes in 83 cities and 23 rural areas in 18 different states. This survey was taken in 1935 and 1936. The National Health Survey was concerned with finding out the general condition of the nation's health, the duration of illness, kind of illness, medical care received, the economic and social factors resulting from the illness and chronic and debilitating illness and accidents which kept individuals from work or from school.

This survey pointed out that the incidence of illness lasting for one week or longer was 57 per cent higher among families with an income below $3,000. Statistics show that the public in this country spends more for automobiles, movies, tobacco, and alcoholic beverages than for medical care. The question immediately might be raised, could part of the family income be appointed for medical care if it were considered as important as expenditures for cars, movies, tobacco, and alcoholic beverages? In considering adequacy of medical care, the distribution of facilities and personnel must be considered. Most hospitals and consequently most doctors, nurses, and other health workers are in large urban centers.

The problem of medical care in many rural areas includes many other aspects of living than simply the medical. For example, proper supervision and protection of water, milk, food supplies, adequate sewage disposal, fly and mosquito control would decrease the incidence of many diseases found more frequently in rural than in urban areas, particularly in certain sections of the country. Public health facilities operating as efficienctly through all rural areas as through large urban centers would reduce the incidence of many diseases and the need for as much medical care as now exists so that the big problem is a general socioeconomic problem rather than strictly medical. Just sending doctors and nurses into an area would not immediately answer the problem. These areas need health officers and sanitary engineers as much or more than they need doctors and nurses and many counties cannot afford to employ the specialized personnel needed. Help from federal government through state and local units is necessary in many instances. According to the United States Public Health Services, about 5,000 communities need new water systems; 7,700 communities with a population of about 9,000,000 need new sewage systems and about 2,800 incorporated communities with a population roughly of about 25,000,000 have no sewage facilities at all.

Another aspect of the adequacy of medical care to be considered is the education of the people in matters of health. Public Health nurses and health officers are well aware of the fact that often people do not know of health facilities available or, if they do know, they may be superstitiously afraid to use them or will not follow out the instructions given because of ignorance. Opportunities for free vaccination, free x-ray, free blood tests, and certain treatments are not often utilized adequately by the general public.

The first national bill for compulsory and sickness insurance known as the first Wagner Bill was introduced in the Senate in 1939. Hearings were held but no action was taken. In 1943, the first Wagner-Murray-Dingell Bill was introduced. This bill was more comprehensive than the first and planned for national compulsory sickness insurance and would have placed the administration of the program under the Social Security Board. This bill provided also for an increase in Federal Old Age and Survivors and permanent disability insurance. Changes were suggested in unemployment compensation and new provisions were made for federal medical and hospitalization benefits and for a system of medical care including laboratory and hospital benefits for every person insured under the Act and to their wives and children. The Surgeon General of the United States Public Health Service was to administer the program and it was to be financed by 12 per cent payroll tax per income up to $3,000 with a 7 per cent tax on the self-employed. The Bill died in committee, but in 1945, the second Wagner-Murray-Dingell Bill was proposed. It reduced the payroll tax to 8 per cent and the tax of self-employed persons to 5 per cent. This bill, however, never came to a hearing.

In November, 1945, President Truman sent his health message to Congress, presenting five basic problems:[3]

(1) The number and distribution of doctors and hospitals
(2) The need for the development of Public Health Service and maternal-child care
(3) Medical research and professional education
(4) The high cost of individual medical care
(5) Loss of earning when sickness strikes.

---

[3]National Health Program, A Message from the President of the United States, November 19, 1945, House Document, 380, Government Printing Office, 1945.

Following this, the third Wagner-Murray-Dingell Bill was introduced into Congress in November, 1945. This bill called for a National
Compulsory Sickness Insurance and covered most of the points of
the second bill but was not definite about the taxation necessary to
finance the program.

The Fullbright-Taft Bill of 1947 (Senate Bill 140) and the Taft-
Smith-Ball-Donnell Bill of 1947 (Senate Bill 545) were other bills proposed in this field. This brief account shows that while many proposals
have been made, there is a strong opposition to any federal compulsory
health insurance, because of the feeling that centralized control of medical practice is against some of the fundamental principles of our country.

The Hill-Burton Bill passed in 1947 was supported by health, medical and hospital groups, including the American Medical Association and
the American Hospital Association. This Bill provides for the expenditures of federal funds for the assistance of states in the building of hospitals and health centers in areas where need has been demonstrated
through state surveys. The Federal government pays one-third of the
cost while the remainder is met by state, county, and private nonprofit
hospital groups. Many of these hospitals have already been built and
they are doing a great deal to relieve shortages in hospital health and
diagnostic facilities. Some of these new hospitals in rural areas and small
towns well equipped and modern are already attracting doctors and
nurses to these neglected areas.

PLANS AND PROGRAMS FOR MEDICAL CARE
UNDER PRIVATE AUSPICES

There has been a very definite growth of voluntary health insurance
programs in this country. One of the best known hospitalization plans
is that of the Blue Cross or Group Hospital Service. As early as 1930,
prepayment plans to cover part of medical care began to be developed
by state medical societies. Many states, such as Michigan and California,
have very extensive programs. In 1946, the Associated Medical Care
Plans, Inc., was organized through the cooperation of the American
Medical Association Council on Medical Service. The purpose is "to
promote the establishment and operation of such non-profit voluntary
medical care plans throughout the United States and Canada as will
adequately meet the health needs of the public and preserve and advance
scientific medicine and the high quality of medical care rendered by the
profession of the two countries." Practically all state medical associa-

tions are now working on some type of prepayment plans. In some of these plans, sponsored by the State Medical Societies, individuals with incomes up to $3,600 are covered and in other instances there is no income limit. Many industries have worked out health plans and health insurance, some covering employees only, but an increasing number include the family. In 1946 a new plan in this field was the Health and Welfare Fund of the United Mine Workers, a fund to be accumulated from wage deductions to be used for "Medical, hospital, and related purposes." It is obvious that collaboration and coordination must be worked out between these various plans. They have grown very rapidly in the last two decades and the development is likely to continue.

It must be remembered, however, that no program for good medical and nursing care, for adequate health instruction and supervision will be effective unless, at the same time, better housing, nutrition, recreation, and education are provided in the community.

FUTURE NEEDS

There are not nearly enough hospitals in the country as a whole to meet the needs of all the people requiring hospital care. However, that is just part of the problem. Some areas have almost enough hospital beds, contrasted with rural and isolated areas where the scarcity of hospital beds is very, very acute. There are three basic problems in meeting hospital needs today: first of all, quantity, to make sure there are enough beds; second, distribution; and third, adequate funds so that hospital construction and maintenance are guaranteed where the hospital is needed.

In the United States the participation of the national government in the provision of medical care has centered around two major proposals. In one, federal grants-in-aid would be made to the states to insure medical care for the indigent. This plan would leave to individuals with the ability to pay, the freedom to make their own plans for medical care. This plan is based upon further development of voluntary programs for insurance and prepayment of medical care which have grown very rapidly in recent years. The second plan is one of compulsory health insurance by the federal government which would necessarily result in a great deal more federal regulation and control of agencies and practitioners providing this care.

It must be remembered that the arguments for and against compulsory health insurance should not be taken to mean that no plans for providing medical care for those unable to pay for it have existed in this country. The present situation is partially the result of poorly planned and poorly integrated programs which have existed in this country for a long period of time.

ABILITY TO PAY FOR HEALTH NEEDS

Looking back over our history, we can see that many plans have been worked out to care for the sick and to provide fairly adequate treatment at little, if any, cost when individuals could not pay for such care. The problem as stated above has been that many of these plans have been inadequate to meet changing local situations and the lack of integration between such plans has meant that, in many instances, individuals have suffered for lack of medical care or lack of knowledge about existing medical care.

The following ways of meeting this problem which have existed in our country for many years might be summarized as follows:

(1)   Voluntary or private hospitals maintained by private philanthropy, often by religious groups, have cared for the poor without charge or for a very low fee.

(2)   Doctors traditionally have taken care of certain patients without compensation or for a very low rate.

(3)   City, county, or state authorities sometimes employ doctors to care for the sick poor in certain localities.

(4)   Needy individuals might be hospitalized and receive medical service, the cost being met by tax funds and the patient to be hospitalized in private institutions if no publicly supported hospitals were available.

(5)   City, county, and state hospitals supported entirely by taxation where individuals could get the necessary care without paying any fee.

(6)   Outpatient departments in connection with public hospitals or private institutions often gave care free or at a very low cost.

(7)   Tax-supported institutions for the care of long term illnesses, such as tuberculosis, chronic illness, and the mentally ill.

A great many discussions have centered around the phrase "ability to pay for medical care." Lack of medical care and health supervision in many families has often been assumed to exist because of inadequate income. Individuals and families in the low income bracket can seldom, if ever, put aside enough funds to meet the sudden and expensive illness which may come to the family. With individuals and families above the low income brackets, the following questions should be considered: to what extent does the inability to pay for medical care result from the lack of planning and budgeting in that the family does not give medical care highest priority in apportioning out the available funds in the family? Another question must also be considered: To what extent does inadequate medical care and health supervision result from the fact that individuals and families do not know of existing low cost or free services in the community or are not willing to avail themselves of these existing agencies? Lack of education in health matters must be considered in all discussions of adequacy of medical care and health supervision.

In considering individual or family's ability to pay for medical care or health supervision, the following factors should be studied:

(1) The condition or conditions requiring medical care and health supervision and the cost of supplying this care
(2) The total resources available by the individual or family
(3) Other demands essential for the individual and his family that are being made on these resources.

Many studies have been made in recent years, both in this country and other countries, covering the health of the individual. All of these studies point out that the United States has made greater progress under its voluntary system of medical care with the resulting good health than almost any other country, except a few small countries with homogeneous population, such as New Zealand. The studies also point out that the white population in this country has better health than the non-white.

Under any system of federal compulsory insurance the cost of medical care would increase because of greatly increased administrative expenses; the tendency of individuals to make unnecessary and sometimes unreasonable demands; and the tendency of some institutions and doctors to use the system to increase their financial advantage.

It is pointed out by many experts that city, state, and federal governments should, at the present time, devote their resources and ability to developments in the field of public health and prevention; to promote health education, particularly in all schools; to teach preventive medicine, not only to the lay public, but to all professionals and subprofessionals in the health field; to promote centers for the training of personnel in the health field; and to enlarge and integrate existing programs for the care of the indigent.

CONCLUSION

The nation's health has become a matter of major importance to all intelligent people in any community. Tax-supported institutions have gradually been expanded and civic health services developed to bring them within the reach of all individuals without regard to economic ability to pay for these services. Voluntary organizations, professional, medical and health associations have also been working to improve health in all of our communities and the cooperation between voluntary and tax-supported organizations in the community is more evident than ever before in our history.

Community planning for health has gone ahead very rapidly in this country since the war. Usually this community planning is a cooperative effort sponsored and carried through by voluntary, as well as tax-supported, institutions and organizations. Publication of a booklet by the Federal Security Agency, "The Nation's Health," has been of great impetus in this program. It has been pointed out that states and communities must ultimately make their own plans and set their own goals for providing better health for individuals in their local areas. Community health councils have been organized and these councils include better representation of nurses today than they have in the past. Nurses are being included in the planning as well as in the carrying out of these activities. These councils including groups of all professional, civic, and consumer representatives should study local needs and make plans to meet these needs through cooperative action and better local organization.

In conclusion, it might be summarized that the goal of solving community problems today can best be achieved by the three approaches of education, rehabilitation, and community service.

STUDY QUESTIONS AND PROJECTS

1. Discuss the changing attitudes of our society toward community problems. How do these attitudes affect community institutions and plans?
2. Study the location of community and health agencies. Are they well located to best meet your city's needs?
3. How many hospitals are there in your community? How are they controlled? How many patients do they provide for? Are the hospital beds in your town sufficient for the people's needs?
4. To what extent is adequate medical care accessible to the masses of American people?
5. How will the Social Security Act affect the nurse in terms of expansion of medical services?

6. Discuss hospital insurance. What kinds are available in your community?

7. Dicuss some of the changing attitudes of society in its acceptance of responsibility for the people's health.

8. What plans recently projected by the Federal government should improve health and health facilities in your community?

REFERENCES

America's Health—A Report to the Nation, New York, 1949, Harper & Brothers.

Colcord, Joanna C.: Your Community, New York, 1947, Russell Sage Foundation.

Ewing, Oscar R., and Lull, George F.: How Shall We Pay for Health Care, Public Affairs Pamphlet No. 152, 1949.

Freeman, Lucy: It's Your Hospital and Your Life!, Public Affairs Pamphlet No. 187, 1952.

Goldmann, Franz: Public Medical Care, New York, 1945, Columbia University Press.

Pink, Louis H.: The Story of Blue Cross, Public Affairs Pamphlet No. 101. Fifth edition, 1948.

Plumley, H. Ladd: Budgeting the Costs of Illness, New York, 1947, National Industrial Conference Board, Inc.

Smith, Lucille M.: Tax-supported Medical Care for the Needy, American Journal of Public Health, January, 1952, pages 56-62.

Stern, Bernhard J.: American Medical Practice in the Perspectives of a Century, New York, 1945, The Commonwealth Fund.

The National Health Council, Your Neighbor's Health Is *Your* Business, Public Affairs Pamphlet No. 180, 1952.

APPENDIX I

FOR TEACHERS

The Curriculum Guide for Schools of Nursing[1] suggested that student nurses be given an introduction to Social Problems in a course called *Social Problems in Nursing Service.* In the years following, articles published in the *American Journal of Nursing* on social and emotional aspects demonstrate increasing interest in this concept. The integration of social and emotional content in each clinical area has also been developing. There is also increased interest in building curriculum content about *patient-centered care.* This means that each patient must be considered as a member of his family and community. In developing this approach to curriculum content, the instructor finds a wealth of material in books, pamphlets, and visual aids.

She may find that the library in the school of nursing does not have much reference material on *Community Problems.* This subject has recently been added to the content of the program for professional nurses. Therefore, it is her responsibility to help build an adequate reference list. The following list of books, magazines, and sources for pamphlets and other visual aids may be helpful. It is suggested that the instructor study educational resources in her community. It may be that arrangements can be made with a nearby college or university library to use certain facilities. This will reduce the cost for the school of nursing.

In the field of community and social problems much free and inexpensive material is available from both governmental and voluntary agencies (see list of agencies at the end of this section). A partial list of sources for films is also included. Sometimes rental may be obtained through the visual aid departments of colleges and universities.

The instructor in charge of this area of subject matter may plan for a short introductory course to be given following sociology. As students get experience in each clinical field, all instructors and super-

---

[1]Published by the National League for Nursing, 1937.

visors should be prepared to help them integrate social and community aspects with the clinical and technical. Teamwork is necessary in this teaching. Different professional personnel from a variety of fields can assist the nursing instructor. The social worker, the occupational therapist, the rehabilitation worker, as well as the public health nurse and doctor have much to contribute.

Such standard books in this field as the following should be available either in the library of the school of nursing or in another educational center in the community:

SUGGESTED BOOKS IN COMMUNITY PROBLEMS*

Burgess, Ernest, and Locke, Harvey J.: The Family From Institution to Companionship, New York, 1945, American Book Company.

Colcord, Joanna C.: Your Community, rev. ed., New York, 1947, Russell Sage Foundation.

Cooley, Carol H.: Social Aspects of Illness, Philadelphia, 1951, W. B. Saunders Company.

Cuber, John F., and Harper, Robert A.: Problems of American Society: Values in Conflict, New York, 1948, Henry Hold and Company, Inc.

Faris, Robert E. L.: Social Disorganization, New York, 1948, The Ronald Press Company.

Fink, Arthur: The Field of Social Work, rev. ed., New York, 1949, Henry Holt & Company, Inc.

Halliday, James L.: Psychosocial Medicine: A Study of the Sick Society, New York, 1948, W. W. Norton & Company, Inc.

Herman, Abbott P.: An Approach to Social Problems, Boston, 1948, Ginn and Company.

Koos, Earl Lomon: The Sociology of the Patient, New York, 1950, McGraw-Hill Book Company, Inc.

Midcentury White House Conference on Children and Youth, Official Conference Proceedings, Raleigh, N. C., 1951, Health Publications Institute.

Phelps, Harold A., and Henderson, David: Contemporary Social Problems, ed. 4, New York, 1952, Prentice-Hall, Inc.

Rennie, Thomas A. C., and Woodward, Luther E.: Mental Health in Modern Society, New York, 1948, The Commonwealth Fund and Harvard University Press, Cambridge, Mass.

Robinson, Canby: The Patient as a Person, New York, 1937, The Commonwealth Fund.

Social Work Year Book, 1951, New York, 1951, American Association of Social Workers.

Straup, Herbert H.: Community Welfare Organization, New York, 1952, Harper and Brothers.

---

*Note: Books and pamphlets in special problem areas are to be found listed at the end of each chapter. Here will be found a broad general list of books and magazines in the field of Community Problems.

Thornton, Janet, and Knauth, Marjorie Straus: The Social Component in Medical Care, New York, 1937, Columbia University Press.

Upham, Frances: A Dynamic Approach to Illness, New York, 1949, Family Service Association of America.

White, William A.: The Meaning of Disease, Baltimore, 1926, Williams and Wilkins Company.

Witmer, Helen, and Koytinsky, Ruth: Personality Development of Children, New York, 1952, Harper & Bros.

SUGGESTED LIST OF PERIODICALS IN THE AREA OF COMMUNITY PROBLEMS

The following list of periodicals is intended to be suggestive only and is not comprehensive enough to cover all special fields. Instructors and specialists in all areas should keep the librarian informed of suitable periodicals for special fields. Librarians in nursing libraries should check with other libraries in the institution which may be used by nurses in order to avoid too much duplication; for example, if a good social work, occupational therapy, or other professional library is available, certain periodicals may be used by nurses there and hence reduce the number that will need to be subscribed to by the nursing library. Some institutions are consolidating all libraries, nursing, social, medical, and patient, under one administrative unit and thus much duplication can be avoided.

American Journal of Nursing, published by the American Nurses' Association, 2 Park Avenue, New York 16, New York, $3.00 for students. $4.00 nonstudents a year.

American Journal of Occupational Therapy, published by the American Occupational Therapy Association, 33 West 42nd Street, New York 18, New York, $5.00 per year.

American Journal of Sociology, University of Chicago Press, 5750 Ellis Avenue, Chicago, Illinois, $6.00 a year.

American Review of Tuberculosis, published by the National Tuberculosis Association, 1790 Broadway, New York 19, New York. $10.00 per year.

The Child, Superintendent of Documents, Government Printing Office, Washington 25, D.C. $1.25 a year.

The Crippled Child, published by the National Society for Crippled Children and Adults, Inc., 11 South LaSalle Street, Chicago 3, Illinois. $2.00 a year. $2.50 in Canada.

Geriatrics, published by the American Geriatrics Society, 84 South 10th Street, Minneapolis 2, Minnesota. $10.00 per year.

Journal of Rehabilitation, published by National Rehabilitation Association, Room 516, Arlington Building, 1025 Vermont Avenue, N.W., Washington 5, D.C. $1.00 a year to members. $2.00 to nonmembers.

Mental Hygiene, published by the National Association for Mental Health, Inc., 1790 Broadway. $5.00 per year. $5.25 in Canada.

Nursing Outlook, published by National League for Nursing by the American Jr. Nursing Company, 2 Park Avenue, New York 16, New York. In preparation.

Parents' Magazine, published by Parent's Institute, Inc., 4600 Diversey Avenue, Chicago 39, Illinois, $3.00 a year.

Public Affairs Pamphlets, published by the Public Affairs Committee, 22 E. 28th Street, New York 16, New York. $.25 each.

Public Health Reports, Federal Security Agency, United States Government Printing Office, Washington 25, D.C.

Social Casework, published by Family Service Association of America, 192 Lexington Avenue, New York. $4.00 per year.

Social Hygiene News, American Social Hygiene Association, 1790 Broadway, New York 19, New York. $5.00 a year.

Today's Health, published by the American Medical Association, 535 N. Dearborn Street, Chicago, Illinois. $3.00 a year.

Venereal Disease Information, United States Public Health Service, for sale by Superintendent of Documents, Washington 25, D.C. $.50 per year.

VISUAL AIDS

Many of the agencies found listed on page 321 have free or inexpensive material available on request. In addition, the following partial list of visual aids may be of value in helping the instructor build up source material in this field. Pamphlet material should be cared for, catalogued, and housed in a central place, preferably in the library, so that it may be available to all. The instructor is referred to *A Library Handbook for Schools of Nursing,* 1953, The National League for Nursing, for help in this.

British Information Services, Film Division, 30 Rockefeller Plaza, New York 13, New York.

Castle Films, Inc., 30 Rockefeller Plaza, New York 13, New York.

Clay-Adams Company, Inc., 141 East 25th Street, New York 10, New York.

Committee on Evaluation of Motion Pictures, New York City, 45 Lafayette Street, New York.

Department of Photographic Illustration, Duke University, Durham, North Carolina.

Eastman Kodak Company, Teaching Films Division, 343 State Street, Rochester, New York.

Educational Film Library Association, Inc., Suite 1000, 1600 Broadway, New York 19, New York.

Erpi, Classroom Films, Inc., 1841 Broadway, New York, New York.

Films, Filmstrips, Slides as Visual Aids in Schools of Nursing, National League for Nursing, 2 Park Avenue, New York 16, New York.

Film Library, Department of Public Health for the State of Illinois, 301 East Monroe Street, Springfield, Illinois.

McGraw-Hill Book Company, Inc., Text Film Department, 330 West 42nd Street, New York 52, New York.

Medical Film Guild, 167 West 57th Street, New York 4, New York.

Metropolitan Life Insurance Company, 1 Madison Avenue, New York, New York.

National Film Board of Canada, 620 Fifth Avenue, New York 20, New York.

National Safety Council, Inc., 20 North Wacker Drive, Chicago 6, Illinois.

New York City Food and Nutrition Program, 45 Lafayette Street, New York 13, New York.

Sources of Visual Aids for Instructional Use in Schools, Pamphlet No. 80, United States Office of Education, Superintendent of Documents, Washington 25, D. C.

U. S. Children's Bureau, Department of Health, Education and Welfare, Washington 25, D.C.

Visual Aid Departments of Many College and Universities.

H. W. Wilson Company, 950 University Avenue, New York 52, New York.

APPENDIX II

AGENCIES

NATIONAL AGENCIES—GOVERNMENTAL

1. Bureau of Employment Security, United States Department of Labor, Washington, D. C.
2. Bureau of Indian Affairs, United States Department of the Interior, Washington 25, D. C.
3. Bureau of Old-Age and Survivors Insurance, Social Security Administration, Department of Health, Education and Welfare, Equitable Building, Baltimore 2, Maryland.
4. Bureau of Prisons, United States Department of Justice, Washington 25, D. C.
5. Bureau of Public Assistance, Social Security Administration, Department of Health, Education and Welfare, Washington 25, D. C.
6. Bureau of the Census, United States Department of Commerce, Washington 25, D. C.
7. Children's Bureau, Social Security Administration, Department of Health, Education and Welfare, Washington 25, D. C.
8. Federal Housing Administration, Housing and Home Finance Agency, Vermont Avenue and K Street, N.W., Washington 25, D. C.
9. Federal Inter-Agency Committee on Recreation, 5138 South Interior Building, Washington 25, D. C.
10. Food and Drug Administration, Department of Health, Education and Welfare, Washington 25, D. C.
11. Immigration and Naturalization Service, United States Department of Justice, Temporary Building X, 19th and East Capitol Streets, N.E., Washington, D. C.
12. Mid-Century White House Conference on Children and Youth, Children's Bureau, Department of Health, Education and Welfare, Washington 25, D. C.
13. National Cancer Institute, National Health Institute, Bethesda 14, Maryland.
14. National Security Resources Board, Executive Office of the President, Washington 25, D. C.
15. Office of Education, Department of Health, Education and Welfare, Washington 25, D. C.
16. Office of United Nations Economic and Social Affairs, United States Department of State, Washington 25, D. C.
17. Office of Vocational Rehabilitation, Department of Health, Education and Welfare, Washington 25, D. C.
18. President's Committee on National Employment of the Physically Handicapped Week, Bureau of Labor Standards, United States Department of Labor, Washington 25, D. C.

19. Psychiatric Social Work Branch, Psychiatry and Neurology Consultants Divisions, Office of the Surgeon General, Department of the Army, Washington 25, D. C.
20. Public Housing Administration, Housing and Home Finance Agency, 1201 Connecticut Avenue, N.W., Washington 25, D. C.
21. Social Security Administration, Department of Health, Education and Welfare, Washington 25, D. C.
22. United States Probation System, Administrative Office of the United States Courts, Supreme Court Building, Washington 13, D. C.
23. United States Public Health Service, Department of Health, Education and Welfare, Washington 25, D. C.
24. Veterans Administration, Vermont Avenue between H and Eye Streets, N.W., Washington 25, D. C.
25. Women's Bureau, United States Department of Labor, Washington 25, D. C.

NATIONAL AGENCIES—VOLUNTARY

1. Alcoholics Anonymous, c/o Alcoholic Foundation, Inc., P. O. Box 459, Grand Central Annex, New York 17, New York.
2. American Academy for Cerebral Palsy, Inc., 4743 North Drake Street, Chicago 25, Illinois.
3. American Association for Adult Education, Inc., 167 Public Square, Cleveland 14, Ohio.
4. American Association of Nursing Homes, 402 North Holmes Avenue, Indianapolis 22, Indiana.
5. American Association of Psychiatric Clinics for Children, 1790 Broadway, New York 19, New York.
6. American Association of Social Workers, 1 Park Avenue, New York 16, New York.
7. American Association of Workers for the Blind, 15 West 16th Street, New York 11, New York.
8. American Association on Mental Deficiency, Inc., Mansfield Depot, Connecticut.
9. American Branch, International League Against Epilepsy, National Veterans Epilepsy Center, Cushing Veterans Administration Hospital, Framingham, Massachusetts.
10. American Camping Association, Inc., Room 1802, 343 South Dearborn Street, Chicago 4, Illinois.
11. American Cancer Society, Inc., 47 Beaver Street, New York 4, New York.
12. American Committee on Maternal Welfare, Inc., 161 East Erie Street, Chicago 11, Illinois.
13. American Council on Education, Inc., 744 Jackson Place, N.W., Washington 6, D. C.
14. American Council on Race Relations, Inc., 4901 Ellis Avenue, Chicago 15, Illinois.
15. American Council on Rheumatic Fever, 1790 Broadway, New York 19, New York.

16. American Diabetes Association, Inc., 11 West 42nd Street, New York 18, New York.

17. American Foundation for Mental Hygiene, Inc., 1790 Broadway, New York 19, New York.

18. American Foundation for the Blind, Inc., 15 West 16th Street, New York 11, New York.

19. American Hearing Society, Inc., 817 14th Street, N.W., Washington 5, D. C.

20. American Heart Association, Inc., 1775 Broadway, New York 19, New York.

21. American Institute of Family Relations, 5287 Sunset Boulevard, Los Angeles. 27, California.

22. American National Red Cross, 17th and D Streets, N.W., Washington 13, D. C.

23. American Occupational Therapy Association, Inc., 33 West 42nd Street, New York 18, New York.

24. American Parents Committee, Inc., 52 Vanderbilt Avenue, New York 17, New York.

25. American Physical Therapy Association, 1790 Broadway, New York 19, New York.

26. American Prison Association, 135 East Fifteenth Street, New York 3, New York.

27. American Prostestant Hospital Association, Station A, Drawer 7, Evansville 11, Indiana.

28. American Public Health Association, Inc., 1790 Broadway, New York 19, New York.

29. American Rehabilitation Committee, Inc., 28 East 21st Street, New York 10, New York.

30. American Rheumatism Association, Inc., 620 West 168th Street, New York 32, New York.

31. American Social Hygiene Association, Inc., 1790 Broadway, New York 19, New York.

32. American Speech and Hearing Association, Inc., Wayne University, Detroit 1, Michigan.

33. American Youth Hostels, Inc., 6 East 39th Street, New York 16, New York.

34. Associated Medical Care Plans, Inc., 425 North Michigan Avenue, Chicago 11, Illinois.

35. Association for the Advancement of Instruction About Alcohol and Narcotics (Applications sent to Dr. John L. Miller, 206 Extension Bldg., University of Wisconsin, Madison 6, Wisconsin.)

36. Association for the Aid of Crippled Children, New York, New York.

37. Association for the Improvement of Mental Hospitals, Inc., 45 East 17th Street, Room 812, New York, New York.

38. Association for the Study of Community Organization, Inc., School of Social Administration, Ohio State University, Columbus 10, Ohio.

39. Baruch Committee on Physical Medicine, 597 Madison Avenue, New York 22, New York.

40. Benjamin Rose Institute, 1000 Rose Building, Cleveland 15, Ohio.

41. Big Brothers of America, Inc., 1347 Broad Street Station Building, Philadelphia 3, Pennsylvania.
42. Boy Scouts of America, Inc., 2 Park Avenue, New York 16, New York.
43. Boys' Clubs of America, Inc., 381 Fourth Avenue, New York 16, New York.
44. Braille Institute of America, Inc., 741 North Vermont Avenue, Los Angeles 29, California.
45. Camp Fire Girls, Inc., 16 East 48th Street, New York 17, New York.
46. Child Education Foundation, Inc., 535 East 84th Street, New York 28, New York.
47. Child Study Association of America, Inc., 132 East 74th Street, New York 21, New York.
48. Child Welfare League of America, Inc., 24 West 40th Street, New York 18, New York.
49. Children's Division, The Institute of Physical Medicine and Rehabilitation, New York University-Bellevue Medical Center, 400 East 34th Street, New York, New York.
50. Commission on Chronic Illness, 535 North Dearborn Street, Chicago 10, Illinois.
51. Committee for the Nation's Health, Inc., 1416 F Street, N. W., Washington 4. D. C.
52. Community Chests and Councils of America, Inc., 155 East 44th Street, New York 17, New York.
53. Council of Jewish Federations and Welfare Funds, Inc., 165 West Forty-sixth Street, New York, New York.
54. Disabled American Veterans, Inc., 1423 East McMillan Street, Cincinnati 6, Ohio.
55. Education-Recreation Council of the National Social Welfare Assembly, Inc., 134 East 56th Street, New York 22, New York.
56. Eye-Bank for Sight Restoration, Inc., 210 East Sixty-fourth Street, New York 21, New York.
57. Family Service Association of America, Inc., 192 Lexington Avenue, New York 16, New York.
58. Federal Council of the Churches of Christ in America, Inc., 297 Fourth Avenue, New York 10, New York.
59. Foster Parents' Plan for War Children, Inc., 55 West 42nd Street, New York 18, New York.
60. Girl Scouts of the United States of America, Inc., 155 East 44th Street, New York 17, New York.
61. Girls' Clubs of America, Inc., 115 State Street, Springfield 3, Massachusetts.
62. Goodwill Industries of America, Inc., 744 North 4th Street, Milwaukee 3, Wisconsin.
63. Hebrew Immigrant Aid Society, 425 Lafayette Street, New York 3, New York.
64. House of the Good Samaritan, Boston, Massachusetts.
65. Immigrants Protective League, Inc., 537 South Dearborn Street, Chicago 5, Illinois.
66. Institute for the Crippled and Disabled, Inc., 400 First Avenue, New York 10, New York.

67. Joint Orthopedic Nursing Advisory Service, 1790 Broadway, New York 19, New York.
68. League for Mental Health, Inc., (formerly the Wonder Welfare League), 42 West Thirty-fifth Street, New York 1, New York.
69. National Association for Mental Health, Inc., 1790 Broadway, New York, 19, New York.
70. National Association for the Advancement of Colored People, Inc., 20 West 40th Street, New York 18, New York.
71. National Association to Control Epilepsy, 22 East 67th Street, New York 21, New York.
72. National Catholic Welfare Conference, 1312 Massachusetts Avenue, N.W., Washington, D. C.
73. National Child Welfare Division, American Legion, Inc., 777 North Meridian Street, Indianapolis 6, Indiana.
74. National Committee on Alcohol Hygiene, Inc., 2039 Park Avenue, Baltimore 17, Maryland.
75. National Committee on Alcoholism, Inc., Suite 454, 2 East 103d Street, New York 29, New York.
76. National Committee on Boys and Girls Club Work, Inc., 59 East Van Buren Street, Chicago 5, Illinois.
77. National Committee on Homemaker Service, 113 West 57th Street, New York 19, New York.
78. National Committee on Services to Unmarried Parents, 1881 Torbenson Drive, Cleveland 12, Ohio.
79. National Committee on Sheltered Workshops and Homebound Programs, 511 North Broad Street, Philadelphia 23, Pennsylvania.
80. National Conference of Juvenile Agencies, Woodbine, New Jersey.
81. National Council of State Agencies for the Blind, Land Office Building, Austin, Texas.
82. National Epilepsy League, Inc., 130 North Wells Street, Chicago 6, Illinois.
83. National Federation of Settlements and Neighborhood Centers, Inc., 214 East 53rd Street, New York 22, New York.
84. National Florence Crittenton Mission, 408 Duke Street, Alexandria, Virginia.
85. National Foundation for Infantile Paralysis, Inc., 120 Broadway, New York 5, New York.
86. National Health and Welfare Retirement Association, Inc., 441 Lexington Avenue, New York, New York.
87. National Health Council, Inc., 1790 Broadway, New York 19, New York.
88. National Hospital for Speech Disorders, 61-63 Irving Place, New York 3, New York.
89. National Industries for the Blind, Inc., 15 West 16th Street, New York 11, New York.
90. National League for Nursing, 2 Park Avenue, New York 16, N. Y.
91. National Multiple Sclerosis Society, Inc., 270 Park Avenue, New York 17, New York.
92. National Probation and Parole Association, Inc., 1790 Broadway, New York 19, New York.

93. National Publicity Council for Health and Welfare Services, Inc., 257 Fourth Avenue, New York 10, New York.
94. National Recreation Association, Inc., 315 Fourth Avenue, New York 10, New York.
95. National Rehabilitation Association, Inc., Room 514, 1025 Vermont Avenue, N.W., Washington 5, D. C.
96. National Rehabilitation Commission, American Legion, Inc., 734 15th Street, N.W., Washington 5, D. C.
97. National Safety Council, Inc., 425 North Michigan Avenue, Chicago 11, Illinois.
98. National Society for Crippled Children and Adults, Inc., 11 South LaSalle Street, Chicago 3, Illinois.
99. National Society for the Prevention of Blindness, Inc., 1790 Broadway, New York 19, New York.
100. National States' Conference on Alcoholism, Division on Alcoholism, State Department of Health, 12 Park Street, Concord, New Hampshire.
101. National Travelers Aid Association, Inc., 425 Fourth Avenue, New York 16, New York.
102. National Tuberculosis Association, Inc., 1790 Broadway, New York 19, New York.
103. National Urban League, Inc., 1133 Broadway, New York 10, New York.
104. Osborne Association, Inc., 114 East 30th Street, New York 16, New York.
105. Planned Parenthood Federation of America, Inc., 501 Madison Avenue, New York 22, New York.
106. Public Affairs Committee, Inc., 30 Rockefeller Plaza, New York 20, New York.
107. Salvation Army, Inc., 120 West 14th Street, New York 11, New York.
108. Save the Children Federation, Inc., 1 Madison Avenue, New York 10, New York.
109. Seeing Eye, Inc., Morristown, New Jersey.
110. Shut-in Society, Inc., 221 Lexington Avenue, New York 16, New York.
111. United Cerebral Palsy Association, Inc., 50 West 57th Street, New York 19, New York.
112. William Hodson Center, Inc., Old Boro Hall Building, Tremont and Third Avenue, Bronx, New York, New York.
113. World Federation for Mental Health (Temporary Office: 19 Manchester Street, London, W. 1, England).
114. World Health Organization, Geneva, Switzerland.

INDEX